The Bighorn

OF

DEATH VALLEY

By Ralph E. Welles
Park Naturalist, National Park Service

and

Florence B. Welles
National Park Service Collaborator

Photographs by the Authors

Fauna of the National Parks of the
United States • Fauna Series No. 6

1961

United States
Department of the Interior

STEWART L. UDALL, Secretary

National Park Service

CONRAD L. WIRTH, Director

United States
Government Printing Office
Washington : 1961

For sale by the Superintendent of Documents
U.S. Government Printing Office, Washington 25, D.C.
Price $1.50

The National Park System, of which Death Valley National Monument is a unit, is dedicated to conserving the scenic, scientific, and historic heritage of the United States for the benefit and enjoyment of its people.

Foreword

In conducting intermittent but intensive research on bighorn sheep in California since 1948, I have developed a deep interest and concern for the species. Over this period of time it has become painfully obvious that our knowledge of the ecology of the animal is extremely rudimentary. The inaccessibility of bighorn habitat, the low-density populations and climate adversities, particularly in the desert regions, have precluded any volume of repetitive, detailed observations. It is only through such observations that the complexity of bighorn existence can ever be even partly understood. Until we have a better understanding, we cannot begin to materially assist the animals in their problems of survival.

It is precisely this type of detailed investigative program that Mr. and Mrs. Welles have conducted. They possess an intellectual ability of unusually high quality and have demonstrated a clarity of purpose and a devotion to the academic approach that mark them as researchers of the highest caliber. By completely disregarding the many generally accepted, although only tentatively supported, facets of bighorn behavior and ecology, Mr. and Mrs. Welles have injected a sorely needed fresh approach to their study. They have produced many highly significant new facts from their very detailed observations.

It is my sincere feeling that Mr. and Mrs. Welles' research has materially advanced our knowledge of the ecology of bighorn. By so doing they have advanced the cause of perpetuating the species as a continuing unique element of our native wilderness.

Fred L. Jones,
Game Management Supervisor,
California Department of Fish and Game.

August 26, 1961.

Acknowledgments

Here are the names of some of the people without whose help this survey and this report would not have been made. On behalf of "Old Mama," "The Hook," "Little Fuzzy," and all the other bighorn in the world, we would like to express appreciation to the following:

Principal Biologist Lowell Sumner, of the National Park Service, without whose wisdom, encouragement, constant support, and editorial assistance this study might not have progressed beyond its initial stages; Dorr Yeager, without whose sponsorship we might never have been in the National Park Service at all; Regional Director Lawrence C. Merriam and Regional Chief of Interpretation Bennett T. Gale for that often intangible but always necessary acceptance which can be found only in "the Region"; Assistant Director, Public Affairs, Daniel B. Beard, himself a biologist, who actively supported and made possible the publication of this report.

Former Superintendent Fred Binnewies, without whose support this study would never have become an official National Park Service project and would have bogged down at Badwater; and Superintendent Granville B. Liles, who carried on where Fred left off.

Park Planner C. Gordon Fredine, through whose efforts the Desert Bighorn Council was established.

Former Chief Ranger Lou Hallock for his work with the 1955 census.

Ranger Matt Ryan for his intelligent inquiring mind, his faithful reports, and his enormous energy, without which we might still know nothing about Twin Springs and Blackwater. And to Rosemary a special necklace of "black pearls."

Bob and Besse Carr for their steady hand at the tiller through the turbulent fiscal seas.

All the National Park Service staff, with special thanks for assistance beyond the call of duty to Park Naturalist Bill Bullard, Ranger-Naturalists Dave Ochsner, Ro Wauer, Ed Menning, Bob Badaracco; Rangers Lee Shackleton and Tom Monroe; and Mike Fahrner, who told us that the Badwater bighorn had finally after 6 years returned to "eating the softer rocks" at Badwater Bay.

The many geologists of the U.S. Geological Survey, whose reports from the back country have filled so many gaps in this story—Hal

Drewes, Wayne Hall, Wayne Ross, Don Mabie, and particularly Jim McAllister for his special report of the ram's "conversation" with him in the Red Amphitheater.

Charlie and Alice Hunt, whose assistance in this project has filled so large a gap that it can scarcely be measured in the time and space at our disposal here.

The staff of the U.S. Bureau of Sport Fisheries and Wildlife at the Desert Game Range, particularly Oscar V. Deming, Lloyd and Estelle McKibben, Newell Morgan, Lydia Berry, Jim Burnham, Clair Aldous, Ged Devan, John Van den Akker, and Dr. Charles Hansen.

Fred Jones, adviser and stanch supporter, Richard ("Bee Seep") Weaver, Vern Burandt, and Gene Gerdes of the California Department of Fish and Game.

Harold Elliott, whose suggestions and generous enthusiasm for our first bungling efforts with long lenses helped so much to prepare us for this work.

Dr. Gertrude Cavins and Dr. Carl Duncan and their West Coast Nature School.

The New York Zoological Society and Dr. Helmut K. Buechner.

Leonard Penhale and the California State Division of Beaches and Parks.

The botanists, Curator Roxana S. Ferris, Dr. Wallace R. Ernst, and Dr. John Thomas, for their encouragement and help in the field, but especially for the permanent installation in the Dudley Herbarium at Stanford University of the specimen collection of bighorn forage plants used during this study.

The miners and prospectors throughout the back country for their interest and cooperation, especially Jim Gill, the foreman of the Pussy Cat mine, and Bob Fordham, Charlie Hammock, "Red" Amey, and George ("Mountain Mover") Ishmael.

Cecil Godfrey for his daily patrol of Furnace Creek Wash.

Ben and Millie Keeney for their vigil at Travertine Point.

Mike Vaniman for his long hours at Badwater.

The countless visitors to Death Valley National Monument who caught the spirit and made many reports that we otherwise would never have had.

And Amy.

Contents

Life History of the Death Valley Bighorn—Continued
General Habits—Continued

Life History of the Death Valley Bighorn—Continued

Maps

Tables

Summary

Death Valley National Monument comprises 2 million acres of extremely picturesque Great Basin desert terrain. Death Valley itself is approximately 190 miles long and from 5 to 20 miles wide. About 550 square miles of the valley is below sea level, reaching the lowest point in this hemisphere at —282 feet near Badwater.

The valley is surrounded by very rugged mountains which rise abruptly to elevations of 5,000 to 11,000 feet, with practically no foothills. These mountains, together with their great alluvial fans, compose the major habitat of the Death Valley bighorn.

Winters are mild, but midsummer temperatures of over 120° F. are not uncommon, and an alltime high for this hemisphere of 134° F. has been recorded. At sea level the extremely erratic rainfall varies between one-tenth of an inch and 4 inches per year, averaging 2 inches. In the mountains the annual total is higher, but it is not recorded. These extremes of climate and of terrain have profoundly influenced the ecology of the bighorn.

The present study was undertaken because very little has been published or known about the day-to-day life history and ecology of the desert bighorn anywhere. It was realized also that studies conducted under the critical environmental conditions of Death Valley might yield findings of a significant and possibly somewhat different nature from those obtained elsewhere.

Intensive fieldwork commenced December 18, 1954, when a month-long uninterrupted series of dawn-to-dusk observations of a clearly identifiable band of bighorn was undertaken. This type of intensive behavior watching set the overall pattern for the study. From December 18, 1954, to March 1, 1961, a total of 1,693 hours was devoted to such observations.

Although the study was conducted chiefly in the Black and Funeral Mountains, it includes a brief preliminary survey of the piñon belt of the Grapevine Mountains. All mountain ranges of the monument were visited many times during more than 6 years of fieldwork.

No single food item can be called a mainstay in the diet of Death Valley bighorn. Grasses, annual nonwoody flowering plants, shrubs, and trees—all are used at times; however the available food supply consists mainly of browse because the region's erratic precipitation does not consistently provide crops of grasses and annual nonwoody flowering plants. Forty-three plant species were observed to be eaten. Use of 12 of these was heavy, 12 moderate, and 19 light. Desertholly (*Atriplex hymenelytra*) received more nearly year-round use than any other plant. A general shortage of food critical enough to threaten seriously the survival of the species has not occurred in Death Valley in the past 10 years, if ever.

Available water supplies constitute a major limiting factor in bighorn numbers and distribution. It appears that Death Valley bighorn need water the year around, drinking every 3 to 5 days in hot and dry weather and every 10 to 14 days in cold weather, with lambs needing relatively more than adults. They can subsist for longer periods without water in an emergency. They seem to utilize permanent water sources and the surrounding forage only when necessary, withdrawing to outlying ranges whenever rainfall, ephemeral water supplies, and forage conditions permit.

As a corollary of this study, a list of more than 300 water sources was compiled from all available records, and to a large extent the list was subsequently checked in the field. Of these, 90 were mapped for the first time, and 43 were established as of prime importance to the bighorn.

A major danger to the future existence of the bighorn lies in a continued and accelerating usurpation of its ancestral water supplies by man.

Bighorn appear to prefer to remain in one home area if conditions allow them to, being born, living, and dying within a radius of 20 miles of their home water supply. However, unlike some other ungulates, they will move rather than starve. The exhaustion of nonpermanent water supplies probably is the most frequent cause for moving.

The general daily activity of bighorn is divided between the effort of securing food and water and resting from that effort, with morning and evening play, especially on the part of the lambs. We have no record of nighttime activity, except in a few instances of their being frightened from their bedding grounds.

By nature, the bighorn would appear to be unwary and trusting, but it quickly acquires a wariness from experience which makes it prefer isolation from human activities. However, deliberate attempts on the part of humans to conduct themselves within limits that are clearly acceptable to bighorn sometimes can lead to a gradual but marked reversal from wariness. In such cases the individual personality of the leader of the band, and her previous experiences with humans, become major factors in determining the degree of herd tolerance to human presence.

Herd leadership possibly holds the key to the future of bighorn-human relationships. If the leader (always a ewe) is unafraid of people, an entire band may become tame within days. This matriarchal leadership plays an important part in the overall life history of the naturally gregarious bighorn, controlling to a large extent group movements and reactions to the environment.

The climbing ability of the bighorn is as phenomenal as legend would have it and can scarcely be exaggerated within reason, but under ordinary circumstances the animals take the easiest route and rest often.

Fighting as an expression of serious hostility on the part of either sex, at any age, seems almost nonexistent.

Bighorn are probably no more nor less sanitary than other ruminants in a natural state, seldom defecating or urinating in their water supplies, but doing both in their vacated beds. Their droppings exhibit an almost infinite range of variation in size, often without correlation to size of animal. Appearances of age or recency likewise can be extremely deceptive. As a result of these variations and many others, the technique of bighorn dropping classification is useful in sign reading, but it demands more study than had been anticipated if it is ever to form an exact science.

Communication among bighorn is in general carried on by the same means as among other similar animals, employing the voice to a lesser degree than some and vision to a greater degree than most. Their sense of smell and hearing is probably average for ruminants.

The mating season is spread over a possible 9 months, reaching a peak in August and September. Since the gestation period is about 6 months, the peak of the lambing season is reached in January and February, with occasional lambs dropped throughout the year except during the peak of the mating season.

In general, the rams travel to meet the ewes during the rut and may visit several spring areas for this purpose.

The "fighting" between males seems to be less of a fight than a ritualistic contest. Serious injury is rare and occurs primarily as a result of some miscalculation or accident. We have seen nothing to indicate enmity as a basis for the bouts. Momentary contestants may feed, water, and travel together between clashes, and the presence of a ewe neither precipitates nor prevents a contest.

A third ram, usually a younger noncontestant, often makes off with the ewe, if there is one present, while the battle continues. Contestants are generally well matched older rams and are deferred to by the younger ones. If a younger, lighter ram challenges an older and heavier ram, he is usually ignored. All the prolonged contests we have seen have been between rams in their prime, with the longest, most grueling bouts taking place between those that are 9 to 12 years of age.

Mature rams appear to be indifferent to lambs, sharing no responsibility for their rearing but presenting no hazard to them.

The ewe during the mating season plays the role expected of the female. Her flight from the male often appears ritualistic in that she waits for him when he pauses in the chase and seems not seriously to seek to outrun him.

The ewe seeks isolation to bear her one lamb, shows solicitude for it during the first few days, but leaves it on its own almost from the beginning.

The lamb begins to learn immediately by emulation of its mother. It eats rough food within 2 weeks, spends most of its time with other lambs when available, learns self-protection through play, is weaned anywhere from a month in rare cases to 7 months in equally rare ones, with a probable average weaning age of 4 to 5 months.

The young ewe becomes essentially an adult at 18 months and can breed then. The ram matures more slowly. It leaves the ewe bands to join the off-season bachelor ram bands at the age of 3 years. About a year later it begins to seek out the ewes at the springs during the rut.

Aside from the cause of a prevalent cough among lambs, very little evidence of disease or parasites was found. Apparently, if a Death Valley bighorn survives its first year, it will have a life expectancy of at least 10 years. Determining the age of animals by counting annual horn growth rings is feasible but becomes increasingly difficult after the first 7 years, for new growth is represented by narrow rings instead of large segments after that age.

With the exception of the ram segregation during the off seasons, the low-density forage and population situation in Death Valley appears generally to preclude the forming of specific herds larger than family groups. The average band appears to be mainly a family group of three to five, with the numbers increasing on good ranges in good years and vice versa.

Except in areas withdrawn from bighorn use by water diversion and human encroachment, distribution of the animals appears to be general throughout most of the monument region wherever adequate water and natural forage exists. There is some indication of an exception to this in the piñon belt of the Grapevine Mountains, where deer are relatively numerous and appear to be unfavorably competitive. More ecological study is needed in all the timbered areas of the habitat.

The number of bighorn is estimated currently (1961) at between 600 and 900.

We believe that the best census method for this region is through the prolonged waterhole count as employed at Nevares Spring in 1957, augmented by an intensive application of the associative principle of sign reading and the system of field identification of individual animals described in the text and shown in the illustrations. We believe that, in Death Valley, traumatic interference with their normal activity by trapping and marking, the use of dart guns, etc., would preclude the type of observation by which the data of this report were gathered.

The specific cause of the annual 90 percent lamb mortality remains a major mystery, with malnutrition heading the list of suspects. Adult bighorn appear generally to die of old age.

We found no evidence of significant predation.

Man and what he has brought with him comprise the only significant threat to the bighorn survival.

The wild burro is part of this picture, but its threat to the bighorn survival is indirect, and present control methods are reducing the threat to a minimum. While all ecological wisdom urges the complete elimination of all exotic species from the biota, it cannot be argued that the burro is eliminating the bighorn, since healthy herds of both species are thriving together on some ranges and have done so for at least 25 years.

Only unchecked human encroachment appears actually to threaten the future status of the bighorn.

Introduction

How and Why this Study was Begun

THIS STUDY was begun inadvertently during our first visit to Death Valley in January, February, and March of 1950.

The Nelson bighorn was being featured in the National Park Service interpretive programs as "one of our most interesting mammals, that crosses from one mountain range to another in the vicinity of Badwater."

The complete absence of any further information about them aroused our interest to the extent that we spent 6 weeks of our time in an increasingly determined effort to see at least one of the elusive creatures if it was at all possible.

We gave up the search with the warm weather of April and decided to apply ourselves to the literature on the Nelson bighorn during the summer and thus acquaint ourselves with its habits and be prepared for a more intelligent search the next winter.

But we discovered that there was, practically speaking, no established body of literature on the species available anywhere. This heightened our interest to the extent that we spent a major part of the next two winters in a fruitless effort to learn something about the bighorn.

We could find no one who knew where to look for them, what they ate, when they had lambs, when the famous fights between rams took place, or anything of the phases of their life history. Such information would be expected to be common knowledge in an area which was a sanctuary for these animals and for all natural features of the desert.

Their behavior and whereabouts became such a mystery that we began to wonder if there were actually any of them left. The fact that during this entire period we had not talked to a single person who had seen a sheep in several years added considerable substance to this idea.

Finally, in March 1952, we found one Nelson bighorn ewe in Echo Canyon and were able to observe her for an hour as she climbed the canyon wall to the tip of the highest peak.

THE BIGHORN OF DEATH VALLEY ✦ 1

Our enthusiasm was revived, and a second phase of our project began.

We had been hearing that sheep were much easier to find at the Desert Game Range, administered by the U.S. Bureau of Sport Fisheries and Wildlife, near Las Vegas in Nevada, and we now decided that since it had taken us three winters to find one sheep in Death Valley we should go to the game range and see how long it took to see one there. We arrived in the latter half of March.

The personnel of the Bureau of Sport Fisheries and Wildlife at the game range were very cooperative and gave us the use of Joe May camp for 10 days. There, in a Joshua-tree habitat at about 5,000 feet elevation, we saw at least 1 bighorn every day, climaxed by 1 day's total of 45.

We followed, observed, and photographed sheep all day, every day, and at night we read a stack of unpublished manuscripts about sheep by Oscar V. Deming, the game range biologist.

We began to learn from what we saw and read. We learned that we were there in the lambing season and that the rams had withdrawn into a separate band in a separate territory. We saw nine rams, all mature, at the top of Wildhorse Pass, in the piñon and juniper country, and we wondered why no young rams were with them.

We learned that there is such a thing as "babysitting" and we saw it; 12 lambs playing and resting on a high cliff in the care of 1 or 2 older ewes, while all the other mothers fed in the dense (and, to lambs, dangerous) vegetation in the wash below.

We saw there were leaders among them and wondered how they were chosen and how they ruled until, as time passed, we saw that they didn't rule at all, but led by example.

We reread some of the few pamphlets and articles we had been able to collect and began to see differences between what was written and what we were seeing. For instance, E. H. Ober (1931) had written that bighorn lambs were born twins and snow white. We could find neither.

Ernest Thompson Seton (1927) had placed the mating season in December, but here in March we were seeing lambs with horns showing and so much greater growth than others that they could be no less than 2 months old; therefore the mating season of these desert sheep had to begin long before December, because lambs were born in January.

Seton also wrote that "the lambs up to 6 months old often bleat exactly as do the domestic kind, but I never heard any sound from the old sheep except a loud snort or 'snoof.'" This was hard to reconcile with the fact that we were hearing ewes call their lambs every day.

So, day by day, the difference between what we were reading and what we were seeing grew to such proportions that we came eventually to the inevitable conclusion that we had apparently stumbled into a virgin field of research; that the life history of the desert bighorn (*Ovis canadensis nelsoni*) was to a large extent unknown; that writers on the subject were rehashing legend and hearsay, as exemplified by J. Ross Browne's account of the Castle Dome country above Yuma (1864, p. 691):

> The country is one of the roughest ever trodden by foot of man. I think it must originally have been designed for mountain sheep, which are said to abound in the vicinity. These animals have prodigious horns, upon which they alight when they tumble down the cliffs. How they get up again is difficult to conjecture. My own impression is that they were born there, and are pushed over by other sheep.

As late as 1960 we still read of "bucks * * * with hollow horns * * * fighting over a harem of six ewes * * * risking attack by wolves * * * and whole bands plunging over 150-foot cliffs" (Barrett, 1960).

Nothing had happened to change this picture much by December 1954 when I was in my second season as a ranger-naturalist in Death Valley National Monument. A recently published booklet on the geology of Death Valley stated what still seemed to be the total story at the local level, "Desert bighorn sheep live in the mountains on both sides of the valley, and are known to cross from one side to the other, but have been seen by relatively few persons."

After our 10-day period of observation, we made other trips to the Desert Game Range. We conducted a weekly interpretive program on the bighorn during the winter season in Death Valley. This stimulated a great deal of interest in both the resident and visiting human population and brought to us many reports from persons who had at some time seen sheep in Death Valley or neighboring country.

We knew by now that conclusions from the study being made by Oscar Deming at the game range would not necessarily be applicable to Death Valley because of the environmental contrasts between the 2 areas, exemplified by the fact that in 3 years of search in Death Valley we had found 1 sheep, while at the game range we had counted over 100 in less than a week—a much greater population made possible by denser vegetation owing to higher elevation, cooler climate, and greater rainfall.

We knew also by now that, incredible as it seemed, no one had ever spent 12 consecutive months in Death Valley for the sole purpose of studying wildlife survival in one of the hottest and driest areas on earth. The field, from a research point of view, was untouched. We decided to go into it.

Meanwhile, sight records of bighorn were reaching us with increasing frequency. We were, in addition to our own weekend excursions, making a concentrated effort to check all other reports reaching us. Through the early spring of 1954 we had received five reports of sheep in Furnace Creek Wash., usually several days after they had been seen. We failed to locate any of these. During the autumn of 1954 we began to get reports of sheep in the Badwater area, and the old story of bighorn crossing the valley at that point once more went the rounds. We checked all reports without success until December 18.

On that day I was on duty at the Death Valley Museum at Furnace Creek Ranch when a young man who was about to leave turned back at the door and said, "By the way, I just got a good picture of some of your goats a while ago, down there at that low place, you know * * *." This was at 4 p.m. I closed the museum, collected my wife and our cameras, and at 4:30 we were photographing a band of six bighorn bedding down about 100 feet above and 100 yards to the north of Badwater. We stayed with them until long after we could see, listening to an occasional sneeze or a rock rolling down in the darkness.

We went back to headquarters at 6 p.m., and at 7 I gave an interpretive program at the ranch. An hour before dawn we were back at the bedding site waiting for daybreak and an answer to the question we had carried with us through the night: Will they be there in the morning? They were, and the present intensive phase of the Death Valley bighorn study had officially begun.

Previous Studies of Death Valley Bighorn

To facilitate the correlation of this report with the results of previous work on the subject, a digest of these reports is included here:

1. In 1891, Edward A. Nelson established the type locality and took the type specimen of the Nelson bighorn in the Grapevine Mountains. They were very common there then, but we find them very scarce there now. Why?

2. In 1917, Grinnell and Dixon found the greatest sheep concentrations at Nevares Spring and in Hanaupah Canyon. They believed the vertical distribution rarely reached below the 1,000-foot level (Dixon, 1935). Mrs. Welles and I lived with a band of bighorn near Badwater below sea level for several months.

3. In January 1935, A. E. Borell visited 26 springs; saw no sheep, but

much evidence of poaching; found the burros ranging at lower levels and did not believe they conflicted with the bighorn (Borell, 1935).

4. In October 1935, Joseph Dixon visited 20 springs; saw no sheep; accepted as trustworthy sight records of 30 sheep in one band at Quartz Spring, 42 in another at Dodds Spring (Dixon, 1935). We have no subsequent official record of either sight or sign at Dodds Spring for many years.

5. In September 1938, the first organized sheep census in the monument's history was made, with Joseph Dixon and Lowell Sumner in charge. With rain falling in some area of the monument every day, 7 men visited 21 sample areas in 14 days, saw 27 sheep and fresh tracks or 38 more, but they made no estimate of the total population. The most encouraging result was lack of evidence of poaching. Plans were laid for more intensive efforts in 1939 (Dixon and Sumner, 1939).

6. In July 1939, the California Division of Fish and Game again gave wholehearted cooperation to Sumner and the monument staff in a prodigious effort scheduled for 2 weeks beginning July 20. In spite of the earlier date for the census, rains overtook them again on July 25, and by the 30th: "Rain in varying degrees of intensity was falling almost universally throughout the Death Valley ranges. Whether or not the bighorn had been restricted to the water-holes prior to the rains, our observations definitely established that the precipitation thoroughly scattered them so that further water-hole censuses were out of the question for 1939."

They counted 35 sheep, which, with 31 counted the month previously by Don Curry, made 66 seen. The Panamint Range south of Emigrant Wash was not covered at all during this survey, but in the areas covered by the 1939 survey the total number of bighorn estimated from sight records, tracks, droppings, and beds was approximately 208. Owing to the scattering of the animals by rains during the survey it was believed that this figure should be increased by at least 50. Using this figure and assuming that the total number of bighorn in the Cottonwoods, Grapevines, Funerals, and Blacks approximated 258, and further assuming that there were at least as many more bighorn in the Panamint Range south of Emigrant Wash, Sumner estimated the total number for Death Valley National Monument at approximately 500 (Sumner, 1939).

Chronology and Scope of the Present Study

The total volume of field data gathered by us is on file in the form of 17 progress reports comprising over 500 typewritten pages copied directly from field notes handwritten at the site of the observations. In addition there are 298 pages of a separate report on water sources. All of these typewritten data are on file with the National Park Service at Death Valley National Monument.

As a yardstick with which to measure the validity of this report, a record of the time spent in actual observation of bighorn, including dates, location, number of animals, age class and sex, and length of time observed is herewith included. (See table 1.)

TABLE 1.—*Observations upon which report is based*

[E, ewe; R, ram; L, lamb]

Location	Date	Number of animals	Hours of observation
Badwater-Natural Bridge area (Dec. 18, 1954–Jan. 24, 1955):			
Badwater....................	Dec. 18, 1954–Jan. 24, 1955.	6 (4 E, 2 L)........	77
Pothole Canyon...............	Dec. 23, 1954.......	5 (3 E, 1 L, 1 R)...	7½
Do......................	.....do............	1 (1 E)............	5
Black Butte.................	Dec. 25, 1954.......	9 (6 E, 2 L, 1 R)...	1
Natural Bridge..............	Jan. 23, 1955.......	5 (4 E, 1 L).......	1½
Do......................	Jan. 24, 1955.......	7 (4 E, 3 L).......	6½
Badwater-Echo Canyon (Feb. 12–Apr. 12, 1955):			
Badwater....................	Feb. 14–25..........	4 (3 E, 1 L).......	132
Do......................	Mar. 1.............	4 (3 E, 1 L).......	5
Echo Canyon.................	Mar. 2.............	6 (5 E, 1 L).......	3
Badwater....................	Mar. 3.............	4 (3 E, 1 L).......	4
Do......................	Mar. 20–30.........	1 (1 E)............	65
Death Valley bighorn census survey (Apr. 5–July 14, 1955):			
Tin Mountain.................	June 7.............	9 (9 R)............	1
Indian Pass..................	July 2.............	5 (5 R)............	5
Willow Creek.................	July 8.............	3 (2 E, 1 L).......	1½
Do......................	.....do............	2 (1 E, 1 R).......	1½
Do......................	July 9.............	1 (1 E)............	1
Do......................	.....do............	1 (1 R)............	1½
Do......................	.....do............	2 (2 E)............	3
Do......................	.....do............	2 (2 E)............	½
Willow Creek, Virgin Spring, etc. (Aug. 19–Dec. 29, 1955):			
Virgin Spring.................	Aug. 19, 1955.......	2 (1 E, 1 L).......	4
Willow Creek.................	Aug. 24, 1955.......	10 (4 E, 1 L, 5 R)...	½
Do......................	.....do............	4 (1 E, 1 L, 2 R)...	½
Do......................	.....do............	2 (1 E, 1 L).......	½
Do......................	Aug. 26, 1955.......	3 (1 E, 1 L, 1 R)...	1½
Do......................	Aug. 31, 1955.......	3 (1 E, 1 L, 1 R)...	½
Do......................	.....do............	1 (1 E)............	3
Virgin Spring.................	Sept. 1, 1955.......	2 (2 R)............	1½
Willow Creek.................	Sept. 11, 1955......	1 (1 R)............	1
Do......................	.....do............	1 (1 R)............	3
Indian Pass..................	Sept. 19, 1955......	6 (4 E, 1 L, 1 R)...	2
Do......................	Sept. 20, 1955......	6 (4 E, 1 L, 1 R)...	6
Furnace Creek Wash...........	Oct. 14, 1955.......	3 (1 E, 2 R).......	4
Virgin Wash.................	Oct. 26, 1955.......	5 (2 E, 2 L, 1 R)...	2
Do......................	Oct. 28, 1955.......	5 (2 E, 2 L, 1 R)...	2

TABLE 1.—*Observations upon which report is based*—Continued

[E, ewe; R, ram; L, lamb]

Location	Date	Number of animals	Hours of observation
Willow Creek, Virgin Spring, etc. (Aug. 19-Dec. 29, 1955)—Con.			
Dead Man's Curve	Nov. 1, 1955	2 (1 E, 1 R)	½
Racetrack Wash	Nov. 29, 1955	1 (1 R)	½
Do	....do	1 (1 R)	½
Virgin Spring	Dec. 2, 1955	3 (2 E, 1 R)	2
Furnace Creek Wash (Dec. 23, 1955–Apr. 17, 1956):			
Furnace Creek Wash	Dec. 23, 1955	2 (1 E, 1 L)	6
Paleomesa	Dec. 28, 1955	5 (4 E, 1 L)	1½
Do	Dec. 29, 1955	7 (5 E, 2 L)	8
Furnace Creek Wash	Jan. 4–10, 1956	7 (5 E, 2 L)	50
Do	Jan. 11–19, 1956	8 (6 E, 2 L)	65
Do	Feb. 2–4, 1956	2 (1 E, 1 L)	12
Paleomesa	Feb. 4, 1956	5 (2 E, 2 L, 1 R)	1
Nevares Spring	Feb. 8, 1956	4 (2 E, 2 L)	2
Furnace Creek Wash	Feb. 9–28, 1956	2 (1 E, 1 L)	116
Nevares Spring	Feb. 28, 1956	10 (5 E, 3 L, 2 R)	4
Do	Mar. 1, 1956	1 (1 E)	2
Furnace Creek Wash	Mar. 1–10, 1956	2 (1 E, 1 L)	39
Do	Mar. 10, 1956	1 (1 E)	1
Do	Mar. 13–24, 1956	7 (4 E, 2 L, 1 R)	77
Nevares Spring	Mar. 26, 1956	3 (2 E, 1 L)	½
Furnace Creek Wash	Mar. 27, 1956–Apr. 8, 1956.	7 (4 E, 2 L, 1 R)	33
Do	Apr. 10–17, 1956	2 (1 E, 1 L)	20
Nevares Spring, Navel Spring, Willow Creek, etc. (May 31–Sept. 8, 1956):[1]			
Nevares Spring	June 19, 1956	2 (1 E, 1 L)	1
Do	June 20, 1956	1 (1 E)	1
Do	June 28, 1956	14 (8 E, 3 L, 3 R)	10
Do	June 29, 1956	2 (2 E)	2
Do	June 30, 1956	3 (2 E, 1 R)	11½
Do	July 1, 1956	12 (7 E, 5 L)	8½
Do	July 3, 1956	1 (1 E)	½
Do	July 4, 1956	1 (1 R)	1
Do	July 10, 1956	9 (5 E, 2 L, 2 R)	8
Do	July 11, 1956	7 (4 E, 3 L)	3
Do	July 13, 1956	2 (1 E, 1 L)	1
Do	July 20, 1956	13 (6 E, 5 L, 2 R)	8
Willow Creek	Aug. 8, 1956	11 (5 E, 5 L, 1 R)	2
Do	Aug. 13, 1956	5 (2 E, 1 L, 1 R)	3
Indian Pass	Aug. 17, 1956	1 (1 R)	1
Nevares Spring	Aug. 25, 1956	1 (1 R)	1
Willow Creek	Aug. 30, 1956	12 (5 E, 5 L, 2 R)	4
Virgin Spring	Aug. 31, 1956	2 (1 E, 1 R)	1½
Monarch Canyon	Sept. 1, 1956	6 (3 E, 2 L, 1 R)	1
Nevares Spring	Sept. 4, 1956	1 (1 R)	2
Do	Sept. 5, 1956	2 (1 E, 1 R)	2
Scotty's Canyon	Sept. 6, 1956	2 (1 E, 1 R)	½
Willow Creek	Sept. 7, 1956	5 (2 E, 2 L, 1 R)	3

See footnote at end of table.

TABLE 1.—*Observations upon which report is based*—Continued

[E, ewe; R, ram; L, lamb]

Location	Date	Number of animals	Hours of observation
Furnace Creek Wash, Navel Spring, Nevares Spring, etc. (Oct. 29, 1956– Feb. 20, 1957):			
Navel Spring	Oct. 30, 1956	4 (1 E, 2 L, 1 R)	1
Furnace Creek Wash	Oct. 31, 1956	1 (1 R)	6
Big Wash	Nov. 3, 1956	5 (4 E, 1 R)	4
Do	Nov. 4, 1956	6 (4 E, 1 L, 1 R)	3
Nevares Spring	Nov. 15, 1956	5 (2 E, 1 L, 2 R)	2
Big Wash	Nov. 16, 1956	11 (7 E, 3 L, 1 R)	3
Do	Nov. 17, 1956	10 (7 E, 3 L)	10
Do	Nov. 18–19, 1956	18 (12 E, 5 L, 1 R)	18
Do	Nov. 22, 1956	5 (5 E)	5½
Do	Nov. 23, 1956	13 (8 E, 4 L, 1 R)	5
Do	Nov. 24, 1956	13 (7 E, 5 L, 1 R)	6
Navel Spring	Nov. 25, 1956	9 (6 E, 3 L)	8
Big Wash	Nov. 26, 1956	4 (3E, 1 R)	1
Do	Nov. 28, 1956	5 (3 E, 2 R)	1
Furnace Creek Wash	....do	3 (2 E, 1 R)	1
Scraper Spring	....do	1 (1 E)	1
Furnace Creek Wash	Nov. 29, 1956	5 (3 E, 2 R)	3
Do	Nov. 30, 1956	7 (5 E, 2 R)	10
Paleomesa	Dec. 1, 1956	6 (5 E, 1 L)	7
Big Wash	Dec. 2–3, 1956	7 (5 E, 1 L, 1 R)	15
Navel Spring	Dec. 5, 1956	3(2 E, 1 L)	2½
Furnace Creek Wash	Dec. 10, 1956	3 (3 E)	4
Navel Spring	Dec. 16, 1956	3 (3 E)	1
Do	Dec. 18, 1956	2 (2E)	½
Big Wash	Dec. 20, 1956	3 (3 E)	5
Box Canyon	Dec. 27, 1956	7 (6 E, 1 R)	3
Nevares Spring	Dec. 28, 1956	6 (3 E, 3 L)	1
Do	Dec. 29, 1956	1 (1 E)	½
Do	Dec. 31, 1956	1 (1 R)	½
Upper Echo Canyon	Jan. 31, 1957	10 (10 R)	1
Do	Feb. 3, 1957	10 (10 R)	1
Emigrant Wash	Mar. 11, 1957	2 (2 R)	½
Red Amphitheatre	Mar. 16, 1957	1 (1 E)	1
Upper Echo Canyon	June 4, 1957	1 (1 R)	1
Nevares Seeps (Aug.11–Sept.10, 1957):[2]			
Nevares Seeps	Aug. 11, 1957–Sept. 10, 1957.	47 (11 E, 9 L, 27 R)	420
Jubilee Pass, Keystone Canyon (Oct. 13–Dec. 5, 1957):			
Jubilee Pass	Oct. 21, 1957	7 (3 E, 1 L, 3 R)	7
Keystone Canyon Fan	Dec. 3–5, 1957	2 (1 E, 1 R)	10
Death Valley Buttes (Feb. 9–16, 1958):			
Death Valley Buttes	Feb. 9–16, 1958	14 (6 E, 6 L, 2 R)	88
Nevares Seeps (June 1–Sept. 12, 1959): Nevares Seeps.	June 1, 1959–Sept. 12, 1959	23 (10 E, 4 L, 9 R)	120
Quartz Spring (May 31–June 1, 1960): Quartz Spring.	May 31, 1960–June 1, 1960.	28 (14 E, 12 L, 2 R)	9
Death Valley Buttes (Jan. 2–Feb. 2, 1961): Death Valley Buttes.	Jan. 2, 1961–Feb. 2, 1961.	27 (13 E, 9 L, 5 R)	28

See footnote at end of table.

TABLE 1.—*Observations upon which report is based*—Continued

[E, ewe; R, ram; L, lamb]

Location	Date	Number of animals	Hours of observation
Badwater (Feb. 10–Mar. 1, 1961): Badwater.	Feb. 10, 1961–Mar. 1961.	12 (7 E, 4 L, 1 R)...	6
Total hours of observation......	....	....	1,693

¹ From July 20 to Aug. 8, summer rains practically eliminated use of the springs by bighorn for the first time since June 1955.

² From before dawn until after dark, every day for 30 days, we recorded the activities of everything that moved on the ground and in the air—420 hours at the site, 253 hours with the bighorn under observation.

The impact of 30 days of unbroken continuity in observation of 1 area and 1 group by the same personnel will be felt throughout this report, since it brought about a revision of our entire approach to the study.

Owing to the overlapping of time of observation of individual animals and the greater body of information involved, the numerical data for this period is presented in a different form. (See Tables 2, 6, and 8.)

Cast of Characters

As our study progressed, 51 different bighorn were observed in the monument frequently enough and at sufficiently close range to receive identifying names in our field notes. The names of these individuals and their identifying characteristics are given here. The subject is discussed further under "Field Identification."

Rams

Black and Tan.......... Prime. Tan with blackish mane, ears, and legs. At Nevares Springs.

Broken Nose............ Heavy, mature ram with crooked, humped nose. Dark, chipped-away patch on left horn. At Nevares Springs. (See figs. 51 to 59.)

Flathorn................ Big dark ram, aloof and suspicious, with a flat area on the top curve of his left horn. At Nevares Springs.

Full Curl............... The oldest ram we knew. Possibly 14 years. Very heavy and badly broomed, but still full-curled horns. Potbellied, but still sleek and intimidated by no one. At Nevares Springs.

The Hook............... Prime. About 8 years old. Slim, dark shiny red (mahogany). High, round close curl, straight nose, and straight neck. Quarter-horse type. Light mark across nose. Beetle browed, left horn broken off leaving jagged, sharp "hook." Right horn split off in jagged point, making identification easy. At Nevares Springs.

Rams—Continued

Kinky.................. Young, mature (5 years old), with widespread horns with a "kink" near tips of both horns. At Big Wash, Echo Canyon.

Knocker.............. Young ram with outsized testicles to match his overactive ego. At Nevares Springs.

Little Joe............. Small young ram with a belligerent disposition that reminded us of a small man we knew by the name of Joe. At Nevares Springs.

Low Brow............. Young ram, with heavy projecting forehead. At Nevares Springs.

Mahogany............. Big, mahogany red, archetype of the desert Bighorn ram. At Nevares Springs.

Nevares............... Called by this place name because he typified the rangy appearance of the majority of the first Nevares sheep we knew. Long body, long legs, long ewe neck, high shoulders. About 7 years old. Definitely mature, but gangling. Hindlegs bent out a little, willowy. Last 10 inches of curve of horns extremely thin and flat, sharper curve or "hook" toward end. On September 2, left horn splintered off 2 to 3 inches. Brown color. Dull pelage.

Nevares II............. Named for older prototype. Younger than Nevares (about 5 years old), but also rangy, ewe necked, high shouldered, long bodied, long legged, horns deeply corrugated, lots of hair back of head with a "shawl" of unshed hair over shoulders. No "hook" on left horn, but left tip turns toward his body, right tip away from body.

Paleface............... Dark gray young ram with whitish face, who herded Droopy for 3 days below Badwater near Keystone Canyon.

Rambunctious........... Aggressive adolescent of the Furnace Creek band. Scar on his back and right side; pronounced sectioning of his horntips. (See fig. 30.)

Roughneck............. Not yet prime. Rough pelage on neck and shoulders fitted his aggressive nature. At Nevares Springs.

Skinny................ Older than Slim. Rough coated, aggressive. At Nevares Springs.

Slim.................. Gangly, high horned. About 3 years old. At Nevares Springs.

The Stranger........... An old "traveling man" on the rut run in March 1956. At Dead Man's Curve.

Tabby................ Blunted full curl, last 6 to 8 inches of left horn chipped thinner and lighter than rest of horns, slimmer than Broken Nose, with extra "tab" of skin on scrotum. Scar on right flank. No eye rings or other facial markings except black spot on nose. No white on front legs or inside back legs. Eight to nine years old. At Nevares Springs. (See figs. 51 to 59.)

Rams—Continued

Tan Rump . . . . Prime. Brown, with tan instead of white rump patch. A traveling ram, with occasional stop-overs at Nevares.

Tight Curl . . . . Mature. Light tan, low shouldered, with peculiar tight curl of right horn, nick near tip of left horn; bases of both horns scarred by heavy fighting. At Nevares Springs, Navel Spring, Big Wash, Furnace Creek, Echo Canyon. (See fig. 25.)

Toby . . . . Tall, bony, high shouldered, scraggly "wig" on back of head. About 8 years old. At Nevares Springs.

Ewes

Big and Little Sandies . . . . The two unmarked sand-colored ewes, perhaps sisters, who were inseparable companions at Furnace Creek. Big Sandy had three faint "warble" scars on the right side. (See figs. 18 and 19.)

Blondie . . . . The distinctively light-colored, young, and slender proportioned glamour girl of the Furnace Creek band.

Brahma . . . . Broken or malformed horns, drooping ears, and the light, blue-gray color of a Brahma cow. She was the lightest colored ewe at Nevares Springs. She had a single-foot gait. About 5 or 6 years old. Had 3-month-old ram lamb, slightly buckskin colored. We knew her for over 4 years.

Brahma II . . . . Brahma II looked like Brahma, but she was the leader of the band on Death Valley Buttes, 9 miles northwest.

Brokeoff . . . . Brokeoff led her forlorn little band to Nevares Springs in 1958. She was tall, gaunt, and gray, with one very long horn and one—what else? Broken off!

Dark Eyes . . . . This was the only ewe we ever knew who seemed to have black eyes. We never could get close enough to her to analyze the reason. At Nevares Springs.

Droopy . . . . The Badwater contender for leadership, with the unique, down-curved horns that led many to think that she was a ram. (See figs. 5 and 6.)

Gimpy . . . . Lame in her right hindleg but a great traveler. Observed at Furnace Creek, Big Wash, Paleomesa. We last saw her, browsing alone, in the Red Amphitheater in 1957.

Little Brownie . . . . The smallest ewe at Nevares Springs except Little Ewe.

Little Ewe . . . . Pale gray. Dainty, gentle mother at Nevares Springs.

Long Brownie .... Named for reddish-brown color and descriptive conformation. Exaggerated Nevares type—long bodied. Only red-brown ewe seen in area. Gives impression of white-socked horse. No lamb. Horns almost as long as Longhorn's.

Longhorn .... Prime. Clear gray, slender, aloof, and with the longest horns we ever saw. At Nevares Springs.

New Mama .... Slender and elegant compared with Old Mama, but a nervous leader of the new band that came in March. At Furnace Creek. (See fig. 37.)

Old Eighty .... The eighth to join the Furnace Creek band. The leader when Old Mama wasn't there. Right horntip missing; pronounced annular hornrings on both horns, 1 set of annual rings deeply grooved. Face whitish. (See figs. 17 and 31.)

The Old Lady .... The mother of sad Little Fuzzy, who had the unrewarding distinction of having a canyon named after him because he died there, half a mile north of Nevares.

Old Leader or The Patriarch. ... The dignified, unhurried old leader of the Badwater band. (See figs. 1, 5, and 7.)

Old Mama .... To whom we owe so much. Old, potbellied, runny-nosed, but tough and worldly wise in bighorn ways. Her right horn was chipped on the inside (rare) near the base, and distinctively broomed at the tip. Her eyes were yellow, with light patches below. At Paleomesa, Furnace Creek, Big Wash, Navel Spring. (See figs. 10 and 28.)

Pearl .... Pearl was a big ewe who got her name because of the peculiar quality of the gray of her coat. She and her lamb lived somewhere on Pyramid Peak and came down across Paleomesa now and then on their way to water at Navel Spring.

Scarface .... An otherwise sleek and beautiful 2-year-old who had apparently fallen from a cliff when she was very young. That she survived the severe facial lacerations and possible skull injuries which left her face the way it was is remarkable. At Furnace Creek. (See fig. 29.)

Whitehorns .... Bad Boy's mother. She had a white patch of hair at the base of each horn, which seemed to extend her horns down the side of her head.

Lambs

Baby Brownie .... She got lost before dawn in the rut run and survived several days alone on Nevares Peak before Little Brownie, her mother, found her again.

Bad Boy .... A 6-month-old who was already pestering the ewes when he came out on Paleomesa in the autumn of 1956. (See figs. 32 and 33.)

Lambs—Continued

Light Neck . . . . Named for whitish patches on both sides of neck. Dark Eyes was this ram lamb's mother. About 7 to 8 months old. Had 6- to 7-inch horns. Still nursing. Dark gray with blackish tints, light neck. Long legs. Horns already showing male characteristics.

Little Brahma . . . . This lamb had begun to look more and more like his mother (Brahma) when we last saw him heading toward Red Wall Canyon at the foot of Nevares Peak.

Little Fuzzy . . . . Named for its "fuzzy" brownish coat. Old Lady was its mother. Scrawny legs, potbellied, like a skim-milk calf, possibly owing to malnutrition, since the mother looked dry. No horns. Looked about 6 weeks old. Found dead August 30 (fig. 44) after being seen alone on August 23. Younger than we thought—perhaps 4 weeks.

Little Whitey . . . . Bad Boy's inseparable companion. A ewe lamb, much lighter colored than he and with white rump, white face (relatively rare), and a peculiar carriage of the head. (See figs. 26, 32, and 33.)

Marco . . . . Six months old. A tough, homely little fellow with a tendency toward travel and independence. Buckskin color (rare) with a blackish mane.

Mischief . . . . Mischief was the first lamb we knew and the only child of the Badwater family. (See figs. 27 and 48.)

Old Mama's Lamb . . . . This lamb had a wonderful time for the first few weeks of its life in Furnace Creek. Then from watching her, however, we began to learn how difficult it is to be a bighorn lamb in Death Valley. (See figs. 34, 35, 36, 37, 38, and 39.)

Life History of the Death Valley Bighorn

Habitat

The terrain of Death Valley itself should not be described without first identifying it as being part of, and surrounded by, the Great Basin, or the Basin and Range Province. The fact that it is situated within this tremendous area, surrounded by other ranges and basins, and is itself the deepest, hottest, and driest of all the Great Basin depressions, accounts in part for the present study.

The physiography of Death Valley has contributed to its climate, its scenic beauty, its geologic interest, its ecology, and its economic and human history in such a way that the composite picture becomes one of a unique and superlative desert area, to be recognized as such and set aside by Presidential proclamation in 1933 as a national monument.

Since this study has been projected by the National Park Service, the 2 million acres of land within the boundaries of the monument comprise the terrain of principal consideration. On the other hand, this arbitrary line in many instances leaves an incomplete biota within the monument boundary, thus forcing a major consideration of the contiguous areas involved.

Death Valley is approximately 190 miles long and from 5 to 20 miles wide, with about 550 square miles below sea level, reaching the lowest land point in this hemisphere at —282 feet near Badwater.

Mountain ranges surround the valley, rising to elevations of 5,000 to 11,000 feet, and there are practically no foothills between them and the valley floor. These mountains are composed principally of metamorphosed sedimentary rock, with the entire span of geologic time represented in the exposures of one ancient layer after another. The mountains arose, however, in relatively recent times, and volcanic activity, faulting, folding, tilting, and uplifting continued through the Pleistocene epoch with such force that erosion was not allowed to become a predominant force until the ice age ended. So the mountains are still new, steep, and relatively devoid of soil.

What might in a less arid climate have become a cismontane soil supply now comprises a third geological feature of Death Valley, the alluvial fans. Composed of billions of tons of detritus spreading out from the mouths of hourglass canyons on both sides of the valley, the fans are still being formed and reformed as floodwater periodically strips the mountains of their supply of decomposing rock which could have become earth.

The entire region may be characterized as one of extreme variability over incredibly short distances. The altitudinal variation is, of course, reflected in the climate. When the then world record of 134° F. was reached below sea level at Furnace Creek Ranch on July 10, 1913, bighorn might have been feeding at 11,000 feet on Telescope Peak in the mild eighties.

During the summer, temperatures of over 120° F. are not uncommon, and nighttime temperatures remain relatively high. In 1959, July recorded an average maximum of 120.1°.

January is consistently the coldest month, with a steady rise in temperature through July and a steady fall through December.

The lowest official temperature of 15° F. was recorded at Furnace Creek Ranch January 8, 1913, the same year as the record high.

Summer and winter, the lowest temperatures occur just before sunrise, with an average differential of 27.2° between 24-hour maximum and minimum readings.

The average number of clear days in a calendar year is 283, and the recorded high is 351. Absence of clouds, the low-density ground cover, and the generally light-reflecting quality of the terrain contribute to an intensity of insolation affecting all life in the area.

The extremely variable rainfall is not adequately conveyed by the official weather records, for the only two stations in operation during the time of this study were less than 4 miles apart and at the same elevation, below sea level. The recorded rainfall averages around 2 inches per year, with a maximum of 4.2 inches in 1941 and a minimum of 0.09 in 1953.

But since, in general, precipitation is correlated with elevation, and since elevations can vary so much in such short distances, it becomes apparent that an accurate record of the rainfall affecting bighorn habitat would involve more weather stations and personnel than are likely to be available for some time. Precipitation can, for instance, be heavy throughout the high mountains and yet none happen to hit the existing weather stations on the valley floor. And the opposite, of course, happens. During an extremely dry year, an isolated cloudburst can catch a weather station, raising the weather chart to "normal" but adding nothing to the vegetation of the sheep range.

The general concept of desert rainfall in North America, including that of Death Valley, is one of two sources and two seasons: winter rains of cyclonic origin from the Pacific, moving across mountain ranges with the rain shadow deepening as it moves eastward, and summer storms from the Gulf of Mexico. A correlation has become apparent between the general pattern of precipitation and the pattern of prevailing wind. In the summers, when there is high occurrence of mountain rainfall, over 90 percent of the wind has been southerly. While winter winds may bring dust-storms from either the south or the north, the prevailing currents appear to come from the north and west, their direction being altered locally by the north and south orientation of the mountain ranges.

Very little work has been done on meteorology specifically for this area, but, presumably, the above generality would be sound despite the local contention that "Death Valley makes its own weather."

Snow is common in the winter to all the surrounding mountains down to the 4,000-foot level, but seldom achieves a pack deep enough to affect winter foraging. Only once in history has snow lain on the valley floor.

It is commonly believed that a relative humidity of zero is to be expected in the summer, but during the period of this survey the lowest determination made was 3 percent, with a summer average of about 10 percent.

That the aridity of Death Valley is commonly exaggerated is indicated in a report from the Scripps Institution of Oceanography (Gorczynski, 1940) : "The Mojave and Colorado Deserts represent the driest area in North America; Bagdad, California, has 70% aridity co-efficient, Death Valley 57%, Yuma 42%, Phoenix 28%, and Tucson 22%, as compared with the middle of the Sahara approaching 100%."

Vegetation, of course, is predominantly xerophilous (i.e., of a type adapted to live in dry soil, sand, or on rocky ridges; characterized by thickening of epidermis, reduction of leaf surface), with a limited, but, to the bighorn, important growth of phreatophytes (deep-rooted plants that obtain their water from the water table or from the layer of soil just above it) in areas of live, perennial ground-water supply.

Because of the high salt content of most of the ground and water at lower levels, and especially on the valley floor, many of these plants must be highly salt resistant.

Away from the relatively few ground-water areas, the vegetation is inclined to be uniformly sparse, the plants widely spaced by the demands of their root systems in the shallow soil and rounded by the equal exposure to light from all sides.

With a few exceptions such as the creosotebush (*Larrea tridentata*) and pigmy cedar (*Peucephyllum schottii*), sometimes known as spruce-bush, the vegetation is light in color, ranging from the silver-white of

616472 O—62——3

desertholly (*Atriplex hymenelytra*) to the dark grays of blackbrush (*Coleogyne ramosissima*), and the yellowish green of rabbitbrush (*Chrysothamnus*).

With the exception of willows and mesquite in ground-water areas, the Black and Funeral Mountains on the eastern side of Death Valley are devoid of trees. The higher elevations from about 6,000 feet up, in the Grapevine Mountains, the Cottonwoods, and the Panamints, support the usual high-desert communities of drought-resistant conifers.

Except for those in the high areas, the plants of the region must be prepared to withstand severe drought conditions, lasting from several months to several years. During these observations we have watched perennial plants lie dormant for at least 6 years, growing drier, more brittle and brown month by month, until even we thought they were dead. No annuals of any kind made an appearance the entire time, and yet when in the seventh year the rains came the perennials grew green again and the annuals appeared as if by magic.

Food

Because of the extreme variability in the quantity, quality, and location of food supplies, food habits and feeding behavior are two of the most difficult pieces to fit into the jigsaw puzzle of the bighorn survival pattern. Almost the only generality that can be made about them is that they are effectively unpredictable.

Kinds

We cannot name any one plant as the mainstay of the bighorn diet. Nor can we say of any area that here they feed in the winter or that here they spend their summers.

The types of food can be described as including, to a locally limited degree, all of the four main groups of plants common to the desert bighorn ranges everywhere—grasses, annual nonwoody flowering plants, shrubs, and trees.

Owing to their shallow root system and the lack of humus in the soil, dependable supplies of grasses can be found only in live ground-water areas, in high washes where runoffs are fairly frequent, and on rolling plateau land at elevations so situated as to make substantial snowfall a dependable feature of annual precipitation.

During the 8 years of this study there have been recorded but two "good flower years." That is to say, years when the casual visitor could be assured of finding enough flowering plants in any one place at any one time to call it a display. At best, these displays are spotty from the valley floor to the mountaintops because the rainfall necessary to their development is spotty, even in the wettest years.

Given enough water and sunlight, annuals on the valley floor and fans at the mouths of canyons may begin to mature in December, as at Badwater in 1954, and spread up the slopes with the advancing seasons through the summer, and if autumn rains are propitious there may be flowers blooming somewhere at some elevation every day of the year. This does not happen every year, by any means, but the fact that it happens some years is of vital importance to the bighorn, because even if the sheep do not find the plants in time to utilize the succulent inflorescence, the dried plants become a vital backlog of food which is no longer dependent on season, sunlight, or rainfall. In fact, much of this supply of food plants seems to become palatable to the bighorn only after it is completely dehydrated.

Present evidence indicates a preponderance of shrub utilization in the diet. The deeper, more extensive root systems of the woody plants and their general resistance to excessive heat, light, and aridity have made some acceptable shrubs available to the sheep at all elevations and at all seasons. The general scarcity of grasses throughout the entire region is, of course, good reason for the bighorn to lean heavily on browsing rather than grazing.

A very limited utilization of the mesquite represents the only tree browsing we have observed in Death Valley.

With very few exceptions, only those plants actually observed by us in the process of utilization are included in this report, because of the difficulty in so many cases of determining whether the browsing was done by sheep, packrats, jackrabbits, or chuckwallas.

On November 17, 1956, a band of nine sheep had been observed for several hours feeding at the base of a cliff 200 yards above the wash in shadow. The plants being used were carefully located by relative number, color, and position for future checking. The next day we found that the dried stems of *Aster* and the small, dark-green leafed *Encelia,* with some dried white bursage *(Franseria dumosa)* had been utilized. This was the first time we had a positive observation of utilization of the dried *Franseria.* But more unusual than that was a patch of green wetleaf *(Boerhaavia annulata)* that had been eaten well back to the ground! I sat down on a large boulder to add this second "first" to my notes when I saw that my large boulder was covered with chuckwalla *(Sauromalus obesus)* droppings, and bits of the wetleaf were scattered around among the small openings beneath. I added wetleaf to the chuckwalla's list, but not to the bighorn's.

The single circumstance of cropping of a plant is no basis for inclusion in a bighorn diet list. The close-cropped, hedged appearance of many *Franseria* plants in the vicinity of Corkscrew Spring had been puzzling for years until June 13, 1957, when a chuckwalla was observed to crawl up into a *Franseria dumosa* bush and, spreading all four legs, to move about on top of the plant in a sort of swimming motion, snipping off the newer shoots in a hedge-clipping effect that explained to us for the first time why so many *Franserias* look the way they do.

Rodents and rabbits are common deceivers in this branch of research. During the Cottonwood Mountains bighorn-burro study in the winter of 1955, the bunchgrass over the entire mountaintop on which we stood was "mowed" to the surface, not by burros (or bighorn) but by rabbits. There was no burro or sheep sign present, but close inspection revealed the ground to be literally overlaid with disintegrated rabbit pellets.

A typical exception to the rule, resulting in the inclusion of a plant that was not seen to be eaten, was recorded on June 5, 1957, in Monument Canyon (1½ miles southwest of the road to Dante's View). On the way up the canyon I was aware of walking through an exceptionally tall and thick growth of *Phacelia* sp. (probably *calthifolia*). I noticed that now and then the tips of some had been utilized, and occasionally even faint track impressions of bighorn showed up in the coarse gravel between plants. The sun was in my eyes, however, and since I was looking for water I did not see what had really happened there until I was on my way back with the sun behind me. When I reached the *Phacelia* beds then, I saw very clearly that many of the flowering plants had been cropped almost to the ground, and that bighorn tracks were around all those cropped, and it was plain to see where the animals had moved from one plant to the other. On the other hand, where no faint tracks showed, no cropping had occurred. Tips broken off but not eaten still retained some color, and the general condition indicated a time lapse of about a week.

Reports from other observers of plants utilized by sheep are not included here for two reasons. Primarily, this list is based on what we have observed, not on what we have read or have been told. Secondly, these exclusions reduce the margin for error to a considerable degree, because mistakes in actual feeding observations are almost as common as those made by a misinterpretation of browsing evidence. Observers with us in the field have repeatedly pointed out incidents of apparent browsing on creosotebush, pigmy cedar, and rabbitbrush (*Chrysothamnus*), when close inspection revealed the presence of a forage plant growing up through the one seeming to be eaten.

Observed utilization of individual species of plants has been so varied as to preclude the effective use of a standard chart of plant distribution and utilization. This, of course, is but a further projection of the great climatic and altitudinal variation which characterizes the habitat as a whole, focusing on the instability of precipitation and the resultant unpredictability of seasonal plant development. While we have found no plant that we can indicate as the most important in the bighorn diet, or one that is more important to rams and one to ewes, etc., some are beginning to attain a general relative status, and as such they are listed. It must be emphasized that none of these plants was ever observed in full year-round utilization, but when they were utilized, it was shown in the following tabulation:

Forage plants observed to be used by bighorn

[Nomenclature follows Kelsey and Dayton (1942); where plant is not listed by them, nomenclature follows Jaeger (1950)]

	Heavy	Moderate	Light
Andropogon glomeratus: Bluestem			X
Aster abatus: Mohave aster		X	
Atrichoseris platyphylla: Parachute plant	X		
Atriplex hymenelytra [1]: Desertholly	X		
Atriplex canescens: Fourwing saltbush			X
Bebbia juncea: Rush bebbia	X		
Boerhaavia annulata: Wetleaf			X
Chaenactis fremontii: Pebble pincushion	X		
Cirsium mohavense: Mohave thistle		X	
Distichlis spicata: Saltgrass			X
Echinocactus polycephalus: Cottontop cactus			X
Encelia farinosa: White brittlebush		X	
Encelia sp.: Brittlebush			X
Ephedra nevadensis: Nevada jointfir		X	
Ephedra sp.: Jointfir			X
Eriogonum inflatum: Desert trumpet	X		
Eriogonum sp.: Eriogonum		X	
Eucnide urens: Stingbush			X
Euphorbia parishii: Parish euphorbia		X	
Euphorbia sp.: Euphorbia			X
Franseria dumosa: White bursage			X
Grayia spinosa: Spiny hopsage			X
Hilaria jamesi: Galleta	X		
Hilaria rigida: Big galleta			X
Hymenoclea salsola: White burrobrush			X
Mohavea breviflora: Lesser mohavea			X
Monoptilon belleoides: Mohave desertstar		X	
Nama sp.: Nama			X
Oenothera brevipes: Golden eveningprimrose	X		
Oenothera clavaeformis: Browneyed eveningprimrose	X		
Oenothera decorticans: Woody bottlewasher		X	
Oenothera sp.: Eveningprimrose	X		
Phacelia sp.: Phacelia		X	
Physalis crassifolia: Thickleaved groundcherry			X
Prosopis glandulosa: Honey mesquite			X
Sisyrinchium sp.: Blue-eyedgrass			X
Sphaeralcea pulchella: Mohave desertmallow		X	
Sphaeralcea: Mallow		X	
Sporobolus airoides: Alkali sacaton	X		

[1] Probably more nearly in general year-round use than any other plant.

	Heavy	Moderate	Light
Stephanomeria sp.: Wirelettuce	X		
Stipa speciosa: Desert needlegrass		X	
Stipa sp.: Needlegrass			X
Tidestromia oblongifolia: Honeysweet	X		

The difficulty involved in ascribing seasonal importance to any of the plants listed will become evident as the varying intensity and time of their use is described.

During the Badwater observations from December 18, 1954, to January 24, 1955, three plants made up 75 percent of the diet of the band of four ewes and two lambs: Desertholly (*Atriplex hymenelytra*), in full bloom from a warm rain in November, 35 percent; honeysweet (*Tidestromia oblongifolia*), having matured in October but still not completely dormant, 25 percent; and Parish euphorbia (*Euphorbia parishii*), 10 percent. The remaining 30 percent was composed of dried annuals of previous seasons, utilized systematically in alternating periods throughout the day, and new green shoots of annuals as they appeared.

When four of the band returned, February 12, they ignored the perennials of their former diet and concentrated on the lush annuals entirely.

We did not see honeysweet utilized again until one of the same sheep returned 3 years later to a fan 5 miles south of Badwater on December 3, 1957. This was the ewe named Droopy, and a young ram, and they divided their attention, when they ate at all, between desertholly and honeysweet.

Groundcherry (*Physalis crassifolia*) and Parish euphorbia, both utilized only slightly less than the first two in January 1955, have not reentered the list since.

Desertholly has maintained a relatively important place in subsequent observations with the exception of about 4 months during the winter of 1955–56, when two bands of bighorn ignored it and honeysweet during their entire stay in the Furnace Creek Wash area.

Bebbia juncea and *Stephanomeria* sp. had, in the meantime, assumed the importance holly and honeysweet had held at Badwater. The two plants in about equal ratio formed roughly 60 percent of the diet of a band of eight bighorn from December 28, 1955, to January 17, 1956. Both shrubs were utilized in all stages of development, from new green shoots to inflorescence and even to previous years' dried materials. *Stephanomeria* was, as a matter of fact, hunted out by scent and pawed free of soil during its early development while it still consisted only of white shoots 3 to 4 inches below the ground. The remaining 40 percent of food, represented more or less equal use of dried annuals, perennial inflorescence both fresh and dry, and *Erigonum inflatum* which ranged from the dried woody stems of previous years down through the green leaves of this year's growth. All of these were pawed up and eaten with almost as much relish as *Stephanomeria.*

However, after 2 weeks *Eriogonum inflatum* was dropped from their diet for a week. *Ephedra,* desertholly, honeysweet, *Franseria dumosa,* and *Grayia spinosa* were available, but they were not utilized until just as the band was on its way out of the wash for the last time on January 18, when some of these were suddenly included again. That day the sheep made feeding history. They had ignored *Ephedra* in all our previous observations, but now, as though marking more changes than one in their pattern, they ate it, the entire band gathering about one bush and eating for 15 minutes. A short time later, we were surprised, to say the least, to find them wiggling their noses down among cottontop cactus (*Echinocactus polycephalus*) needles to lap up the "cotton" with evident relish. For the first time in over a week, they also stopped at *Eriogonum* patches and sent up great clouds of dust as they all pawed for the freshest shoots before moving on.

Dried *Aster* and *Encelia* tops came in for their usual share of use on this particular day, but the greatest surprise was the use of dried cottontop cactus thorns and of stingbush. The 6-month-old lamb known as Bad Boy chewed away on dried, blackened cottontop cactus thorns for a full 15 minutes. He was joined, though without much relish, from time to time by three or four others. We had seen evidence of possible use of stingbush before, but this was the first time we had actually observed it. They browsed, not on the succulent undergrowth, but on the dried prickly tips. This was not just nipping and passing on, but real feeding for several minutes. Dormant desertholly was included during the period of observation referred to, but *Hymenoclea salsola* and *Franseria dumosa,* high on many lists of bighorn forage plants, was still untouched. Some *Grayia spinosa* and *Boerhaavia* tops were browsed.

A single ewe and lamb followed the same pattern from February 2 to March 13, 1956, when they were joined by four more adults and another lamb. From March 13 to April 1 this band of seven fed almost exclusively on *Bebbia* and *Stephanomeria.* For 1 week they mixed the lush green *Bebbia* and *Stephanomeria* of the washes with the dormant vegetation of Paleomesa above the washes toward Pyramid Peak. This change was similar to the one made by the previous band just before they left the wash for the last time—dormant desertholly, *Encelia, Aster, Eriogonum,* and *Grayia spinosa* leading the list, as though the sheep were gradually breaking themselves into a change they knew was coming. They alternated their feeding in the wash with lengthening periods on the mesa, until one final feast on April 8; and then, with the forage in the wash the most luxuriant it had been all year, they left.

Two days later two of the ewes and a lamb returned and for 2 days ate nothing but the inflorescence of *Hymenoclea* and *Franseria dumosa,* with *Bebbia* and *Stephanomeria* suddenly secondary on the list. They had been gone for 3 days when the first ewe and her lamb returned alone. They were back on *Stephanomeria* and *Bebbia* again, with only desultory nipping now and then at *Hymenoclea* and *Franseria.*

This brief utilization of *Hymenoclea* and *Franseria,* it should be emphasized, was only of the inflorescence, lapping the buds and blossoms into the mouth with the tongue and then tossing the head to strip only the flowering parts from the plant. This is the only time we have seen this happen. Previous observations had shown no utilization of *Hymenoclea* whatever, and it stands today as the only record, although this is one of the most widely distributed plants in the wash community.

Franseria utilization had been previously recorded as varying from extremely casual and intermittent use to none at all. It is not only common in washes but is likely to be associated with the creosotebush-saltbush (*Larrea-Atriplex*) communities throughout the Death Valley region. Heretofore, nothing but dried inflorescence had been taken. We were not to observe further utilization of *Franseria* until October 2, 1957, when a band of seven browsed for several hours vigorously on whole *Franseria* plants for the first and only time during this study.

Bebbia and *Stephanomeria* resumed their importance in sheep diet in October 1956 and retained it until the end of December 1956. Then with the exception of a few weeks of travel use in and out of Nevares Spring we observed no utilization of either plant from January 1, 1957, to August 1958. Furnace Creek Wash, Big Wash (a tributary to Furnace Creek Wash), and all the washes above Navel Spring were as lush with it as they had ever been in 8 years, but repeated and extensive surveys there disclosed no bighorn use and only an occasional sign of an animal or small band crossing the washes, apparently on their way from the back country to Navel Spring for water.

So *Bebbia* and *Stephanomeria* have begun to emerge as extremely important to the bighorn in years of drought when practically the only areas that get enough moisture to produce green feed are the washes that form the stem and "handle" of the huge drainage fans near and beyond the base of such mountains as Pyramid Peak. These two plants are doubly important in that they are almost as acceptable to the bighorn in their dormant stage as in any other. In this stage they may rest unused but in perfect storage for several seasons, should general rains in the higher country provide enough forage to make regular use of the washes unnecessary.

From these observations it seems reasonable to suggest a correlation between the relatively dry months in the high country from November 1954 through December 1956 with the concurrent use of the washes, and the immediate and continued disuse of the washes with the resumption of relatively regular and heavy rainfall in the back country.

The importance of *Eriogonums* and *Encelias* should not be underestimated, since they are utilized at all stages of growth, have a wide altitudinal distribution, and are likely to be found in use almost as regularly, if not in such quantity, as *Atriplex hymenelytra*.

Most of this study has been conducted below the 4,000-foot level and has therefore not included much of the *Ephedra* range, but on those occasions when sheep did come in contact with it observations indicated a moderate to heavy use of it at higher elevations. The same observations were made with regard to *Atriplex canescens, Grayia spinosa, Stipa speciosa, Hilaria jamesii,* and *Hilaria rigida*.

The importance of some plants will be emphasized later in connection with water and the special part they play in bighorn watering behavior. In general, however, it should be pointed out here that the amount and kinds of food found near or at a water supply can be the determining factor in the survival of many animals every year.

During our 30 days of continuous observation at Nevares Spring in the summer of 1957, we found a great variation in the utilization of the available food supply. With our 12- and 16-power glasses from our general observation camp, we could check the use of any of the 40 plants listed below, which we believe comprise all plants of the Nevares community:

Plants of the Nevares Spring Area*

[*Species identified at Stanford University by Roxana S. Ferris, assistant curator of the Dudley Herbarium, and Dr. Wallace R. Ernst. **Utilized by bighorn during 30-day observation period]

Gramineae—Grass Family:
Andropogon glomeratus (Walt.) B.S.P.—Bluestem**.
Arundo donax L.—Giant reed.
Distichlis spicata (L.) Greene—Saltgrass**.
Imperata hookeri Rupr.—California satintail.
Sporobolus airoides Torr.—Alkali sacaton, or hairgrass dropseed**.
Cyperaceae—Sedge Family:
Fimbristylis thermalis Wats.—Hotspring fimbristylis.
Schoenus nigricans L.—Black sedge.
Scirpus olneyi Gray.—Olney bulrush.

Juncaceae—Rush Family:
  Juncus cooperi Engelm.—Cooper rush.
Iridaceae—Iris Family:
  Sisyrinchium sp.—Blue-eyedgrass**.
Orchidaceae—Orchid Family:
  Epipactis gigantea Dougl.—Giant Helleborine.
Saururaceae—Lizard's-tail Family:
  Anemopsis californica (Nutt.)Hook.— Yerba mansa.
Polygonaceae—Buckwheat Family:
  Eriogonum inflatum Torr. and Frem.—Desert trumpet**.
  Eriogonum sp.—Eriogonum**.
Chenopodiaceae—Goosefoot Family:
  Atriplex hymenelytra (Torr.) Wats.—Desertholly**.
  Suaeda sp.—Seepweed.
Amaranthaceae—Amaranth Family:
  Tidestromia oblongifolia (Wats.) Sta.— Honeysweet**.
Mimosaceae—Mimosa Family:
  Prosopis juliflora var. torreyana (L.) Benson—Western honey mesquite**.
  Prosopis pubescens Benth.—Screwbean, or tornillo.
Zygophyllaceae—Caltrop Family.
  Larrea tridentata (D.C.) Coville—Creosotebush.
Euphorbiaceae—Spurge Family:
  Euphorbia parishii Greene—Parish euphorbia**.
Tamaricaceae—Tamarisk Family:
  Tamarix aphylla (L) Karst (*T.* articulata Vahl.)—Athel.
  Tamarix pentandra Pall. (*T. gallica* L.)—Salt cedar.
Losaceae—Loasa Family:
  Eucnide urens Parry.—Desert rocknettle, or stingbush**.
Cactaceae—Cactus Family:
  Echinocactus polycephalus Engelm. and Bigelow—Cottontop cactus**.
  Opuntia basilaris Engelm.—Beavertail cactus.
Lythraceae—Loosestrife Family:
  Lythrum californicum Torr. and Gray—California loosestrife.
Labiatae—Mint Family:
  Salvia funerea M. E. Jones—Death Valley sage.
Compositae—Sunflower Family:
  Aster abatus Blake—Mohave, or desert, aster**.
  Baccharis sergiloides Gray—Squaw waterweed.
  Bebbia juncea var. *aspera* Greene—Sweetbush, or rush bebbia**.
  Cirsium mohavense Jepson—Mohave thistle**.
  Encelia farinosa Gray—Incienso, or Encelia**.
  Franseria dumosa Gray—Burro-weed, or white bursage**.
  Gutierrezia microcephala (D.C.) Gray—Threadleaf.
  Peucephyllum schottii Gray—Pigmy cedar, desertfir, or sprucebush.
  Pluchea sericea (Nutt.) Coville—Arrowweed.
  Solidago confinis Gray—Goldenrod.
  Stephanomeria—Wirelettuce**.

Only 18 of the 40 species were utilized at all, and some of these may have been eaten accidently through their juxtaposition with other plants.

Of the grasses, alkali sacaton (*Sporobolus airoides*) was commonly and heavily used, with *Andropogon* a poor second and *Distichlis spicata* a poorer third. Utilization of *Prosopis juliflora* was very light as we had expected, but the surprise plant of the summer was the Mohave thistle (*Cirsium mohavense*). Both fresh and dry inflorescence of the thistle were devoured voraciously by the ewes, casually by the lambs, and not at all by the rams!

In a sense it can be said that use of the phreatophytes (deep-rooted plants adapted to live in moist situations) is seasonal in that they are utilized only when bighorn are coming in to water during hot and dry seasons.

The point that must be emphasized here is that the dry seasons are not limited to the seasons of the year, but may, and often do, last for several years at a time. So in a broader sense the word seasonal should probably be applied to the pluvial cycles which play such a dominant part in the survival patterns of the bighorn.

During our extended reconnaissance work preceding the 1955 census, we found no utilization of spring areas for several months prior to and including June. During this period when the burden was removed from the spring-area vegetation it should not, however, be presupposed that it had been shifted to any other one area or elevation. Much has been said about the bighorn leaving the springs for the high country when the rains come. The use of a broader term than high country is indicated by the 4-month observations below sea level in the Badwater area. Localized rainfall brought on the vegetation which brought the sheep down from Lemonade Spring to the fans in only that one area of the Black Mountains. At the same time, other bands were being observed at the expected higher elevations above the supply of ephemeral food plants at Badwater.

So it would appear difficult if not impossible to discuss bighorn food by season without discussing water and rainfall and their effect on vegetation and their use in relation to wet and dry periods that do not coincide with the calendar year.

For example, forage demands on spring areas was constant for 18 months from July 1955 until January 1957, when pressure on the spring vegetation was relieved by general rains until August. After that date came a 3-month period of use at the springs again; then rainfall once more released the sheep into the back country and to the vegetation there which they had not been able to utilize until the arrival of a wet cycle or season. The distance from free water is the limiting factor in the availability of much of the best forage in the monument and is counteracted only by rainfall when it comes.

Much work remains to be done on the back-country phase of bighorn life history. We have observed bands at 4,000 and 5,000 feet elevation in upper Echo Canyon, where presumably the Nevares

Spring bighorn browse when conditions allow them to remain away from their permanent water supply. With only a few hours observation obtainable, *Hilaria* sp., *Stipa speciosa,* and *Ephedra* sp. were the only plants we could definitely add to the bighorn food list from there.

On June 7, 1955, we observed a band of nine rams in the Cottonwoods at an elevation of 8,000 feet. They traveled and browsed so rapidly that no positive identification of plant utilization could be made. However, in the July census of the same year, Fred Jones reported from the same area the utilization of the following plants: Littleleaf mahogany (*Cercocarpus intricatus*), *Sphaeralcea ambigua,* winterfat (*Eurotia lanata*), low sagebrush (*Artemesia arbuscula*), *Stipa speciosa, Ephedra,* snowberry (*Symphoricarpus longiflorus*), and desert peach (*Prunus fasciculata*).

The relative importance of ephemeral plants as forage is not yet defined. The probability that some flower is blooming at some elevation in the monument every day of the year may be an important factor in bighorn distribution. That variety of diet is of great importance to them is indicated by their habit of incompletely using a plant or an abundant supply of plants. Abandonment of an area owing to exhaustion of ephemeral food supply has not been observed here. The Badwater band left the area while these annuals were at their peak. The last one to leave after feeding entirely on the blossoms of *Atrichoseris platyphylla* for 10 days left a lush field of the plants nodding shoulder high (to a sheep) on the fan, to become part of a "hayfield" for use in another year.

The big flower year of 1958 brought a band of 14 bighorn down from the Grapevine Mountains to an elevation of 1,600 feet at Death Valley Buttes on February 9, where they stuffed themselves for 8 days on *Oenothera* and *Chaenactis* with a seasoning of *Encelia, Monoptilon, Mohavea,* and *Phacelia* thrown in. Then they went back into the Grapevines while the flowering plants were at their optimum production. We were inclined to attribute this exodus to the fact that substantial stands of flowering annuals and perennials were appearing at higher elevations farther away from roads and human molestation.

At 6,000 feet elevation the same self-limiting utilization of ephemeral plants had apparently taken place on Funeral Peak when we surveyed the high trails there June 6, 1957.

The last group of plants to be considered has been labeled "supplementary food" because of the singular aspect of its utilization. Growing *Echinocactus polycephalus* was observed eaten but once, August 23, 1957. At that time, an entire plant, including many of the thorns, was devoured by a mature ram in half an hour. (See fig. 43.)

The lapping up of the "cotton" from among the thorns of cottontop cactus (*Echinocactus*) was engaged in casually by both ewes and lambs on two or three occasions, but the manner and extent of their use of the dried thorns, shells, and roots of long-dead *Echinocactus* plants illustrates the universal tendency of the bighorn to ingest dead wood and plant fiber.

On February 19, 20, and 26, 1956, a month-old lamb ate ordinary gravel in Furnace Creek Wash, and one mature ewe did likewise near Navel Spring on November 25, 1956. These are the only indication that supplementary minerals may be added to the diet in a separate form.

We have very few observations indicating an age class and sex differential in food utilization. Isolated .incidents, of course, prove nothing, but can, in some instances, point toward possibilities. In February 1956, a 4-week-old lamb ate creosotebush (*Larrea tridentata*), Kleenex, and paper bags, which serves as a reminder that the young of all species go through an experimental stage of trying to eat everything they can get into their mouths. So to that extent, young bighorn probably ingest a number of items not relished by their elders. The most pregnant of the ewes at Furnace Creek Wash was the most avid devourer of the "milky" new shoots of *Stephanomeria,* and only ewes and lambs were observed eating thistles at Nevares Spring. However, the fact that only one ram was observed eating cottontop cactus is no reason to conclude that ewes and lambs do not.

In general, evidence points strongly toward lambs, both male and female, beginning to learn during the first week of life to eat everything their mothers do, and by the time they are 2 weeks old they are, to a limited degree, actually doing it.

As far as we have been able to determine, there are no areas of sheep range in Death Valley that are occupied separately by rams, or by bands of ewes during lambing. Bands of rams have been observed without ewes and lambs in certain areas, but limited data prohibit conclusions that ewes and lambs do not use the same areas at times and utilize the plants there.

Shortages

A general shortage of food critical enough to threaten seriously the survival of the species has not occurred here in the past 10 years, if ever. There have been several dry cycles severe enough to affect other species, but the bighorn status during those times can be inferred from the situations that had developed by the end of the particularly dry summer conditions which prevailed throughout the monument in 1956.

On June 7 of that year we found Hanaupah Canyon the driest we had ever seen it, with no food in the canyon washes or on the mountain walls above them. Nine burros, all bony, were subsisting with difficulty on a diet of watercress.

Three days later in Wildrose Canyon we found no flowers, no insects or birds, no lizards, rodents, cottontails, or jackrabbits. One dead coyote, reported to us 5 days earlier, had already been picked clean when we found it. As we approached the carcass, a live coyote in very poor condition got to its wobbly legs and made off. Miners throughout the area reported the least wildlife they had seen in many years. Yet on November 25 with the 2-year drought still unbroken, we observed 18 bighorn at Navel Spring in optimum condition. This was the largest band we had seen anywhere at that time.

Overgrazing has been caused in the past by domestic stock—cattle in the Grapevines and Cottonwoods and wild burros in the Panamints, Cottonwoods, and Black Mountains.

The cattle pressure has been alleviated in the Grapevines and Cottonwoods. Burros have been eliminated from the entire Amargosa Range and are being controlled in the Panamints and Cottonwoods. If present policies of the National Park Service continue in effect, there need be no further shortages induced by an exotic influence.

The only natural shortage of food to be expected, then, involves a shortage of water, and the two become a kind of inseparable bipartite hydrofloral factor of the greatest importance to bighorn survival. If food supplies become too attenuated between water supplies either in distance or time, bighorn survival is threatened.

Back-country forage in the case of Navel and Nevares Springs, for example, covers an area of extremely rough terrain from 8 to 12 airline miles, or a probable 12 to 20 sheep-travel miles, deep. Therefore, a bighorn in an extended dry cycle, if still dependent on its permanent water source, would have to make a 40-mile trip to utilize the farthest limits of its reserve source of food. This would eliminate the very young, the very old, and the sick.

In our 30-day observation at Nevares Spring we found that during the driest, hottest weather the ewes and lambs came to water every 3 to 5 days. (See Table 2.) It was not too uncommon for them to remain within observation range from 4 to 6 hours after drinking. And since bighorn apparently do not habitually travel during the night, it seems obvious that they were making no effort to reach the relatively lush forage of the back country before they returned for water. It would seem doubtful if they could reach it in time to make the trip of any practical value during their longer periods away from water. Hence, the longer the hot and dry period continues, the more likely that a compound shortage of food and water will become acute.

TABLE 2.—*Visits of sheep to Nevares Spring, August and September 1957*

[E, ewe; L, lamb; R, ram]

Date	Temperature (° F.)	Number of sheep observed	Age class and sex	Time seen	Hours observed
August:					
11......	116	3	1 E, 1 L, 1 R..	6 to 7 p.m................	1
13......	117	1	1 E............	4 to 5 p.m...............	1
14......	117	11	3 E, 3 L, 5 R..	10:45 to 11:25 a.m.......	1
15......	115	3	1 E, 1 L.......	11 a.m. to 5 p.m........	6
			1 R............	2 to 5 p.m...............	3
16......	120	2	1 E, 1 L.......	8:45 to 9:45 a.m.........	1
17......	122	10	1 E, 1 L, 2 R..	6:10 to 8:45 a.m........	2½
			1 E, 1 L.......	7:45 to 8:15 a.m........	½
			1 E, 1 R.......	2 to 3:30 p.m..........	1½
			1 E, 1 L.......	2:30 to 3:30 p.m.......	1
18......	121	10	1 E, 1 L, 2 R..	6 to 10 am..............	4
			2 E, 2 L, 2 R..	10:30 a.m. to 2:30 p.m.....	4
19......	116	1	1 R............	6 to 7 a.m..............	1
20......	110	9	1 E, 1 L, 2 R..	5:45 to 7:45 a.m........	2
			1 E, 1 L.......	7 to 8:30 a.m...........	1½
			1 E, 1 L.......	7:15 to 9:45 a.m........	2½
			1 R............	5:15 to 7:15 p.m.........	2
21......	108	5	1 R............	5:45 a.m. to 12:15 m. and 4:30 to 7:30 p.m.	9½
			1 E, 1 R.......	6:30 to 8:30 a.m........	2
			1 R............	7:15 to 7:45 a.m........	½
			1 R............	5:45 a.m. to 12:15 m. and 4:30 to 7:30 p.m.	9½
22......	111	6	1 R............	9:15 to 10:45 a.m.......	1½
			1 E, 1 L, 1 R..	9:45 to 10:45 a.m.......	1
			1 R............	10:45 to 11:45 a.m......	1
			1 R............	1:45 to 6:45 p.m........	5
23......	115	7	1 R............	6 to 7 a.m..............	1
			1 L............	6:45 to 7:45 a.m........	1
			2 R............	9:30 to 11:30 a.m.......	2
			1 E, 1 L, 1 R..	4:30 to 7:30 p.m........	3
24......	117	11	1 R............	8:15 to 11:45 a.m.......	3½
			2 E, 2 L, 2 R..	8:45 to 11:45 a.m.......	3
			3 R............	1:45 to 3:45 p.m........	2
			1 R............	3 to 7:30 p.m...........	4½
25......	112	5	2 E, 1 L, 1 R..	8 a.m. to 2:30 p.m.......	6½
			1 R............	9 a.m. to 2:30 p.m.......	5½
26......	114	2	1 R............	9 to 10:30 a.m..........	1½
			1 R............	6:15 to 7:15 p.m........	1
27......	112	12	1 E, 1 L.......	7 to 7:30 a.m...........	½
			1 E, 1 L, 1 R..	7:15 to 7:45 a.m........	½
			1 R............	7:45 a.m. to 2:45 p.m......	7
			1 R............	9:30 a.m. to 2:30 p.m......	5
			1 R............	1:15 to 3:45 p.m........	2½
			1 E, 1 L, 1 R..	4:15 to 5:15 p.m........	1
			1 E............	6:30 to 8 p.m...........	1½
28......	118	7	1 E, 1 L, 1 R..	7 to 8:30 a.m...........	1½
			1 E............	7:30 to 8:30 a.m........	1
			3 R............	1:30 to 6 p.m...........	4½
29......	117	2	1 E, 1 L.......	1:30 to 2:30 p.m........	1
30......	101	3	1 E, 1 L.......	6 to 6:15 a.m...........	¼
			1 R............	6:15 to 7:15 a.m........	1
31......	104	4	1 E, 1 L, 1 R..	7:30 to 8 a.m...........	½
			1 R............	10:15 to 11:30 a.m.......	1¼

[E, ewe; L, lamb; R, ram]

Date	Tempera-ture (° F.)	Number of sheep observed	Age class and sex	Time seen	Hours observed
September:					
1........	106	4	1 R............	1:30 to 2:00 p.m.........	½
			1 E, 2 R.......	4:45 to 6:45 p.m..........	2
2........	109	8	1 R............	6:45 to 7:45 a.m..........	1
			1 R............	9:30 to 9:45 a.m..........	¼
			1 R............	9:45 a.m. to 3:15 p.m......	5½
			2 E, 2 L, 1 R..	3 to 6:15 p.m.............	3¼
3........	111	5	1 R............	6 to 7:30 a.m.............	1½
			1 R	8 a.m. to 12:30 m. and 5:45 to 7:15 p.m.	6
			1 E, 1 R.......	1:15 to 3:45 p.m..........	2½
			1 R............	1:30 to 3:45 p.m..........	2¼
4........	112	7	1 R............	7 to 8 a.m................	1
			1 R............	8:30 to 9:30 a.m..........	1
			1 R............	9:45 to 10:45 a.m.........	1
			1 R............	2:50 to 3:05 p.m..........	¼
			1 E, 1 L.......	5 to 6:30 p.m.............	1½
			1 R............	6 to 7:15 p.m.............	1¼
5........	111	10	1 R............	6 to 8 a.m. and 6 to 6:30 p.m.	2½
			1 E, 1 L, 4 R..	6:30 to 8 a.m.............	1½
			1 R	10:30 a.m. to 12:30 m. and 1 to 2 p.m.	3
			1 E, 1 L.......	1 to 2 p.m...............	1
6........	117	7	1 E...........	6:30 to 7:30 a.m..........	1
			1 R............	6:45 to 7:45 a.m..........	1
			1 R............	7:45 to 10:45 a.m.........	3
			1 R............	8:30 a.m. to 12:30 m. and 6:15 to 8:15 p.m.	6
			1 E, 1 L.......	9:15 a.m. to 8:15 p.m......	11
			1 R............	2 to 8 p.m...............	6
7........	117	3	1 L...........	8:30 to 10:30 a.m..........	2
			1 R............	10:30 a.m. to 6:30 p.m.....	8
			1 R............	4:30 to 6:30 p.m..........	2
8........	118	8	1 R............	6:45 to 7:15 a.m..........	½
			1 E...........	9 a.m. to 1:30 p.m........	4½
			1 E, 1 L.......	9:30 a.m. to 1:30 p.m......	4
			1 R............	9:30 a.m. to 1:30 p.m......	4
			1 R............	4:15 to 6:30 p.m..........	2¼
			1 E, 1 L.......	4:30 to 7 p.m.............	2½
9........	117	6	1 R............	6 to 7:30 a.m.............	1½
			1 R............	8 to 10:30 a.m............	2½
			1 R............	8:45 to 9:45 a.m..........	1
			1 R............	10:30 a.m. to 12:30 p.m....	2
			1 E, 1 L.......	5:45 to 6:45 p.m..........	1
10.......	113	3	1 R............	10 a.m. to 1:30 p.m........	3½
			1 R............	11:15 a.m. to 6:45 p.m.....	7½
			1 R............	7 to 7:30 p.m.............	½

Water unequivocally enters the picture as a compounding factor, because the lack of it near enough to the food supply effectively eliminates the supply itself. One rainstorm and the shortage immediately ceases to exist as long as pothole water lasts, and perhaps longer if precipitation is heavy enough to bring on new plant growth, whether annual or perennial. A zone of succulence is apparently a fair, if temporary, substitute for free water as far as the bighorn is concerned.

That the nature of feeding periods and the amounts eaten contribute substantially to the survival of the bighorn in Death Valley is indicated by the difficulty encountered when attempting to trace sheep by browsing sign. Habitually they tend to move so steadily and to eat so little of any one plan that browsing sign is often difficult to find even in areas where plants have been carefully noted during observed browsing periods. The animals' habit of nipping from a plant in passing rather than standing and devouring it to the ground, not only leaves a supply of food for their own future or for other animals but allows for a healthier plant recovery, ground cover, and finally, intact watersheds with a minimum of soil loss and a maximum of water retention.

Bighorn feeding behavior is as variable and unpredictable as bighorn food habits. The length of time and the time of day they may feed is influenced by so many overlapping factors that it becomes almost impossible to say what is dominating their browsing activity at any given time. A list would certainly include the following: The nature of food, the general condition of the animals when they find the food, the type of leadership present, the weather, the terrain, and the time and distance from water. Herd composition, age class, and sex, with especial reference to reproduction, may temporarily dominate both feeding and watering behavior.

The most compelling and pervasive influence is the quality and quantity of the food available. All age classes and sexes spend less time eating when food is rich and abundant. The six ewes, six lambs, and two rams in the flowerbeds on Death Valley Buttes for 8 days in February 1958 alternated average feeding periods of 90 minutes with average rest and play periods of 3 hours. The Furnace Creek Wash band, with the same age class and sex ratios represented but lacking the abundance of ephemeral food plants, reversed the ratio, alternating 3-hour feeding periods with 1-hour rest periods as a rough average.

The Badwater band, in early winter, with the ram ratio absent and also lacking an abundance of ephemerals, was perhaps the most regular in its feeding behavior of any band we have observed. Of no other band have we been able to be so definite. They browsed among the crags from the first streaks of dawn until sunrise; worked down to the fan from 8 to 9 a.m.; fed in the washes and on the fans until 10

616472 O—62——4

or 10:30; then had their siesta for 30 to 45 minutes; and went back up the slope to browse at higher elevations until noon. Then they took another siesta for 1 to 1½ hours. They repeated this pattern in the afternoon, with a siesta at 2 or 2:30; fed on back to the edge of rising elevations at dusk; and then climbed up to 100 to 500 feet by dark. Occasionally we heard them moving for an hour or 2 after dark.

The unusual regularity of the Badwater feed schedule appeared to be largely due to the personality of the old leader, sometimes called The Matriarch. The strength of her leadership was constantly emphasized by the persistent but futile efforts of another ewe to abrogate her regimen. (See "Herd Leadership.")

For 8 days the leader arose at dawn, led the band down and out on the fans, chose the feeding grounds and siesta sites, led the way to the potholes and pawed the first water, and chose the time and place for night bedding. They alternated an average of 50-minute siestas with 2-hour-and-15-minute feeding periods.

When the leader returned on February 12 with only three of her band, she again took up a regular schedule, but ephemeral abundance was now reflected in longer resting and shorter feeding periods— 70-minute siestas compared with 50 minutes in December, and feeding periods of 1 hour and 54 minutes compared to 2 hours and 15 minutes before the ephemerals matured.

The band of five which joined the ewe known as Old Mama and her lamb in Furnace Creek Wash, March 13, 1956, were gaunt, rough coated, and in every way indicated undernourishment in appearance and action. They buried their heads in the large *Bebbia* and *Stephanomeria* bushes and stayed for several minutes at one bush, then ran to the next. For the first few days they were reluctant to leave the wash for resting, and often in the morning would break into a run and bypass Old Mama on their way into the wash. After about a week their hunger seemed to abate to the extent that they more or less followed the patterns of the old leader.

Weather sometimes controls the length and time of feeding periods, especially for bands watering at lower elevations, where almost no feeding is done by some bands in the middle of hot and humid days.

During dry cycles when sheep may have to travel farther and farther from their water source they tend to line up in traveling through those areas where forage is exhausted. But as soon as they reach food supplies again they spread out and slow down enough to nip a plant as they pass it. This tends to produce longer and more mobile feeding periods. The same is true of the more barren and cliffy terrain, where the low-density ground cover necessitates longer browsing periods than is the case in washes and spring areas.

It is possible that one of the reasons for age class and sex segregation is to be found in differences in food habits and feeding behavior. During the rut, ewes with still nursing lambs are trying to grab as much green forage from the spring areas as they can get, with the added harassment by the rams. So for days at a time, getting food at all is on a catch-as-catch-can basis for both ewes, lambs, and rams.

On the other hand, the pregnant ewe apparently intensifies her search for succulents with the imminence of parturition, and at the same time begins to feed alone and farther away from the rest of the band.

During the spring the rams are likely to be found in mobile bands farther away from water than the ewes and lambs, suggesting a wider browsing range and a greater tolerance for dormant vegetation.

The tendency to browse in the early morning and late afternoon and evening is pronounced only in the hottest weather at lower elevations.

We have no definitive data on amounts eaten. We know that amounts vary with the quality as well as the quantity of food available, and this variation appears to be maintained by choice.

The average browsing time at Nevares Spring was 37 minutes. This comprised a series of the shortest browsing records we have, but no exhaustion of supply motivated abandonment of browsing.

Generally speaking, there appears to be among the bighorn very little aggressive competition for food. Rams in the rut fight for hours, then placidly feed side by side. Sometimes an older animal may oust a younger one from a particular choice plant, and lambs tend to get into the middle of plants like *Bebbia* or *Stephanomeria,* from which they may be removed by their elders. A maturing young ram occasionally will get rough and jostling with adult ewes, but he quickly withdraws if the ewe resists him at all.

The importance of herd leadership in food habits and feeding behavior is becoming increasingly evident. It begins in the first few days of the lamb's life when it is learning by emulation to do everything its mother does, even to the point of trying to help her chew her cud and straining to defecate when its mother does. Leadership in this sense may materialize from any quarter and does not always come from the accepted leader of the band. The youngest in the band may be the boldest and often leads the way in minor enterprises.

On the other hand, when droughts become severe, bands tend to dissolve. As the 1957 summer advanced and the drought continued, we seldom saw more than three bighorn browsing together, usually a ewe, her lamb, and a ram temporarily en famille.

A Factor in Bighorn Distribution and Survival

As a factor in the distribution and survival of bighorn, food habits and feeding behavior emerge close to the top of the list, for we have here what amounts to a conservation program a la bighorn, with four main points: (1) By eating very little of any one plant at a time, the bighorn seldom destroy a plant by browsing. (2) By constant traveling while feeding, they allow plants to recover. (3) By wide dispersal in small bands they further minimize browsing damage. (4) By their ability to subsist for indefinite periods on completely dormant and even dead plant material, they can with immunity survive droughts resulting in the decimation of many other species of desert animals. (5) Their apparent ability to substitute green forage for free water allows them to reach distant food supplies that otherwise would be unavailable to them.

Water

Water requirements of the bighorn in Death Valley can be separated from food requirements only with difficulty since they are so interrelated. It has already been pointed out that under certain conditions the quantity and quality of available food supplies may control the need for free water. Perhaps the word "need" should be defined to clearly include "wanting" or "preferring" as well as "necessary." All of the existing data apply only to what the bighorn prefers in water needs. We know nothing as yet about how much free water it must have to survive. The hypothesis that it can survive with no free water at all will not be discussed here because we have found no evidence to support it.

What is indicated here is a constant need for water, varying in intensity with changes in weather, forage, and activity.

Requirements by Season

In simplest terms, the demand for water increases as the supply decreases. Summer conditions, with longer days and related increases in insolation, aridity, and rate of surface evaporation, are aggravated by the explosive activity and heightened metabolism of the rut. The hottest, driest days (tables 3, 4, and 5), unless relieved by summer rain, coincide with the height of the running and fighting stage of the mating season in late July through August and into September.

TABLE 3.—*Official air temperature record, Death Valley National Monument headquarters for July, August, September, and October 1957*

	July Temperature (° F.)		August Temperature (° F.)		September Temperature (° F.)		October Temperature (° F.)	
	Max.	Min.	Max.	Min.	Max.	Min.	Max.	Min.
1	116	89	121	86	106	72	102	76
2	116	92	119	92	109	75	94	71
3	118	85	118	93	111	79	93	73
4	120	86	117	92	112	82	90	64
5	122	88	115	88	111	80	88	63
6	119	92	109	84	117	81	88	62
7	115	92	107	80	117	83	88	63
8	119	85	111	81	118	87	89	60
9	120	89	116	81	117	87	95	62
10	119	97	116	88	114	90	95	65
11	116	89	116	90	111	84	94	62
12	116	93	115	85	109	83	83	60
13	115	90	117	87	108	79	83	68
14	114	85	117	93	106	78	85	68
15	118	85	115	90	105	77	82	67
16	120	91	120		101	78	90	63
17	118	89	122		101	73	92	64
18	114	90	121		95	70	92	64
19	113	88	116		99	74	91	65
20	113	87	110		98	79	89	69
21	112	87	108		102	79	71	58
22	110	81	111		104	73	76	51
23	110	81	115		106		81	56
24	115	79	117		107	75	86	59
25	117	82	112	79	108	77	89	62
26	117	81	114	69	107	81	81	65
27	114	87	112	84	105	81	85	58
28	118	90	108	75	108	74	90	63
29	119	91	107	77	106	80	87	62
30	121	91	101	71	105	82	83	60
31	121	93	101	72			78	65
Average	117	88	114	84	107	79	87	64

NOTE.—Average for July 1959: 120°.

TABLE 4.—*National Park service ground temperature readings in Furnace Creek vicinity, May–November 1957*

Date	Ground temperature (° F.)			Air temperature (° F.)
	Station No.1	Station No.2	Station No.3	
May 3	132	146	138	102
May 21	139	152	150	105
June 3	156	168	165	117
June 16	158	174	164	121
July 1	164	180	174	123
July 14	160	178	173	122
July 30	157	179	166	120
Aug. 11	157	180	168	....
Aug. 28	150	178	164	....
Sept. 10	144	178	158	....
Sept. 22	136	168	148	....
Oct. 9	130	165	148	....
Oct. 21	115	152	134	....
Nov. 14	110	144	126	....

TABLE 5.—*National Park Service ground temperature readings at Badwater and Tule Spring, May, June, July, and August 1958*

Date	Ground temperature (° F.)		Date	Ground temperature (° F.)	
	Badwater (south)	Badwater (north)		Tule Spring (north)	Tule Spring (south)
May 5	150	142	May 4	144	148
May 31	160	140	May 25	154	142
June 13	154	154	June 13	154	152
June 28	160	160	June 27	156	154
July 12	168	170	July 12	190	178
July 26	164	170	July 26	184	176
Aug. 14	152	162	Aug. 14	160	162
Aug. 30	154	152	Aug. 30	162	162
Sept. 27	160	156	Sept. 27	158	158

This report includes four tables pertinent to water requirements. Table 2, the Nevares Spring sheep record, shows the dates, temperatures, and age class and sex tabulations, the arrival and departure times, and the number of hours observed. Variability is again immediately noted, with high temperatures being the most stable item recorded. The number of animals watering in 1 day ranged from 1 to 12, with no apparent correlation between the hottest days and the number of sheep coming in to water. The first 3 weeks of observation disclosed a preponderance of ewes and lambs on the scene, and the last 10 days show more and more rams. There appears to be no correlation between age class and sex and the time spent by the animals within our range of observation.

Amounts Taken

The question of time preference for watering, as shown in table 6, indicates a definite leaning toward the morning hours, a curious abstinence during the noon hour, a 50 percent resumption of activity shortly after noon, and an irregular decline to sundown. It is worth noting that the highest incidence came before sunrise and the lowest after sunset, with only one animal coming in so late during the entire 30 days.

TABLE 6.—*Hourly record of bighorn drinking at Nevares Spring, from Aug. 11 to Sept. 10, 1957*

Sex and age of animals	Number of animals drinking during morning hours from—							Number of animals drinking during afternoon hours from—							
	5–6	6–7	7–8	8–9	9–10	10–11	11–12	12–1	1–2	2–3	3–4	4–5	5–6	6–7	7–8
Ewes and lambs	2	11	14	10	7	10	2	0	5	3	4	8	4	3	0
Rams	3	18	9	9	11	12	2	0	11	4	2	6	1	3	1
Total	5	29	23	19	18	22	4	0	16	7	6	14	5	6	1

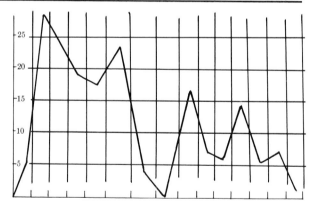

The ground around the spring areas usually was swept at dusk to eradicate the sign and was examined at dawn for sign of nocturnal watering. There was no evidence of nighttime use, but on several occasions animals were found standing at the springs or heading away from water at first visibility.

Actual drinking time of individual animals is partially recorded in table 7. While this record is far from complete, it offers a fair cross section of all age classes and sexes and is sufficiently repetitious in incidence to justify analysis. There are more records of rams than ewes and lambs for two reasons. In the first place, there were more rams to be recorded; and in the second, very often when the ewes and lambs came to springs surrounded by tall grass we were unable to determine actual drinking time. The rams seldom used these areas and when they did their greater size made it possible to determine by body movement whether they were eating or drinking.

TABLE 7—*Drinking time of bighorn at Nevares Spring, 1957*

[E, ewe; L, lamb; R, ram]

Date	Number of animals, by age class and sex	Drinking behavior	Drinking time (minutes)
August:			
15.........	2 (1 E, 1 L).........	....	5
16.........	2 (1 E, 1 L).........	....	11
16.........	1 (1 R).............	Drank intermittently for 45, 50, 30, 29, 20, and 10 seconds.	2½
16.........	2 (1 E, 1 L) (above)..	2d drinking...............	1
17.........	2 (1 E, 1 R).........	After chase..............	10
18.........	4 (1 E, 1 L, 2 R)......	2d drinking...............	3
18.........	6 (2 E, 2 L, 2 R).....	....	5
19.........	1 (1 R).............	....	3
20.........	3 (1 E, 1 L, 1 R).....	....	3
20.........	2 (1 E, 1 L).........	....	7
21.........	1 (1 E).............	....	8
22.........	1 (1 R).............	....	2
23.........	1 (1 R).............	....	2
23.........	3 (1 E, 1 L, 1 R).....	....	6
24.........	1 (1 R).............	2d drinking...............	3
25.........	1 (1 E).............	....	8
25.........	1 (1 R).............	....	3
26.........	1 (1 R).............	....	1
27.........	1 (1 R).............	....	4½
27.........	1 (1 R).............	....	10½
27.........	1 (1 R).............	....	3
27.........	1 (1 R).............	Drank for 3- and 2-minute periods, intermittently.	19
27.........	2 (1 E, 1 L).........	....	7
27.........	1 (1 R).............	....	4
28.........	2 (1 E, 1 L).........	....	6
28.........	1 (1 E).............	....	8
29.........	2 (1 E, 1 L).........	....	5
30.........	1 (1 R).............	....	2½
31.........	1 (1 R).............	....	6
September:			
1.........	1 (1 R).............	....	1½
2.........	1 (1 R).............	....	5
3.........	2 (1 E, 1 R).........	....	7
4.........	1 (1 R).............	....	6
4.........	1 (1 R).............	....	10
4.........	1 (1 R).............	....	5
4.........	1 (1 R).............	....	4
5.........	1 (1 R).............	....	2½

TABLE 7—*Drinking time of bighorn at Nevaras Spring, 1957*—Continued

[E, ewe; L, lamb; R, ram]

Date	Number of animals, by age class and sex	Drinking behavior	Drinking time (minutes)
September:			
6............	1 (1 R)............	....	3
7............	1 (1 L)............	....	3
7............	1 (1 R)............	....	7
7............	1 (1 R)............	....	4
8............	1 (1 R)............	....	2
9............	1 (1 R)............	....	2½
9............	1 (1 R)............	....	6
9............	1 (1 R)............	....	4
9............	1 (1 E)............	....	3
9............	2 (1 E, 1 L)............	....	6
10............	1 (1 R)............	....	12

NOTE.—Average drinking time: Ewe—6.8 minutes; lamb—3 minutes; ram—4.2 minutes; ewe and lamb (together)—6 minutes; ewe, lamb, and ram (together)—6.1 minutes; for all animals—5.3 minutes.

Aside from these records of time spent in drinking, we have nothing but estimates of amounts drunk by individuals. On August 19, 1955, a ewe at Virgin Spring drank close to 3 gallons of water, and her 7-month-old but still nursing lamb drank about half a gallon. On January 16, 1956, after 3 weeks without water, the Furnace Creek Wash band of eight traveled 4 miles to Navel Spring, drank all of the then available 7 or 8 gallons of water, and with at least two of the number still thirsty went a mile back on Paleomesa for the night. We "bedded" them there, camping for the night in freezing weather to find them on their feet at their bedding site at dawn. None came back to drink. On March 24, 1956, a band of four ewes, two lambs, and one ram made the same trip, found 12 gallons of water and left 2, for a probable average of over a gallon and a half for the adults and less for the lambs.

Finally, in table 8, we have approached the question of how long they voluntarily go without drinking. In this table no attempt is made to define the limits of time involved. It is offered as an indicator only, since it records the relative time lapses for only one area with one segment of the entire population for 1 month of one summer, and it discloses a variation so wide as to suggest that in this phase of the life history of the bighorn repetition of observations may be multiplied by generations without definition.

However, some points in Table 8 immediately become apparent. The number of times each animal appeared during the 30 days ranged

TABLE 8.—*Bighorn watering record at*

Animals watering	Date and temperature (° F.)													
	August													
	11 116°	12 115°	13 117°	14 117°	15 115°	16 120°	17 122°	18 121°	19 116°	20 110°	21 108°	22 111°	23 115°	24 117°
Ewe and lamb	X													
Ram	X													
Long Brownie			X											
5 rams				X										
3 ewes				X										
3 lambs				X										
Old Lady					X		X						X	
Fuzzy					X		X					X		
Tabby					X									
Little Ewe						X								
Marco						X								
Dark Eyes							X			X				X
Light Neck							X			X				X
Longhorn							X				X			
Brahma							X			X			X	
Little Brahma							X			X			X	
Mahogany							X				X			X
Slim							X				X			X
Knocker							X			X			X	
Short Horns								X						
A ewe								X						
Widow								X						
3 lambs								X						
White Socks								X						
Rambunctious								X						
Lefty								X			X			
Low Brow								X						
Arrow Collar									X					
Little Brownie										X				X
Baby Brownie										X				X
Roughneck										X		X		
The Hook										X		X		X
Full Curl											X			
Nevares											X			
Deer											X			
Scrubby											X			
Humpy											X			
Rambunctious II													X	
Little Joe														X
Tan Rump														X
Flat Horn														X
Skinny														X
Tight Curl														
Toby														
Low Curl														
Nevares II														
Stocky														
Broken Nose														
Curly														
No. 27														

		August—Continued							September							
25 112°	26 114°	27 112°	28 118°	29 117°	30 101°	31 104°	1 106°	2 109°	3 111°	4 112°	5 111°	6 117°	7 117°	8 118°	9 117°	10 113°
														X		X
X					X									X		
X					X									X		
		X		X				X			X					
		X		X				X			X					
X			X							X				X		
		X				X		X				X		X		
		X				X		X				X		X		
															X	
		X								X				X		
	X									X		X				
							X					X				
			X													
										X		X				
			X							X	X				X	
			X							X	X		X		X	
				X				X								
X		X	X			X			X			X			X	
			X							X	X					
		X						X				X				
		X														
		X														
							X									
		X														
														X		
X	X	X														
		X								X	X	X	X			
			X								X					
						X									X	
								X	X	X	X	X			X	
								X								
									X		X	X				X
												X				
																X

from once only for several to 10 visits for The Hook, who made his first appearance on the 10th day of observations and thereafter set the summer's record for frequency of drinking. It seems safe to conclude that he had been watering at some other spring and decided for some reason to stay on here.

With the exception of three, the one-time visitors were all rams making the rut-run from one spring to another. Three lone rams drank on at least 4 consecutive days. This may indicate a greater need for water on the part of rams but it may not, because the ewe has but one reason to come to the spring and that is for water. She shows up only when prompted by thirst. The ram, on the other hand, may be drinking every day solely because of proximity to water, while on his primary business of racial propagation. This in itself creates a greater expenditure of energy in him than it does the ewe since she is concerned only with her own oestrous cycle, whereas his interest and activity quickens with the sight, sound, and scent of every ewe in the herd. The evidence points toward a greater use of water by rams during the rut. We recorded three instances of rams coming in twice in 1 day but none for ewes.

Table 8 indicates that under these conditions resident ewes and lambs come to water every 3 to 5 days on an average. This means going from 1 to 3 full days without water. The almost double length of time for some animals suggests alternate appearances at two springs, possibly combining Scraper Spring, 5 airline miles to the north, with Nevares to make one home area. How much time rams take or how far they travel on their jaunts from spring to spring is not known. Two of the rams were both known from Navel Spring area 12 airline miles to the south, and both appeared to be heading north toward Scraper Spring when they left Nevares.

The irregularity of five of the ewes seems to indicate multiple use of springs by some ewes as well as rams. A typical instance to support this conclusion occurred at Nevares Spring at 9:30 a.m. on September 5, 1958. It was already 105° in the shade when three bighorn came in from the south on the "Needle's Eye Trail." They were a ewe, a 9-month-old lamb, and a yearling ram. They were the poorest sheep we had ever seen there, walking slowly as though exhausted, heads down, and every rib was showing. The ewe was a true Nevares type, with high shoulders, rangy build, and long, high horns. Was it Longhorn or Long Brownie? As she came closer we knew it was neither. The right horn was broken off—nearly half gone. This could have happened to Longhorn or Long Brownie, but the remaining horn, as long as theirs was, had a hook toward the tip which was unique with this ewe. This one was older, too, at least 10 years old, with conspicuous gray patches at the base of the horns very much like White Horns of Furnace Creek Wash. Long horns are characteristic of the Nevares-type sheep, but the horns of this one were long even for them.

Although we hadn't seen this ewe before, this was not her first time in. She went slowly but directly to Old Spring and began to drink, and the young ram and the lamb joined her, whereupon she trotted 10 yards down to Trail Pool and drank again. The youngsters followed her there and they drank for 5 full minutes. The ewe and yearling then moved a few feet away and stood still, absorbing their water, but the lamb continued to drink for another 2 minutes. Then all three of them stood, filling out like a dried prune fills out when it comes in contact with moisture. This striking bodily transformation following recovery from dehydration is discussed under "Watering Behavior."

For half an hour, these three bighorn ate grass (*Sporobolus airoides*), and then the ewe and yearling started up the mountain, but the lamb went back to Old Spring and drank for another 3 minutes, ate grass, and expanded while the ewe and yearling waited a hundred yards up the mountain. None was poor looking then. They looked too full and fat to move, and although it was only 108° in the shade they panted, open mouthed, as they moved into the shade and went into siesta at 11 a.m.

How long it had been since they had drunk or how far they had traveled to get to water will never be known, but their fatigue was great. They rested until 4 p.m.—5 hours—then came down into the wash and browsed on *Bebbia* for half an hour. After that they returned to the spring area and grazed for 2 full hours on alkali sacaton, bluestem, black sedge heads, Mohave thistle, and mesquite. At 6:30, after feeding within a few feet of water, they left without drinking again and stopped to browse the first desertholly they came to. They were still browsing on holly when darkness fell.

At 3:15 the next afternoon this ewe and her lamb and the yearling ram came back and again drank at Old Spring. This was the first record we had of a band coming in on consecutive days. Rams have often done it, but not mixed groups. Again, the fatigue of the day before was emphasized and the importance of food supply at spring areas became increasingly clear, for they fed today as voraciously as yesterday.

After a half hour of energetic grazing they drank again, the ewe and ram for 1½ minutes and the lamb for 2¾ minutes. The lamb, as yesterday, eating and drinking for a longer time than the others.

At 4:05, the lamb again leading, they went across the wash and into the shade of the Cut Bank. They rested there until 5:30, when they began browsing northward on *Bebbia* and *Encelia* and disappeared in the South Wash as the sun went down.

Where they had come from, or why, we never knew, but we saw them often after that and they grew fat and sleek as the summer ended. Their move from one home to another was successful.

Our evidence to date indicates that if bighorn are near enough to water in hot weather they will probably drink every day, but 1 full day to 3 full days without watering is at least common preference. We have no evidence to support the idea that they might survive with no free water at all, even in the winter or at higher elevations. On December 20, 1954, we followed a band of ewes and lambs to water in a tinaja (or "tank"—a cavity in the rock, often full of sand or gravel, holding water for a time after runoff) at sea level near Badwater. They came again to the same tinaja the next day and found it dry. The following day they climbed several miles up into the Black Mountains to Pothole Canyon, a mile north of Badwater; and while we did not see them drink there, later investigation disclosed their contact with water.

On January 16, 1956, we followed the first Furnace Creek Wash band of eight bighorn 4 miles to water at Navel Spring. They traveled from an elevation of 3,000 feet to an elevation of 1,800 feet in 40° weather. Another band of seven made the same trip in March.

On February 2, 1957, at an elevation of about 5,000 feet a band of 10 rams traveled 2 miles through snow to break the ice and get a drink immediately after a storm, in freezing weather.

In addition to these isolated and special instances, the dry period from July 1955 to January 1957 found dozens of bighorn watering regularly throughout the entire 18 dry months. The interval between visits to water during the winter was much longer than in summer, ranging from 10 to 14 days instead of from 1 to 3.

Young lambs show some evidence of requiring water oftener than adults, as in the case of the ewe, lamb, and yearling ram previously described. Old rams past their prime are often found farther away from known water sources than bighorn of any other age class or sex.

Shortages

"Water shortage" in Death Valley is a term requiring some definition, since it is related less closely to amount of water, but very importantly to the time and distance from an available supply.

One of the problems inherent to the area in general is our lack of knowledge of available water sources. During this study we have found many sources of "permanent" water, once known and utilized by man but unmapped, forgotten, and no longer known to the present inhabitants of the region.

"Forgotten Creek," which we located February 11, 1955, is a series of springs, some of potable water and some not, culminating in a creek nearly a mile long. It is the center of old game trails converging down out of the Grapevine Mountains; but it is, mysteriously, unused at the present time. The remnants of a barbed wire barrier across the mouth of the canyon and a rusty tin star from a plug of chewing tobacco are the only signs that other men once knew of its existence.

Corkscrew Spring on Corkscrew Peak, elevation 4,000 feet, when first investigated by us on December 8, 1956, turned out to be an ancestral bighorn stronghold of the first order. Fire Spring, a thousand feet below it, discovered earlier in the autumn by Lowell Sumner, was as mysteriously unused as Forgotten Creek, until in December 1960 we discovered that, like Willow Creek, it had inexplicably been put back to use by bighorn.

One of the most significant rediscoveries of a water supply was that of Twin Springs, June 11, 1957, at an elevation of about 4,000 feet, 5 miles southwest from Stove Pipe Wells on Tucki Mountain. Tucki is said to be an Indian word for sheep, and yet as far as we had known there was no free water in the Panamints north of Blackwater Spring, which meant none at all on Tucki. Geologist Charles B. Hunt reported a salty spring at Shoveltown at the base of Tucki Mountain, with old game trails and old sheep sign, indicating past use of the area. In April 1958 the West Coast Nature School brought us fresh bighorn sign from upper Mosaic Canyon on the north side of Tucki. There had been no recent rains in the area to produce pothole water. This indicated either that there was a permanent source we knew nothing about or that they were drinking from the Shoveltown salt spring. An unlikely alternative was that they were ranging 20 airline miles north from Blackwater Spring.

The most plausible of these alternatives was the existence of an unknown water supply. We began to hunt and inquire. Park Ranger Matt Ryan at Emigrant Station became interested, and his inquiries finally produced results. Through an oldtimer in Beatty, Nev., he heard of "a big spring on the mountain above Stove Pipe Wells Hotel." Ryan asked Mrs. Peg Putnam of Stove Pipe if she had ever heard of it. She had, and showed him a tiny green spot high up in the upper drainage of Mosaic Canyon.

On June 11, 1957, Matt Ryan and I climbed for 6 hours through remarkably steep, rough, and barren terrain to a point about a mile below Tucki's 6,700-foot crest. There we found, amid chin-high columbines blooming in a knee-deep green island 100 yards long, another ancestral stronghold of the bighorn, 16 airline miles from its closest neighbor and supporting a population leaving as much sign as we had found anywhere with the possible exception of Willow Creek.

During the summer of 1959 our attention was divided between the bighorn study and a survey of the water resources of Death Valley National Monument. For 4 months everything that looked like a spring, that appeared on any map as a spring, or that had been called or named a spring in a book, magazine article, scientific report, or by longtime residents of the area, was considered by us, its present status established, and its location verified and mapped.

Of the more than 300 sources entered in the Death Valley water book in 1959 (Welles and Welles, 1959), 132 were given names for the first time, 90 were mapped for the first time, and 43 were established as of prime importance to the bighorn. In the first year following the completion of that report, nearly a dozen "new" springs were described and mapped for the first time, and probably many more will follow.

But the natural water shortage which has existed throughout the region since the "little ice age" 3,000 or 4,000 years ago will continue, since it is one of time and place: Time, in the sense that rainfall is infrequent and its occurrence unpredictable; place, in that permanent sources are too far apart to permit full utilization of the forage areas between them.

There is some evidence pointing toward a gradually increasing aridity in the entire region, but whether this is a cyclic phenomenon or a long-term trend is not yet known. Changes over and above the usual erratic yearly variations in precipitation are virtually imperceptible.

Caused by Man

There is a present and perceptible danger inherent in the mining laws and their administration which has in the past allowed the complete diversion to human use of many water sources, which in turn has rendered thousands of acres of forage in former bighorn habitat unavailable, and so has become a limiting factor in distribution and survival. During the depression years scarcely a spring could be found without a prospecting camp or a "mill" site within a few feet of it, and in some places they were built directly over the water itself. Thus a shortage was created of such severity that by 1935 bighorn were believed to be practically extinct in this region. Fortunately, large numbers of these camps and mills were abandoned after the depression.

Caused by Wild Burros

It is quite commonly believed that wild burros create a water shortage by usurpation and that where burros drink bighorn refuse to water. All ecological wisdom points to the desirability of freedom from exotics of all species, and from that point of view this report adds volume to the hue and cry for drastic control of the feral burro. But in the interest of accuracy and freedom from prejudice it is urged that the issue of burro control not be joined to the bighorn issue alone.

The early summer of 1960 found the emphasis of the bighorn project once more diverted, this time to the wild burro. The results of this survey were a shock to the bighorn world. Burros and bighorn will and do water at the same springs. Burros must pollute water at times to have received such widespread condemnation for it, but this survey disclosed none of it. They do contribute indirectly and substantially to water shortages by destroying the emergency food supplies on the way to and in watering areas. The entire controversial subject of burro-bighorn interrelationship is discussed in detail under "Competitors and Enemies."

Natural

In addition to local manmade shortages owing to proximal installations or the boxing in and complete diversion of the water, natural causes may eliminate considerable amounts of water from availability. It is commonly believed that earthquakes sometimes shut off water sources, but we have no firsthand evidence of this. Floodwater, however, by burying smaller springs under tons of detrital material, has closed three known water sources during the time of this study. These three springs, Scotty's, Navel, and Hole-in-the-Rock, were subsequently restored to use by us, but the others that are lost each year and not restored are a responsibility neither accepted, delegated, nor discharged as yet by anyone.

Acceptance of New Sources

Bighorn acceptance of new or rehabilitated water installations appears to be no problem in Death Valley. During the summer of 1956 the sheep returned and used all of the rehabilitated springs within weeks of the work being done, and Lowell Sumner saw bighorn drink at Virgin Spring within the hour of installation of a new tank. One half hour after a new tank was dug at Trail Pool at Nevares Spring, a ram chased a ewe across it, and while the ewe avoided it by a tremendous leap, the ram plunged into it and immediately abandoned the chase for a long drink of muddy water.

October 10, 1955, saw the final installation of the orientation exhibit building on Dante's View. The workmen left a tub of water exposed there for the weekend and Monday morning found the tub empty and surrounded by bighorn tracks and droppings. The closest known water source is Lemonade Spring, 5 airline miles north of Dante's View. This "adaptability" to a new condition is comparatively rare compared with the "elasticity" of behavior shown by their return to former water sources that have been restored. The distinction between adaptability and elasticity will be discussed further under "Watering Behavior." Upper Willow Creek Spring is completely surrounded by a dense willow thicket wall about 20 feet deep, and the water flows through an understory cover of black sedge 2 or 3 feet high. This spring had not been used for many years when we first visited it in 1951, nor was it used until the summer of 1956. We had accepted the commonly held belief that bighorn avoid watering anywhere that their lines of vision and routes of escape are obscured, and we assumed that they bypassed this spring for the more open spring half a mile below for that reason.

On August 8, 1956, we found a band of 11 bighorn emerging from trampled-out tunnels through the willow wall, the black sedge matted down below water level as bighorn stood on it to drink. The open trails to the former watering place down canyon were deserted. This area, previously considered untenable (figs. 8 and 9), was used with apparent freedom throughout that particular dry season, but was abandanoed with autmn rains. For some undetermined reason, perhaps due to a change in herd leadership, it has remained unused since. The "tunnels" have grown closed, the tall black sedge once more stands waist high, and the sheep trek half a mile farther down the canyon to drink.

On January 31, 1957, on a ridge above Echo Canyon at 4,400 feet elevation, we found a mine shaft with a partial block at the mouth from a cave-in from above caused by runoff of rainwater, which then ran back into the tunnel, filling it to a depth of about 18 inches. Old trails and droppings showed that bighorn had found the water and drunk from it. Not only had they drunk at the mouth of the tunnel, as the water receded, they had followed it back nearly 40 feet and turned a corner in almost pitch darkness to get a drink. The sign pointed to a more or less annual use of this mine shaft as a temporary water supply.

In contrast to the above records which indicate a propensity for the acceptance and utilization of water under surprisingly adverse circumstances, there is a considerable body of evidence pointing toward excessive wariness, even fear, associated with the act of drinking under what might be considered the very safest of watering environment. To mention one of many recorded examples, Raven Spring, of the Nevares Seeps, is situated in open flatland at the very terminal of a made-to-order escape route up Nevares Peak. The flat terrain and lack of ground cover would seem to preclude the possibility of ambush, and it is accepted with complete confidence by some bighorn every day. However, others approach it with obvious anxiety, and in some instances, even with terror.

Watering Behavior

To characterize bighorn watering behavior as unpredictable seems empirically safe here, but the glib postulate that the most consistent thing about the bighorn is its inconsistency should be carefully weighed. Repeated observations often present a simple answer to an apparently complex problem, and a conceivable consistency emerges here in the hypothesis that the variable individual behavior of watering bighorn should not be correlated with the environmental characteristics of an observed water source but with the experience that the individual animal has had in connection with the act of watering.

Some bighorn show signs of acute anxiety while still at some distance from water and are overcome by indecision, turning this way and that, back and forth, sometimes for an hour or more, then finally in apparent desperation dashing to the spring, where they may or may not actually drink before dashing headlong away to what seems to them a safe distance. Eventually this exhausting activity usually subsides sufficiently to allow them to satisfy their thirst, but the condition of the animals is likely to reflect their anxiety and tension in less weight and lacklustre pelage, which suggests a habitual approach to a constant problem. The problem seems to become less acute as the size of the band increases and as more stable leadership is offered, but the symptoms seem never to be completely absent until the sheep so afflicted are beyond the sight, sound, and scent of water per se, whenever and wherever found.

Some bighorn have this problem, others do not. Those that do apparently associate the mere presence of water with danger to themselves. This might be a socially "inherited" family or group fear, which can be communicated from one individual to others, possibly even over a span of more than one generation. Or it might be the traumatic experience with a predator or a poacher on the part of one individual. An accident in the spring area or a snakebite could contribute substantially to either an individual or a group fear. On two occasions we have found sidewinders (*Crotalus cerastes*) buried in the sand within a few inches of the position where both front feet and the muzzle of a bighorn would have been had it come in to drink at the time.

Acute fear is more likely to be evidenced by animals alone or in small groups, but this is not always true. Young rams, 2 or 3 years old and probably making the rut-run alone for the first time, almost always manifest more or less acute anxiety as part of their watering behavior, while the mature rams, from 9 years up, seem to have out-grown it entirely. Some ewes with young lambs are extremely fear-ful while others show no nervousness whatever, approaching the spring with steady confidence, drinking leisurely, resting and brows-ing around the water for hours before taking an unconcerned de-parture. Larger bands of a dozen or more seem relatively fearless unless the water source lies in a restricted area with limited escape routes, such as Navel Spring in its box canyon with only three routes of ingress and egress. Even under these conditions some bands, hav-ing satisfied themselves as to security, will relax for a time in the shade of the cliffs.

So it appears that watering behavior among bighorn varies with the individual and is consistent only with the individual's experience with water, and therefore remains unpredictable.

Bighorn preferences as to potability of water appear to be as un-predictable as their behavior. Keane Spring, Monarch Spring, the main Nevares Spring in the Funerals, and Fire Spring on Corkscrew Peak in the Grapevines, all with running streams of potable water, are sometimes ignored while small, still, seep pools a quarter of a mile away are drained daily in hot weather. Dozens of speculations as to this behavior present themselves, but none are resolved. The same applies to questions as to why some bighorn kneel to drink and others do not; or why, in 30 days at Nevares, only 4 out of 47 sheep drank twice the same day; or why an entire herd will utilize a spring one year and abandon it the next as at Willow Creek; or why they use a source for only a few days or weeks every 2 or 3 years, as at Hole-in-the-Rock, to which the bighorn returned on September 17, 1958, for the first time since October 1956, drank the tank dry, explored the 15-foot tunnel to its end and pawed holes in the mud for more.

Individually these observations are inconclusive, but collectively they suggest an elasticity in the bighorn adaptation to aridity and in its utilization of water which is of great significance, shared only by food as a factor in the survival and distribution of the race.

Since the use of the word "elasticity" may be considered uncommon in this connection, Webster's definition of "elastic" is included here as the best description of this phase of the bighorn survival pattern: "Springing back, having the power of returning to its original form; rebounding; springy; capable of extension; having the power to recover from depression."

A separate consideration of some of the components of this definition is productive:

1. *Having the [astonishing] power of returning to its original form.*

Our reports prior to the summer of 1957 contain many references to the relative physical condition of animals observed. During the 30 days at Nevares we finally became aware of a correlation between apparent physical condition and the temporary degree of dehydration of the animal at the time of observation. The word temporary is scarcely adequate to emphasize the dramatic quality of the change that occurs in the dehydrated bighorn both during the ingestion of water and in the period of rehydration of the body which follows. We often witnessed a metamorphosis so complete that is was difficult to believe that the animals leaving the spring area were the same as we had seen approaching it.

For example, at 8:45 in the morning of August 16, 1957, with the temperature already at 100°, an emaciated ewe and lamb stood at Old Spring and drank for 11 minutes. Their pelage was rough and dull, their legs spindly with knobby joints and taut, stringy muscles. Hipbones, ribs, and skulls lay close under drawn and shriveled skin.

We wondered aloud as we watched them drink: What caused this forlorn condition? Was it some illness? Lung-worm? Not enough food? Not the right kind of food?

As they drank their sides filled out, then began to protrude until by the time they had finished drinking and sought shade for resting there was a pathetic incongruity between the distended bellies and the shrunken limbs of the animals.

The ewe nibbled briefly at desertholly as she moved slowly toward the shade of a mesquite, but the lamb seemed too full, walking slowly with its legs wide apart. A half hour after drinking they left the shade and began the grueling climb up the face of Nevares Peak.

There was nothing unusual about what they were doing; we had watched it many times—routine watering behavior of a bighorn ewe and lamb at a desert spring in the summer. What had happened to them in the last few minutes was also normal routine. I had seen it before, many times; another such instance involving three animals has been described in "Amounts Taken" under "Water." But somehow it had never before fallen into place. Now it did. I was watching the ewe and lamb climb, briskly, easily, in the gathering heat, and I was marveling at how two animals in such poor condition could do this when I suddenly realized that they were no longer in poor condition! The potbellies were gone, the legs were no longer spindly, and the muscles were smooth and rounded beneath the glistening hides of animals in perfect health. Now I suddenly realized that the apparent emaciation of their bodies when they had first appeared at the spring half an hour before was a symptom, not of bad health, but of acute dehydration. This rapid recovery from it, this complete rehydration in so short a time seemed little short of miraculous when observed in full context and relativity. It is one of the most significant single observations we have made, since we have come to believe that without the possession of this extreme physiological elasticity there would probably be no desert bighorn as we know them today. Once noted, the metamorphosis, the "miracle at the spring," was recorded many times.

The next morning, August 17, we recorded a young ram, also shriveled like a dried prune, standing drinking at Raven Spring. This time we consciously watched for it for the first time—the filling out of the tissues of the body, very much as the dried prune would fill out if dropped in a glass of water. At first just a highly inflated look as he drank time after time—but within half an hour he was no longer potbellied but smooth and straight in the body. His hind quarters were filled out and rounded, his neck no longer stringy looking—slim to be sure, but rounded and sleek.

Gauntness is commonly associated with dehydration in all animals, but in these other animals the shrinking of muscles to such an extreme scrawniness of the limbs and neck and a general skeletal protrusion, as well as the apparent dullness and roughness of pelage, usually ascribable to malnutrition and disease, is not associated with an ability to recover promptly, easily, and almost routinely as with the bighorn. The camel of the Sahara Desert does equal or possibly surpass the bighorn in this respect, for it can lose more than 25 percent of its body weight through dehydration without being seriously weakened. It exhibits a similar emaciation on being deprived of water and a comparably dramatic filling out of the tissues about 10 minutes after drinking (Schmidt-Nielsen, 1959). Whether bighorn possess insulation, and body temperature tolerances, of the same magnitude is unknown, but it would appear likely that the mechanisms are comparable. The shrinking of body tissues and shriveling of the skin are considered symptomatic of a fatal or near fatal degree of dehydration in the human body (Adolph, 1947). Park rangers at Death Valley have observed a similar shriveled appearance, followed by a rapid transformation to near normal, in persons whom they have rescued from near fatal dehydration. In man, under desert conditions, a loss of 12 percent of body weight through dehydration is fatal.

2. *Having the power to recover from depression.*

All evidence points toward the economic depression of the thirties as an even worse depression for the bighorn of Death Valley in that scarcely a water source existed during that time that was not usurped by mining interests which not only robbed the sheep of their water supply and the forage made available by it but raised poaching to a significant volume for the only time in the known history of this region.

The recurrent droughts (such as the 18 months during 1955–56) reduce the standard of living for bighorn to a depression status from which they regularly recover. We realize that other species in different environments from that of Death Valley likewise show great elasticity in population recovery. Deer afford a good example.

3. *Being capable of extension.*

At Raven Spring, 10 a.m. on September 10, 1957, a full curl ram (Broken Nose) drank his fill and went into the shade of Red Wall Canyon, half a mile north of the spring. At 11:20 another full-curl ram (Tabby), dull-coated, lame, and generally emaciated in appearance, was hustling toward the spring when Broken Nose arose from his shaded siesta and challenged him. Tabby, who either had had no water for 42 hours (September 8 at 4:30 p.m.) or had just finished an 8-airline-mile trek through the mountains from Indian Pass on a day when official temperature was 113° in the shade, met the challenge and fought his well-rested, completely rehydrated opponent for 2 hours with no apparent handicap and at no discernible disadvantage whatever.

Each charge of a battling ram entails the expenditure of a tremendous amount of energy. The adversaries stand from 15 to 40 feet apart, rear, and on their hindlegs race toward each other to the proper point, then, with every ounce of energy they can muster, hurl themselves through the air and meet head on at a speed in the neighborhood of 30 miles per hour (Cottam and Williams, 1943). A few minutes recovery time may be allowed or it may not. Tabby and Broken Nose blasted each other something over 40 times in 2 hours. Ten minutes after the fight had ended in a draw, Tabby came in to water and drank for 12 minutes, ate a few mouthfuls of grass, and went into siesta until 5:45, when he went back to the spring grasses and grazed until 6:30. Then, having last drunk 5 hours before, he headed into the South Wash, sleek and fat, walking briskly and rapidly in 102° of heat.

On August 17, 1957, with the official maximum temperature at 122°, Buddy [Mrs. Welles] spotted two pale bighorn racing across the foot of the mountain three-fourths of a mile to the north. I estimated their speed at 25–30 miles per hour through terrain that we could scarcely walk across with safety.

As they raced nearer, with only the briefest hesitations in their head-long flight, it became evident that it was a ram chasing a ewe. As they came opposite us, the ram (a young one, 3 years old) lunged at the ewe's flank with his horns, and they put on an incredible burst of speed which ended only at Long Spring a quarter of a mile from us.

They drank for perhaps 10 minutes. Then, bulging with water, they began the chase again. The ewe started to run toward the mountain, and the ram headed her off, turning her back toward the spring.

She tried to go around him on the other side. He turned her back like a cutting horse working with cattle, or a sheep dog with sheep.

She tried to get away half a dozen times, but he ran faster, lowering his horns and forcing her to stop and turn back.

Then suddenly, as though by common consent, the activity ceased as abruptly as it had begun. The ram sought shade on one cliff and the ewe another, leaving us to put our cameras away gratefully, for by now they were almost too hot to touch, since our wet-bath-towel cooling system had long since stopped functioning.

What we had been observing was a phase of mating activity which we were to record again and again. One such incident lasted for 3 days with no apparent depletion of energy on the part of either animal, although as far as we could determine they had no water during the entire time.

Their ability to extend their energy to incredible limits is put to what is probably its severest test when a band already severely dehydrated reaches a water source to find that it is no longer available. When this happens, their willingness and ability to extend their expenditure of energy to the ultimate inclusion of another water source within the limits of their home area may be one of the principal reasons that they have outlived so many contemporaries of 11,000 years ago.

The above observations are made more significant by the total absence in other forms of desert life in the Southwest of such strenuous and prolonged activity in excessively high temperatures.

A Factor in Distribution and Survival

Too much emphasis can hardly be placed on the importance of their use of food and water as factors in the distribution and survival of the bighorn. In the violated ecology of the Death Valley region, their hardiness has been amply proved, but human encroachment, with its attendant results, is the denominator of eventual destruction unless its pressures can be kept from increasing each year.

The elasticity described above should not be confused with adaptability or flexibility, since we could not support a very strong claim for either in the bighorn. With the exception of occasional prompt use of new water sources discussed previously, evidence points toward a prevailing inability to make quick adaptation to a major change of environment. The mortality ratio from shock also runs high in most efforts to transplant bighorn from one area to another. The wild burro, on the other hand, seldom injures himself in captivity and has never been known to suffer from shock, much less die from it (Welles and Welles, 1960).

Flexible means easily bent, pliant, yielding to persuasion—characteristics not yet noted in the bighorn.

And, finally, it must be emphasized that this elasticity which we have considered so thoroughly here is limited to the conditions of their natural habitat and to the uninhibited employment of all their instincts for survival.

Home Area

We have insufficient evidence for defining the home area of a bighorn beyond the generalization that an individual sheep is born in an area containing adequate food, water, and shelter to insure survival under normal conditions. As long as the bighorn can maintain satisfactory access to these three requisites, it will probably utilize the same area all its life.

Some home areas probably include only one source of free water, others more than one. The size of the area of land involved in any one home area is inherently variable because of the great instability in the pattern of precipitation, which may allow an entire herd to subsist within an area of 4 or 5 square miles one year but require 20 square miles the next.

We know that at least a nucleus of a resident band returns to the same water source or sources year after year. For five summers we watched old Brahma, the leader at Nevares Peak, bring the same band back to water at Nevares Seeps. The water source seems to be the determining factor in the location of the home area. Loss of either food or water from either natural causes or exotic pressure would appear to be the main cause of abandonment of one area for another.

Since the bighorn is essentially gregarious, it does not claim individual territorial rights as do some animals. Some old rams appear to prefer solitude, and ewes, even the leaders of the band, will isolate themselves during lambing; but we have seen no instance of overt defense of privacy.

We have no evidence of demarcation of home areas of bands by age class or sex in this region. Bands of rams appear to occupy the same general area as ewes and lambs, with the possible exception that they may be able to range farther from water, but even this is unproven. Temporary extension of the home area is probably brought about occasionally by a ewe getting caught in a tide of rams in the rut-run and carried from one spring to another before the fervor of oestrus subsides.

Owing to their greater activity during the rut, rams probably include a greater number of water sources and therefore a greater foraging territory in their home area. However, it seems likely that the average bighorn lives and dies within 20 miles of where it was born.

Trails

The importance of trails in the life of the bighorn is not yet fully understood because no specific study has been made of their use, but in the Death Valley region some facts are beginning to appear:

Trails connect one food supply with another and in many places one water supply with another, and when a spring dries up the presence or absence of long established trails to another source conceivably could make the difference between life and death. Evidence indicates a major role for the trail system in race propagation. During dry, hot weather the spring areas bear the brunt of rut activity, but during wet or cool rut weather the rams prowl the trails and intercept the ewes in passage from one area to another.

While bighorn have a remarkable ability for negotiating more or less perpendicular terrain, they seldom use this ability unless pressed, with the result that their trails almost always conform to contours and follow the easier routes. Since the trails are relatively level, they are also utilized as readymade bedding sites. Manmade trails and mine roads also are pressed into this extratransit service, and the resultant beding sign becomes part of the record of bighorn population and movement. Many of the manmade trails also are connecting links between water supplies in remote areas, and so it is sometimes difficult to distinguish between them and bighorn trails, except that they are usually about twice as wide. To walk on a bighorn trail, a man usually must place one foot more directly in front of the other than on manmade trails because bighorn trails averaged about 8 or 9 inches wide.

From the top of Echo Mountain, on the north side of Echo Canyon, the pattern of trails approaching Nevares Spring from the north can be seen, showing the main trail connecting Nevares with Indian Pass and becoming absorbed in the converging fan of trails as it approaches the Nevares area. These main, or connecting, trails we have called highway trails. This particular one contours the base of the Funerals, maintaining an average 1,000- to 1,500-foot elevation, and it is deep and dusty by the end of the rut-run in December.

On December 25, 1957, with Charles and Alice Hunt, we followed the Nevares highway trail north for several miles. It led past a spring that had been extinct, according to Geologist Hunt's calculations, since the late Pleistocene, or from 10,000 to 15,000 years. But the trail is still in use because the outcropping of travertine that marks the site of the dead spring happens to be en route to still living sources of water.

So, in addition to the part they play in the everyday life of the bighorn, trails are invaluable to the human observer as clues to the past as well as the present status of the species.

Activity

Fixed patterns of daily activity are very difficult to trace in bighorn. As with most animals, their time is divided roughly by the business of getting enough to eat, enough to drink, enough rest, and reproducing their kind. In the young, a period of play may occur in the early morning and late evening. But we have found little evidence of daily routine among bighorn. They usually leave their night beds at dawn, but they may "sleep in" until noon. They are likely to take from one to three siestas during the day, but they may take none.

Their activity is governed to a large extent by their relationship to their supplies of food and water, and since availability of these supplies is varied more by wet and dry cycles than by calendar seasons, it is difficult to define seasonal activity by months. The tolerance of high temperature by bighorn has already been established. That they have an equal tolerance for cold is suggested by the facts that a newborn lamb seems impervious to freezing weather and that we have no record of any change of activity because of low temperatures.

An extremely general description of daily activity would run as follows: The bighorn are likely to rise at dawn; if young are present, they may play for a short time and on occasion be joined by adults; they may feed for a period of from 1 to 3 hours, then rest for 1 to 3 hours. Alternating of feeding and resting periods continues throughout the day, with the band usually climbing to a higher elevation for bedding at dusk.

General Habits

Wariness

As previously described under "Watering Behavior," the degree of wariness in bighorn varies with the individual. This is evident not only in its watering behavior but in its relationship with its entire environment.

By Age Class and Sex

Nothing seems to suggest a significant variation in wariness by age class or sex except for ewes with newborn lambs. Prior to lambing, the 10-year-old leader of the Furnace Creek band, known as Old Mama, had become so unafraid of us that on one occasion when I turned suddenly away from my camera I bumped into her where she browsed so close behind me. Yet when she returned with her lamb on February 2, we could not get within 200 yards of her. Pictures taken of the ewe and lamb during the first 2 weeks after birth showed that instinct always placed the lamb on the far side of the mother when observers were in the vicinity, but after 2 weeks the lamb began to be more independent and less fearful. However, Old Mama had not completely regained her placid self-confidence when she finally left the wash in the middle of April.

"Freezing"

"Freezing" seldom has appeared to be a part of the defense mechanism of the bighorn in Death Valley. We have repeatedly approached young lambs where they were left by their mothers and they have never "played dead" the way young fawns are likely to do. Bighorn of all ages will often stand motionless for many minutes, even an hour or so, while observing their observers, but they will do the same thing when unaware of being observed. However, as further described under "Climbing Ability," I once had a ram freeze not more than 50 feet from me and remain absolutely motionless for 20 minutes until my eyes fell on his, when he stiffened, snorted, and dashed away.

Curiosity

Much has been said about the curiosity of the bighorn, but it is difficult to draw a line between a curiosity tinged with wariness and a suspicion tinged with anxiety. An effort to determine whether something is dangerous seems more an act of suspicion or caution than of simple curiosity. A ewe with a newborn lamb may make a great effort to keep an intruder in sight, not from curiosity but from apprehension, and yet if the observer is unaware of the lamb's presence he might be inclined to label the motivation of the ewe's action as curiosity.

On two occasions we tried to climb above the Badwater band to photograph them with the valley as a background. As we began to circle them the sheep watched us, first with apparent curiosity at this unusual behavior, and then as it became apparent to them that we were about to cut off their escape route to the mountains their curiosity gave way to a deeper interest. They watched with increasing fear as we slowly tried to work around them. When we would start to pass above them they would first huddle and watch as long as we stood still. But as soon as we started again they would break into a run, making a circle around us, and continue climbing until they were above us once more.

After his great fight with Broken Nose, Tabby repeatedly came out from his siesta to "blow" and stare at Buddy [Mrs. Welles]. "Blowing" is a sign of apprehension, not of curiosity.

On December 1, 1956, Tight Curl, a 9-year-old-ram, demonstrated another variation of the reaction loosely labeled curiosity. At 9:20 in the morning, Old Mama and a band of four were in the wash at Travertine Point. We followed them up on the mesa as they browsed, with no new observations until about 12 noon. They had been bedded while we lunched about 150 yards away. Two prospectors began descending Pyramid Peak from their claim about 1½ miles away and 1,500 feet higher up. The ram began to be uneasy about them and stared at them for some time with growing anxiety. Then he began to make a sound we had never heard before. It was in no way like the "blowing," snort, or cough we have always associated with alarm and warning from bighorn. This sound, which he made every 2 or 3 minutes for half and hour, was more like a nasal growl.

His uneasiness had nothing to do with us, because during this time he never once looked at Buddy, who worked with her camera closer to him than ever before. His attention never left the distant figures, and he kept up his "growling" until suddenly, without ever looking at Buddy, he made a rapid retreat over the ridge to the north.

It would appear that curiosity in bighorn varies with the individual and is seldom the sole motivating factor in bighorn behavior. It is, therefore, difficult to discuss except in its relationship to anxiety, suspicion, and fear.

Occasionally the mixed motivations are resolved into an acute stage, and flight clarifies any doubt as to the cause of observed behavior.

Length of Retreat When Frightened

The length of retreat when frightened is unpredictable and varied, since the experience of the animals involved dictates the individual reaction to any given set of circumstances. And, of course, the degree of fright varies from the slight shock engendered in a lamb by a rolling stone to the devastating, sometimes mortal, shock so widely recognized as a problem in the capture, physical restraint, and transport of adults in transplanting projects.

Just what determines the bighorn evaluation of danger beyond its individual experience is not known. Instinct, of course, plays an undetermined role in it, but it seems unwise to conclude that the bighorn is instinctively afraid of anything, because present evidence points more toward conditioned behavior than toward inherited reaction.

How far an animal may run from the sound of the human voice, therefore, may depend on whether it is startled by an unrecognized sound or is frightened by an audible reminder of a remembered traumatic experience.

Response to Humans and Equipment

This can be particularly apparent in bighorn reaction to humans, human behavior, and manmade equipment. As a matter of fact, bighorn appear to have no more of a fixed pattern of reaction toward humans than humans have toward bighorn. In both instances the reactions vary, according to the experience one has had with the other, from complete indifference to overwhelming concern, and it is necessary for the observer to understand that the bighorn's attitude and reaction toward him is a conditioned response to his own (and other human) behavior toward the bighorn.

It must be remembered, too, that emotions are contagious among bighorn just as they are among humans, and 1 frightened bighorn may engender fear in a band of 10. Yet the quickly regained confidence of a leader among them may immediately overcome this fear simply by her not participating in their reaction to it. If a band is temporarily without a leader, however, this fear may result in a panic and headlong flight to an environment of relative safety.

Since the relationship between people and bighorn involves the third primary factor in bighorn survival in Death Valley, and realistic measures for their protection, it seems pertinent at this point to discuss the bighorn-human relationship in further detail:

Because few people ever see a bighorn, the species has acquired a legendary reputation of unapproachable wildness which has no foundation in fact. In order to clarify the picture somewhat, this report will trace the development of bighorn reaction to humans as observed by us from the point of view of the multiuse designation of the area as (1) a national monument, (2) a resort and recreation area, (3) a mining district, and (4) a wildlife sanctuary.

The first bighorn we found in Death Valley, in March 1952, lived up to the popular concept of bighorn behavior. When first observed, this animal was 200 yards ahead of us, running across the wash and up the mountain to a distance of a quarter of a mile before pausing amid completely camouflaging surroundings. After watching us anxiously for a few minutes, it continued its rapid ascent of the mountain until an hour later it stood, a black dot against the sky, on the farthest promontory of the range, where it watched us until our jeep disappeared at a turn in the canyon over a mile away.

Later the same year during the peak of the lambing season in the relatively dense population of the Nevada Desert Game Range, we found the popular concept of wildness breaking down. We were advised that it was a poor time to be photographing bighorn there because during the lambing season the ewes were very "spooky" and difficult to approach. The first four or five bands we found demonstrated the soundness of the advice. The ewes with lambs were extremely wary and unapproachable. However, we soon discovered that if we remained in full view of the sheep and did not try to stalk them, we had much greater success in achieving proximity.

Within a very few days after we stopped trying to conceal ourselves from them, they began to stop running from us. After 10 days among them, we were able to photograph a "babysitting" (one mother remaining with all the lambs while the other mothers leave to forage or drink) from a distance of 100 yards. The same evening at sundown we climbed along, keeping a distance of no more than 50 yards, with a band of 11 ewes and yearlings as they went up for the night. They scarcely glanced in our direction as they bedded down within 100 feet of where we stood.

Our one contact with rams of the area was traditional. We surprised nine of them in siesta on the edge of the piñon habitat. They leaped to their feet and into a huddle for one quick look at us, then fled at full speed without stopping until they disappeared into a canyon half a mile away. Such precipitous flight naturally precludes continued contact and the possible lessening of alarm through further modifying experience.

We were astonished one day at lunch by an old ewe, with two yearlings in tow, who approached to within 100 yards of us, bleating eagerly as she came as though she thought we were other sheep. She seemed to realize her mistake rather suddenly, stopping short, staring at us for a moment; then, with a snort, she bounded away, the yearlings following with much less evidence of alarm. We have, of course, found this type of approach to humans by bighorn to be a quite common experience among fieldworkers in bighorn areas. This singular reaction is not limited to an age class or sex but has been observed repeatedly in lambs, ewes, and rams, with motivation undetermined in all cases.

The two observations we have of lambs approaching us were both made during a period when the lambs were lost from their mothers, and so it would seem safe to assume that this circumstance contributed to the reaction. One of these instances occurred at 8:30 a.m. on September 7, 1957, as I was checking the Seeps at Nevares Springs. I heard a cough up the mountain and soon I saw a lamb, coughing badly as though it had asthma. It was watching me, and soon its coughing stopped and it began a lively run down toward me, bleating. I stood still, wishing I were somewhere else so I wouldn't keep it from water.

It came down to within 100 yards of me, looking at me all the time and bleating eagerly every few steps. I realized then that this lamb was not just preceding its mother down the mountain; it didn't know where its mother was! It "spooked" when it got close enough to see I wasn't a sheep (or so it seemed) and went bounding back up the mountain.

On the morning of September 9 at dawn, I searched the spring area thoroughly through binoculars, decided that nothing was coming in, and went down to check for any sign made in the night after we had swept the ground free of previous sign. I had examined Raven and Long Springs with negative results and was approaching Old Spring when a big red ram leaped up out of Round Pool, 150 yards away.

I stood still and he stopped and looked steadily at me for perhaps 2 minutes; then he unconcernedly walked toward me as far as Old Spring, 75 feet away, and proceeded to drink his fill, drinking about 2 minutes at a time. Between drinks he raised his head, with his mouth dripping water, licked his lips, and yawned once. Meanwhile, he studied me in a speculative sort of way. After three drinks and study periods, he walked up on the bank on my side of Old Spring to within 50 feet of me, where he gave me a thorough going over, and I him.

When finally he was through studying me he walked past me within 30 feet and started north. When I turned and took a step or two after him, he was alarmed and ran up the mountain about 50 yards before he stopped and turned back for a moment, then began a high-headed "spooky" climb away.

Subsequent encounters with this ram, whom we named Mahogany, found him maintaining a distance of around 200 yards.

Our interim reports are replete with similar records of this singular type of reaction to humans, which is usually cited as an example of extreme curiosity on the part of the sheep. But once more the use of the word curiosity must be questioned as a specious, anthropomorphic oversimplification of a complex area of bighorn behavior. Curiosity is defined by Webster as meaning "A desire to learn or know; a desire to learn about things that do not necessarily concern one; inquisitiveness." This is a simple, limited motivation toward learning for its own sake with no further objective either stated or implied, and we find no clear evidence to support this human characteristic as an identifiable bighorn attribute.

It seems more likely that a complex array of animal instincts contributing to self-preservation in one way or another is at work in most of such instances. Ewes, frustrated in oestrus by the absence of rams, may be seeking substitutes just as rams in the absence of other rams with which to battle will charge into boulders, or tree trunks, or even a mountainside as will be described later. Just as adults in frustrated mating fervor may be seeking substitute sex objects, the lost lamb may be seeking a substitute mother. In any case, such evidence suggests a temporary aberration induced by the stress of an individual experience or emotional need, unshared by other animals at the time.

In the interest of bighorn conservation, particular attention has been paid to these singular instances of bighorn behavior because of a keenly felt necessity of seeing them in proper perspective. The temporary nature of such reactions must be emphasized and the absence of repetition by the same animal noted. Of more importance still, it should be remembered that this is actually atypical behavior engaged in by a small percentage of the population. Although such behavior heightens interest by its relative rarity, it can be dangerously deceptive if used as a basis for planning bighorn-human relations of the future. It is only when the reaction of an individual is shared by its companions that it is likely to become measurably important in bighorn management and protection.

The leader of the Badwater band seemed to have little fear of humans. She maintained her distance from them with a placid insistence which suggested that her lack of fear was based on a confidence generated by experience which had taught her that a certain distance from humans meant safety from them. Since the reaction of a leader appears to a considerable degree to be communicated, the entire band responded to our presence with increasing indifference, until by March the hundreds of park visitors on the highway below them were ignored completely unless someone disturbed the accepted conditions by leaving the highway and beginning to approach them. This action usually brought the band into a preflight huddle, and, if the approach was continued, ended in retreat up the mountain.

This was a mild presentation of the most formidable problem facing the Death Valley bighorn today—human encroachment. Whether it is the relatively harmless but insistent approach of the photographer, the less prevalent but still considerable activity of the poacher, or the possibly overwhelming usurpation of water sources by a mining boom, the question is always there: How much human encroachment can the bighorn tolerate without jeopardy?

The development of another acceptable bighorn-human relationship began in the winter of 1955, when we commenced our 18-month association with the Furnace Creek band. We made no effort to follow them any more than was necessary to keep them within observing range of 12-power glasses. We remained unobtrusively in the open at all times and withdrew if our proximity became disturbing. We took pictures all day, recording their eating behavior and habits as they moved slowly but steadily over the rolling hills and up and down the

616472 O—62——6

sides of the bisecting canyons, paying no attention to us as long as we kept a distance of about 100 yards. Here was something new in our sheep observations: These animals seemed not to care whether we were above or below them, and they made no effort to keep between us and an avenue of escape. There was no cliffy terrain within a mile of where they fed, but this did not disturb them in the least. As a matter of fact, they fed closer and closer to us as the day wore on, until just before noon they bedded down with their backs to us less than 200 feet away.

Their progress in bighorn-human relationship was rapid from then on, until by January 5 they fed directly down to the highway and gave an astonishing exhibition of indifference to people and winter traffic. They foraged right on the shoulder of the highway on fresh green shoots of *Stephanomeria*. Cars passing caused them only to stop eating to watch but did not frighten them! Then, for the first time, Old Mama, their leader, led them across the highway.

The next day they all crossed the highway repeatedly. This began to worry us. They were becoming a traffic hazard and people were piling out of their cars with loaves of bread to feed them! By now this band was feeding to within 5 or 6 feet of us, which was fine for making study pictures of horn formation, eating behavior, identification markings, etc., but was dangerous for the sheep.

On January 10 they set an alltime precedent for Death Valley when the entire band stood stock still in the middle of the highway and blocked traffic. (See figs. 13 and 14.) Old Mama walked between two cars with people standing within 4 or 5 feet. On several occasions she fed to within the minimum focal range of our cameras, too close for pictures.

By the 12th, 20 to 30 cars of people a day were coming into the wash to see and photograph the sheep. In order to avoid accidents to sheep and visitors as well as to avoid contributing to the formation of a pauper band of bighorn in Death Valley, we tried scaring the sheep off the road, running at them, honking horns, shouting, throwing gravel, and firing guns over their heads. They would move 100 feet or so away, then stare at us curiously as much as to say, what are you doing that for?

Never before had Death Valley bighorn reacted this way to humans, for the simple reason that never before had humans reacted this way to gradually gain their confidence. In the instance of both the Badwater band and the Furnace Creek band, we had set up new, nondisturbing conditions for a bighorn-human relationship which were accepted by them with a startling alacrity and completeness.

The first and probably the most important of these new conditions was the fact that we came and stayed in the area where they fed, bedded, and watered, but did not disturb them or interfere with their activities in any way, nor did we allow anyone else to engage in aggressive actions of any kind. As much as possible, we kept constantly in sight of them throughout the daylight hours, because we soon discovered that they became suspicious of us only when we disappeared for a while and especially if we reappeared closer to them.

The Badwater band never overcame its nervousness while on pavement to the extent of crossing the highway, but the Furnace Creek band was crossing freely within a week. The leadership of the two bands may have had much to do with the difference, but also of great importance was the fact that the Furnace Creek sheep found the choicest food on the shoulders of the road. However, in itself the presence of a fresh, lush growth of *Stephanomeria* on the road shoulders and berms was not new. The new condition was that when the sheep were feeding on the shoulders we stopped all cars, called the attention of the park visitors to this rare opportunity for observing bighorn, but curbed the inclinations of some persons to pursue them. The bighorn quickly accepted their protected status as being permanent and appeared to take it for granted that all cars would always stop for them. This created a traffic hazard.

Response to Noises

Probably the most unexpected phase of this development of bighorn reaction to humans through their voluntary acceptance of these new conditions was their refusal to be disturbed by our violent, noisy efforts to frighten them. They no longer attached a sense of danger to cars, roaring motors, honking horns, shouting people, or exploding cartridges.

That this acceptance hinged on its being voluntary on their part and was possibly limited by an association only with the Furnace Creek Wash area became apparent when they ventured out on the fan below Deadman's Curve on January 16 and headed for Navel Spring and water. Perhaps it was a sense of being pursued that made them nervous. In any case, once they left their established feeding ground, we were not allowed within 200 yards of them.

All morning they moved rapidly, feeding comparatively little, down the wash nearly to the Ryan Junction, where they turned directly across the face of the hill toward Navel Spring.

In spite of our efforts to reach the spring first, the sheep made the last quarter of a mile so much faster than we thought they could that they had been at the spring for 10 minutes at least before we got there.

As we entered the narrow mouth of the box canyon occupied by the spring, the entire band led by Old Mama "spooked" and bounded up to a promontory 100 feet to the south. They stopped there for a while but continued to regard us with apprehension. These were the same sheep that had fed to within 2 or 3 feet of us when out in the open. Apparently they had a fear of being trapped in the box canyon. Old Mama and Little Whitey did not come back down for another drink, but one by one, with the greatest distrust of us, the others did.

Oddly enough, Old Eighty, usually the wariest of the band (fig. 17), was the first to reach water. She descended a few steps at a time, mincing sideways in her determination not to let us out of her sight. She then stopped and looked back up at the others who remained fixed, staring down at us. Then she looked quickly at us, tossing her head. Finally she turned back as though to give it up, hesitated, turned quickly, and plunged the remaining distance down to water. Once there, she was still too nervous to drink much—one swallow at a time, then throwing up her head to look more fully at us.

The sound of the cameras made her jump away although she had heard the sound many times before. One of the other sheep starting down dislodged some small rocks, and the sound of these, to which she would have paid no attention elsewhere, now threw her into a panic from which she didn't recover until she was back up with the others. The one who had caused her fright was in turn frightened by her flight and dashed back with her to the top, where they all stood in what we call the "spook huddle"—heads close together and held high, with all senses keyed to the alert.

We finally withdrew entirely from the canyon before they would return to drink.

Some of the nervousness, wariness, suspicion, and fear seemed to stay with them for the 3 days that we followed them after this watering. They never went back to Furnace Creek Wash to stay, only passing through it on their way across the mesa to the foot of Pyramid Peak.

About January 16, Old Mama became nervous and restless. Her unborn lamb was kicking harder every day, and approaching parturition might have been urging her toward seclusion. She seemed to be trying to elude not only us but the other bighorn as well, and this seemed to kindle a general anxiety among them all. Three days later we could not get within 50 yards of them. On this day they disappeared on Pyramid Peak after 3 weeks of close association with us in the wash. As a specific band, they never returned to Furnace Creek. Individual members of the band have been observed in Big Wash, on Paleomesa, and in the washes back of Navel Spring. Possible reasons for this apparent abandonment will be discussed in later chapters.

When Old Mama returned on February 2 without the band but with her newborn lamb, she was as wild and unapproachable as tradition would dictate—with one exception: She was still unafraid of cars, and quickly taught her lamb that only when cars disgorged people was any attention to be paid them. (This eventually led to the lamb's being struck by a car and left for dead on the highway. See "Growth, Behavior, and Care of the Young.")

Old Mama appeared on the one hand to cling to the accepted conditions guaranteeing her security and complete freedom of terrain and highway, but on the other she imposed a new one involving the requisite distance between her lamb and the tidal wave of eager photographers which poured into the wash when news of her return with a lamb was broadcast. She raised her lamb there for 10 weeks, and when she left in April her new, indifferent aloofness was as unbreachable as ever.

In the meantime, however, she had been joined on March 14 by a band of five new bighorn—three ewes, a 2-year-old ram, and a lamb about the same age as her own. These sheep were wild, apparently were not used to cars on the highway, and might have been seeing humans close up for the first time. Their reactions to humans, to Old Mama, and to Old Mama's reaction to humans, therefore, became of great significance to the study of the development of bighorn-human relations.

The new sheep were startled into an anxious huddle by the jeep door slamming in the wind after I got out to set up a camera. Led by the mother of the new lamb (not Old Mama and her lamb), they began a wary withdrawal across the wash when I was 200 yards distant. The wariness gave way to panic as I crouched over the movie camera, and they hurtled up the mountain for another 100 yards before they seemed to notice that Old Mama and her lamb were still standing placidly in the wash below them. They looked from me to her and back again, gradually relaxing as I made no effort to get closer to them. When I got back in the truck and waited, they little by little worked their way back down to the old leader, and eventually began to browse close to her, with one eye on her and one on me, like a sailor with one eye on the barometer and the other on the sky.

For the first week the mother of the second lamb, by then known as New Mama, competed with Old Mama for leadership and tried repeatedly to lead the band out of the area. On several occasions she succeeded in getting them about half a mile up toward Pyramid Peak before they inevitably began to look back at Old Mama feeding in the wash. Then, usually led by the 2-year-old ram, they would rush pell-mell back to the old leader, followed reluctantly by the unsuccessful contender.

The new band continued to take their cue from Old Mama, gradually relaxing toward us until March 24 when we followed them to water at Navel Spring. As with the other sheep previously, they (including

Old Mama) because nervous, anxious, and alarmed at our presence in the box canyon with them. It might have been a coincidence, but, just as with the first band, they disappeared after watering but returned after 4 days absence and resumed normal activity in the wash. By the time they left we had formed an entirely new concept of the relative importance of the matriarchal system in bighorn behavior.

On April 7, 1956, we found that two miners had moved into the very center of the Furnace Creek feeding area and were preparing to set off a heavy charge of dynamite just as the band fed toward them from the Big Dip, a short distance east of Travertine Point. Three of the sheep, led by Old Mama, actually went up on the ridge above where the miners worked, and after watching them for a few minutes lay down and went to sleep on a ledge 100 yards above the impending detonation. The other four members of the band did not see their leader ascend the ridge and continued to browse in the wash below. Those in the wash were out of sight from us when the blast occurred. We were watching Old Mama and her three companions at the time but they never moved or stopped chewing their cuds. The cloud of dust from the blast attracted their attention to the extent that they watched it for a few minutes as it billowed up in the sunlight.

We found the other four sheep a mile below the scene of the blasting, and the contrast in their behavior was notable to say the least. While we were still half a mile away, we saw them huddled on a promontory at the edge of the wash, and as we approached, the symptoms of anxiety we had come to associate with the loss of a leader began to develop. At 9 o'clock that morning these four sheep had fed behind Old Mama to within 30 feet of us; now, without her, their tension visibly increased when we stopped our jeep 100 yards away. As we stepped out of it, they fled as though they had never seen a jeep or people before.

We watched from a quarter of a mile away the rest of the day as they moved restlessly from one point to another, feeding ravenously for a few minutes in the wash, then suddenly dashing frantically for a high spot again. Between times they looked for Old Mama and the others, up and down the wash and across it and back up toward Pyramid Peak.

As the day wore on, it became apparent that temporarily at least a new leader was being born, for the three younger ones began to turn to the older ewe and await her decisions and to follow suit.

Toward evening we made an experimental approach, thinking that with a new leader becoming established among them anxiety might be lessened, but such was not the case. Here the importance of the quality or nature of existing leadership was suddenly underscored, because as we walked slowly toward them, the new leader stood transfixed until we were about 100 yards away, when she bounded away in precipitous flight, which ended only on the distant rim of Paleomesa.

What becomes increasingly apparent is a correlation between the success of bighorn-human relations and the nature of the leadership present on both sides of the entente. The following points must be emphasized and remembered in the formulation of any plan for the future of the bighorn in Death Valley:

1. The prolonged and continuous associations we have had with the various bands of Death Valley bighorn from 1954–61 was not accidental. It was part of a plan of action.

The formulation and execution of a plan involving more than one person carries with it an assumption of leadership, and this plan implicitly involved all persons in Death Valley in that their cooperation was sought and substantially received. It resulted in a marked increase in the number of reports of sheep sightings to reach National Park Service headquarters. One of these was the Badwater band, another the Furnace Creek band, and still another the 14 bighorn on Death Balley Buttes—all serve as good examples of the cooperation that developed.

2. In all three instances, the development of our relationship with the three bands was about the same and was made possible by our control of (or leadership in) the human reaction toward them. Only by our continuous and unobtrusive presence were we able to convince the sheep that humans could be an acceptable condition of their environment.

3. Once the bighorn had accepted us, we felt compelled to insist that other humans visiting the area refrain from disturbing the conditions which had proved acceptable to the sheep.

4. While it is quite probable that the majority of these observations would never have been made had we done other than present ourselves without overtures and waited for them to set the distance between us, it is also quite probable that even these conditions would not have proved acceptable were it not for the type of bighorn leadership present in each band. All three old ewes had apparently never had any reason to associate humans with danger to themselves, and their initial wariness soon gave way to a placid unconcern. Contacts were made with other bands in both the Badwater and Furnace Creek areas, but such contacts could not be maintained because of the flight of the leaders. If the leadership is fearful, conditions involving proximity of humans may never be acceptable to the band.

5. It must be considered more than coincidence that nowhere in the Death Valley region have we observed, nor do we have a record of bighorn continuing to water at a source which has become the

headquarters of humans. It would appear that the continued presence of people at or near a water supply has to the present created unacceptable conditions for the continued utilization of that source by the bighorn. Whether it has been the mere presence of people at the springs or whether further acts of aggression took place to trigger abandonment is not known. Whether controlled conditioning to human proximity at or near water sources could bring about permanently acceptable conditions for continued use of one water source by both humans and bighorn in Death Valley is not known and could be determined only by controlled experiment.

Herd Leadership

While herd leadership has emerged as an important factor in the life history of the bighorn, very little is known as to the quantity and quality of control exercised by the leader.

An indication of the quality of control is found in the response of bighorn to sounds whether natural or otherwise. The reaction of individual animals to a particular sound would, of course, vary with the experience of the individual with that sound. Our efforts to "spook" the Furnace Creek bands off the highway were quite illuminating. When standing 15 or 20 feet behind them as they fed with their heads down, facing away from us, the first sudden, loud clapping of hands accompanied by a loud shout produced an immediate huddle and a bounding away for perhaps 15 feet. A walking retreat followed, but the leader, Old Mama, then began to lag and come to a stop at about 75 feet while the others continued away to a distance of 50 yards. Here they stopped and fixed their attention on Old Mama while she "evaluated" the situation. In a very few moments she dismissed this incident and returned to browse; the others immediately returned to her and also began browsing.

A few minutes later we again clapped and shouted, but with a modified repetition of results. Old Mama jumped and took only two or three steps away while the others "huddled" a few feet beyond her, watching her, not us. The third time produced practically no reaction. Old Mama raised her head and looked at us, while the others, without moving away at all, looked first at her then at us for a moment and returned to browsing. Thus, it would appear that leadership is by example, somewhat as among the more primitive tribes of the human race (Hockett, 1960).

Certainly superior physical strength or prowess plays no part in attaining the position of leadership. Old Mama was obviously the poorest physical specimen of the band, and, in common with many leaders we have known, much the oldest.

In contrast to the status of the primitive human leader, there is no respect or deference attached to the bighorn leader. We have many observations of the leader being routed out of a bed she had just made and occupied scarcely long enough to warm it. Sometimes there are bullies in the bands, but we have yet to see one of these as leader.

Competition for leadership sometimes arises between two ewes. The Badwater band afforded one of our best opportunities to study this. An old ewe who carried her head at a distinctive tilt and had a large bump on her left horn was unquestionably the leader. But there was also a contender for the throne, "Droopy," as we called her because of her unique dropping horns. (See figs. 5 and 6.) Droopy always traveled close behind or side by side with the leader. But the two tended to feed separately from the others and sometimes rested apart from them.

On many occasions Droopy seemed to make persistent efforts to lead the band in a different direction from that chosen by the leader. She would do this by turning off on a ridge which the leader had already browsed by. The other four (who usually traveled and fed in a close group) would follow Droopy for some distance before noticing that the leader was not in front of them. Then they would stop and look around for the leader, whereupon Droopy would seem to increase her pace until she reached some high point where she would stop and look back at the others.

Sometimes Droopy's attempts would last for half an hour. The leader would calmly feed or watch as though it had nothing to do with her, as the four in between looked first at her, then at Droopy, while Droopy turned this way and that as though trying to persuade them to follow her. They never did. In the end they turned back toward the leader, leaving Droopy alone on her little hill. She would sometimes remain aloof for an hour, but eventually she would rejoin the band, passing all others until she once more took her place second in line.

At times it is difficult to distinguish an actual leader, because while feeding in travel, the band will follow, for a short distance, the first to diverge in any direction.

Especially when alarmed, the first one to bolt will likely be followed for a short distance. Then leadership becomes more apparent, because as soon as a safe altitude or distance is attained the real leader will stop for an evaluation of the danger, and the others will go into a huddle a short distance beyond her and await her decision.

Definite travel of any distance, however, such as a change in feeding territory, a search for water, or a climb to night bedding grounds, is always led by the same individual—one of the oldest ewes in the band.

On January 12, 1956, we witnessed a most unusual episode on the face of a cliff about a mile above the Natural Bridge. One of the outstanding characteristics of the bighorn is the casual self-confidence with which it approaches and traverses seemingly impassable terrain. On this occasion, however, it took a great deal more than casual self-confidence on the part of the leader to extricate her little band from an impasse.

The band of seven were moving at a fast walk, with occasional short bursts of running, along what appeared to be a well-defined trail across the face of a nearly perpendicular slope, when the leader suddenly stopped, stared for an instant straight ahead, then turned suddenly and ran back, the rest of the band turning and running with her. A few minutes later, she returned to the same spot and stopped again. While the others watched, she surveyed the cliff ahead, raising and lowering her head from time to time, taking one cautious step forward, then backing up.

We could see then that a part of the old trail had fallen away, leaving a chasm about 8 feet across. The trail immediately approaching it was apparently about 6 inches wide, running across a sheer cliff in a slight curve, making it a very difficult approach, even for a bighorn.

The leader finally gave up again, turning quickly, and running back to the others.

During the next half hour each of the others made more or less the same approach—the hesitant back-and-forth movement along the cliff toward the edge of the chasm and final flight back to the band.

One of the yearlings was followed out to the edge by the leader, and, as it hesitated, the leader suddenly gave it a strong push from behind. The yearling was pushed off, but, instead of leaping across, it flipped around and dropped down, managing to regain its footing about 3 feet below its former position, where it stood for some time before cautiously inching its way back to the trail.

Now the leader backed away from the ledge and with no more vacillation "took a run at it." Two leaps negotiated the dangerous curving approach, and a third cleared the 8-foot chasm itself. The others, after some obvious screwing-up of their courage, followed suit—except two who got panicky and ran back along the trail, searching frantically for some other way across. In the end they too made it, only to find the entire band in a cul-de-sac. They milled about again after going back to the dangerous crossing and staring up and down the cliff across which they had come, apparently deciding that even they couldn't make it back that way. After half an hour of this futile effort to find a way of escape, they dismissed the whole thing by lying down for a siesta, placidly chewing their cuds or stretching out in complete relaxation!

Forty-five minutes later they all arose as though at a signal. The leader, as if in accordance with a previous decision, walked to a ledge above a dry falls cut back into the cliff. Without any hesitation, she leaped and began a hair-raising 50-foot descent, zigzagging back and forth from one side of the falls to the other until she reached the talus slope at the foot of the cliff. She never looked back once she started, and even after reaching the talus slope she kept on going at a broken canter across the badlands. The others followed her lead without hesitation or mishap, and the entire band disappeared in a southeasterly direction toward the upper drainage of Natural Bridge canyon.

In none of the instances where competition has developed has the current leader been disturbed by the competition activity. This is probably because of the likelihood that the activity is not truly competitive in the sense that the contender actually wants to replace the leader. It seems more likely that the contender simply wants to go somewhere or do something else but doesn't want to do it alone. The true leaders among bighorn seem to be those self-sufficient ones who have reached a point in life of knowing what they themselves want to do and of being determined to go about doing it regardless of what the others want to do. There is no evidence here to indicate any concern on the part of the leader for the welfare of the band. In fact, the very lack of concern about everything, an overall fearlessness in her approach to the business of survival is indicated as prerequisite to the status of leadership. It seems possible that such matriarchs may have developed their independence through having outlived former elders of the band whom they themselves may have followed during earlier phases of development.

Possession of the quality of leadership, however, does not insure a following, for some who have it live alone. This in turn indicates a possible matriarchal influence in the choice of a leader and in band formation.

Rams of all ages appear to accept the temporary leadership of ewes whenever both sexes travel together, but a ram has never been observed by us in the role of leader except to other rams. The same suggestion of patriarchal influence is usually present in the sense of tribal, rather than paternal, leadership.

Lambs, having less experience with pain or fright, will often precede fearful adults into feeding or watering areas where the conditions are unknown and as yet unaccepted. Many times we have observed a band of sheep standing in a gaunt fearful huddle above a spring for minutes while a lamb works its way down to water. Once it was there, drinking and still safe, the others would break huddle, rush down and join it—sometimes displacing it in their drive to fulfill their need for water.

Here again, of course, no overt act of leadership is involved. The lamb reacted according to its experience and found conditions acceptable for watering. By going on in and drinking, it created acceptable conditions for the others.

While some leaderships are undoubtedly outgrowths of family ties, others are probably accidents of propinquity, as suggested by Old Mama's inheritance of the second band of blond strangers in Furnace Creek Wash, none of whom shared her identifying family characteristics in any way. She seemed to tolerate, rather than welcome, their attachment to her for about a month. Then she separated herself from them and their dependence on her.

The conflicting loyalties or instinctive dependencies indicated here will be discussed further under "Herd Composition."

The phenomenon of matriarchy as a factor in the survival pattern of the bighorn can be readily traced to the inception of postnatal training as the day-old lamb wobbles forward in its first instinctual drive to emulate its mother's way of living. (See "Growth, Behavior, and Care of Young.") Through her example many of the decisions are made of what, where, and when to eat, to drink, to rest, and to sleep. Through her the lamb learns what to fear, what to trust, and when and where to seek a new home.

The leaders have been our liaison with the other bighorn.

Gregariousness

How gregarious the bighorn is seems to depend on the relative abundance of its food supply—in good years the bands are likely to be much larger than in bad years. The natural tendency seems to be toward group living, but it is by no means a fixed pattern. Dry years or cycles with their correlated depletion of water and food supplies find the bands dividing into smaller and smaller groups as the cover thins and a given area supports smaller numbers of sheep. (See "Herd Composition.")

Play

Bighorn play (and training) may begin within a few hours after birth. We once watched a ewe place her forehead against that of her 8-hour-old lamb and gently but firmly shove it off its feet. The sprawling lamb eagerly returned for the same treatment. This happened three or four times before it forgot to get up and went to sleep.

Playing reaches its peak among the young in the spring or whenever food is easiest to get, in the morning and evening when it is cool, and when they are likely to have more companions to play with.

On February 9, 1958, a band of 14 blond fat bighorn were reveling in the lush vegetation of a "good flower year" on Death Valley Buttes. All afternoon they had basked in the sun, but as the day had cooled off their activity increased. The two older rams began to challenge each other in true bighorn fashion; and the little ones even tried now and then to emulate them, standing on their hindlegs, cocking their heads sideways, and advancing a few halting steps toward each other, and even bumping horns a little as their forefeet dropped back to earth.

As darkness approached, their playing increased still more. All ages and sexes began butting playfully at each other, bouncing into the air, twisting and kicking as they sailed downhill for 15 or 20 feet at a bound. Sometimes they went nowhere, and just jumped up and down in one place, twisting and turning as they did so.

Presently they began destroying the lush new green of the desert shrubs in their exuberance, trampling, pawing, and thrashing their horns in them and sometimes grabbing large mouthfuls before darting away. This activity continued until after dark and began again at daybreak, when for over an hour we were treated to the greatest playing exhibition we had ever seen. Round and round on a steep loose talus slope they raced, leaping, bounding, kicking, butting the air, each other, plants, rocks, or just butting. The 3-year-old rams backed off and "let each other have it" from about 10 feet apart with a clonk perfectly audible from where we watched three-quarters of a mile away.

They found a crumbling cliff at the edge of the slope and there the youngsters gathered, seeming to enjoy the feel of the edge giving way under their feet, leaping off into space with the greatest delight, and scampering around and back up again. There was much shoving going on too, apparently in an effort to shove each other over the edge. The two 3-year-olds joined in this and were pushed about even by the youngest of the merrymakers.

The six older ones, the ewes, disappeared into a ravine leading up to the top of the ridge, where first the six lambs and then the two rams soon followed. Within what seemed no more than a few seconds we first heard, then saw, all 14 racing pellmell across a talus slope a quarter of a mile east of the ravine into which they had disappeared. Even the old "ladies" were playing then, as round and round they raced for several minutes. Then as though at a signal they all stopped and began to graze.

While most of the playing is usually in the morning or evening, optimum conditions may bring it on at any time. The next day at 1:30 p.m. four of the youngest began playing on top of a boulder about

4 feet high and just big enough for all four to stand on. Once there they tried to push each other off. Three times when two were on top of the rock alone, they stood and "sighted" just as their fathers do. Both male and female lambs do this at times, but the males do it much more. It consists of cocking their heads and sighting down their noses as adult rams do in battle before the charge.

We supposed that the good grazing and cool weather were responsible for such excess energy. We had seen lambs do this before, but only once before had the ewes joined in, and that was on March 31, 1956, before a big rain in Furnace Creek Wash. This band in Furnace Creek had deviated from the usual routine by sunning themselves on big flat rocks until well after noon. Finally at 1:30 they all began to rise and stretch. The young ram was the first to get on his feet and browse away a short distance. They all browsed around the bedding area for a few minutes and then started down the hill; once they started down, their behavior changed.

It was a cloudy, cool day with the smell of water in the air, which may have affected them. They took little extra runs this way and that all the way down, until as they came out on the bench just above the wash above the Big Dip one of the lambs suddenly started to run full tilt down the slope of a bench and then plowed all four feet into the slope, raising a cloud of dust from which it reappeared running wildly back up the slope toward the bench and across the bench about 100 feet to the foot of the mountain. There it turned, while all the others watched, and raced across the bench again. This time when it reached the crest of the bench slope, instead of running down, it shot straight out into the air in a leap at least 30 feet long before it landed in the gravel of the wash below.

Upon landing it continued to bound and bounce into the air 3 or 4 feet, progressing more or less in a circle, kicking and writhing this way and that. By now, the others were affected by these antics and the entire band in varying degrees joined in what by now had a remarkable resemblance to a wild dance of some sort. Even Old Mama shed her dignity long enough to round the circle a time or two—and her lamb, although it was lame, joined in a tentative effort now and then. This went on for probably 3 minutes and was over before we even thought of getting pictures of it.

It seems obvious that the training begun at an early age by the mother is continued in the form of play, and play, therefore, assumes a greater role than simple recreation in the life of the growing bighorn as it does for most young animals. (See "Growth, Behavior, and Care of Young.")

It would appear that a lamb raised alone would be at somewhat the same disadvantage in later competition as a human child would be without playmates or a formal education. A lone lamb in a band, like a child, compensates for the lack of contemporary playmates by playing solitary games and by pressing adults into sometimes reluctant participation in its program. In contrast to the group games on Death Valley Buttes, we observed several weeks of playtime activity by single lambs in both the Badwater and Furnace Creek bands.

On February 21, 1955, as darkness fell, the Badwater band started straight up the face of a cliff 2 miles north of "The Bay." The 6-month-old lamb as usual chose this precarious (so it seemed to us since we could scarcely see the ground to walk on) time to gambol and frisk about on the near-perpendicular face of the cliff. (See fig. 48.) At one time it leaped a 4-foot chasm, kicking its heels and tossing its head as it did so.

The next day after the noon siesta the lamb, on rising, had a very playful session with its mother who, for once, responded. Such a lamb often tries to play with the ewes, who usually ignore it until they become irritated and butt it away. Later, this lamb ran to its mother again as though teasing, thrust its nose into nursing position, and quickly gave a surprisingly strong shove, nearly knocking the ewe from her feet. Then before the ewe could regain her balance and whirl on the lamb, it had dashed away, gleefully kicking its heels as it went.

In Furnace Creek Wash on February 15, 1956, the 2-week-old lamb was very active and playful. At one time the ewe was feeding between two large rocks. The lamb ran and jumped on one rock, from there to its mother's back, then to another rock, and scampered off up the side of the wash. There it walked bravely, ears forward, head up, looking up the canyon side, up and down the canyon. Suddenly it looked back and could not see its mother. Its ears came down and back, the bravado vanished, and small bleats and a panicky run brought it back to within sight of its mother.

That play is sometimes directly blended with serious activity is suggested in the habitual off-season sex play of young ewes and the rams up to their third year, before the latter have finally left the family group for the winter ram herd. This "play" occasionally re-sults in actual copulation and may contribute substantially to the spread of the lambing season in Death Valley. Playful sexual behavior begins within the first few weeks of life and continues to maturity.

Memory

We have no conclusive data on the subject of bighorn memory. Many incidents, which at first appeared to be attributable to memory, have with repetition shown such prominent instinctual characteristics that labeling is approached with hesitation. That bighorn have some memory goes without saying, but efforts at quantitative or qualitative determination of its dimension would seem unwise in view of the still unmeasured potentialities of their eyesight, hearing, sense of smell, direction, equilibrium, and physical coordination.

Such questions as these arise: Does a bighorn know its way through the mountains because it has been there before and remembers its way around, or does its physical and sensorial equipment make it possible for it to follow where other bighorn have gone although no trail is visible to us? When we first began observing bighorn at Nevares Spring, was their apparent terror in approaching Round Pool caused by a remembered traumatic experience, the lingering scent of a passing predator, the remembered crack of a poacher's rifle, or was it a socially "inherited" reaction having nothing to do with the present, a family or group fear handed down from generations and conditions long since nonexistent?

Climbing Ability

Their climbing ability has long held a legendary status in bighorn lore, tall tales growing taller and widening their scope as new facets of wonder "spring like the bighorn from nowhere!"

The true record of their prowess in mountaineering is incredible to the casual observer, because their normal habits of travel are deceptively easygoing in appearance to the point of laziness, and sensational demonstrations of the peak of their phenomenal abilities are so rare that they are seldom seen by any but the most persistent or fortunate observers.

The normal undisturbed manner of bighorn travel, whether up or down, is leisurely and along the lines of least resistance, with frequent rests along contouring trails. They appear prone, especially in the summer, to conserve their energy as much as possible.

The climbing training of the young through play and emulation of their elders has been discussed under "Play" and will be more fully developed under "Growth, Behavior, and Care of Young." The adults' application of their highly developed climbing abilities to their every-day activity is phenomenal but is usually executed with such deceptive ease that it often passes unrecorded.

During the 1955 census at Willow Creek, I had been standing near the blind above the springs examining the entire area through binoculars for about 20 minutes when I decided to go into the blind itself to see if I could get some idea of how successful a hunter would be in keeping the area in view from that point. As I started toward the blind, I suddenly realized that a magnificent full-curl ram was, and had been during this entire time, standing directly below me, not more than 50 feet away. He stood with his massive horns lowered, looking up, the translucent amber of his eyes startlingly noticeable from where I stood. He had apparently "frozen" in this attitude and held it ever since I had appeared 20 minutes before. Outstaring a bighorn can become a tiring job. We have observed them many times maintain complete immobility for hours at a time.

When my eyes fell on his, although I had moved nothing else, he knew I had seen him for the first time. His head raised slightly and a tremor ran through his body as muscles tightened. For a count of five he stood, then blew loudly once through his nose. Four leaps took him across a boulder-strewn gully, a sharp turn to the right and he was gone. It took me 2 minutes to follow him to the point where he had disappeared. As speedily as possible, more or less on all fours, I attained the summit of the point above the blind, a distance of perhaps 50 feet across a precipitous incline of smooth solid rock strewn with talus. As I reached this point, the ram appeared at the crest of a ridge about 200 yards away. He looked back for an instant and then disappeared beyond this ridge. I checked my watch, entered the time in my notebook—12:32. When I looked up, the ram was in sight again, approaching the crest of the second ridge away, where he came to a full stop. In my glasses I watched him turn, instantly relax everything but his senses, draw one deep breath from his exertion, and then lapse into immobility again. The distance, as carefully as I could estimate it, was a quarter of a mile. I had previously tried to work my way along the route he had taken and after half an hour had given it up because of the loose boulders of 3 to 4 feet in diameter piled one on the other against the almost perpendicular walls of the canyon.

I had first seen him at 12:30. It was now 12:34. He had covered this distance in 4 minutes at 15 miles per hour.

The ability to "bounce" from one wall to another in ascending or descending has already been well illustrated under "Herd Leadership," in the instance of the 8-foot section of a cliff trail that had recently fallen away, leading to the entrapment of a band.

A highly developed sense of balance was demonstrated by a young ram on a cliff below Keystone Canyon on the evening of December 3, 1957, The old ewe Droopy and this young ram had been under observation since daylight, and as darkness fell the last we could see of her she was lying down, placidly chewing her cud. The young ram was standing 10 feet above her on a loose ledge looking down at her. The ledge began to crumble under him, and she got up and moved from under the falling rocks. Completely unperturbed, he just spread all four feet out a little and rode down the small landslide until it stopped; whereupon he simply relaxed where he stood. She lay down again a few feet away. As we left them there, they were chewing their cuds in the moonlight.

Their agility and ability to regain their equilibrium in the air was demonstrated on August 28, 1957, when three mature rams, old acquaintances of ours, were jousting in South Nevares Wash.

I had gone into the drainage below them and was close enough, I hoped, for good pictures of jousting. Two of the rams made a running jump and got up a 15- or 20-foot bank. The third one, Toby, started to do the same thing, but The Hook caught him full in the face as he hit the crest and knocked him over backward. Toby spun around in the air like a cat and came down on his feet. The Hook stood waiting at the top for him to try it again, but he went around and came up a safer way.

On March 17, 1956, the second Furnace Creek band fed down to the junction with Whitewash Canyon, turned up that canyon at 12:30, and at 12:45 climbed out on to a jutting, narrow, intersecting ridge that ended in a 75-foot drop. Here they pawed five beds and went into siesta until 2 p.m. The ridge was so narrow that as the others were getting up to leave, the ram (still asleep) fell off it and scared the whole band as well as himself. He caught himself about 10 feet down, shook himself vigorously, and unconcernedly climbed back up.

While we have not yet observed rams "tumbling down cliffs and alighting on their prodigious horns" (Browne, 1864, p. 691), we have recorded above the type of incidents that give rise to such reports. Here is another example in which my own activity is given in detail as well as that of the ram because of the apparent influence of my presence in determining the climax:

On August 14, 1957, I arrived with pick and shovel at Navel Spring at 11:30 a.m. By 1:15 the sun came into this box canyon and I gave up shovel work for the day and took all equipment back out to the truck. I found it was 135° in the cab of the truck, there being no breeze where the truck sat in the cut.

I loaded up and drove back out of the cut to get some breeze, pulled out the extension of the truck top for shade (fig. 4) and was preparing to eat lunch when I saw a big ram coming over the skyline above the spring. Glasses showed it to be an adult ram, hurrying along in a half trot, mouth open in the heat. He stopped now and then to look around, seemed to see me and the truck, but paid no attention.

He dropped into the spring by the north trail and crossed below the mesquite to the tanks. He stopped in the opening and gave the area the wonderfully wary, head-up going over that is so becoming to rams. He seemed a little disturbed by the evidence of my digging at the tunnel. Then he dropped out of sight, which I hoped meant he was getting that much-needed drink. I was glad I came out to where I did because he probably wouldn't have come in if I had been much closer.

But suddenly he bounded back after he had been in there but a minute. He raced across the opening to the first ridge at the foot of the north trail. Then he stared back down at the spring trying to see what frightened him. It was probably a rock dislodged from the cliff overhead by a flock of linnets, who were doing that all morning as I was working at the spring. (I was hit a stinging whack on the arm by one rock about an inch through. Another larger one whizzed past my head by inches.)

The ram seemed to think some one was pelting him with rocks from some place he could not locate. He stared down awhile and then moved to another spot and stared again. He faced toward me twice to give me the once-over, but almost instantly he dismissed me in favor of the "rock thrower." Finally he started to leave, although he could not have drunk his fill in so short a time. He reached the overhanging ledge which runs along just above the trail, on his way out, his mouth now really open. He tried to walk in the shadow of the ledge, even to the extent of squatting down as he walked to get out of the sun. He stopped, pawed briefly, and lay down, mouth wide open, with his muzzle and one horn still in the sun. My thermometer read 100° where I was.

He was on his feet, almost at once, startled again by something. He came out from under the ledge and looked up as though it might have been another rock from above. There was a strong breeze up there carrying the dust away as he pawed three times and lay down again.

I began my lunch. In 10 minutes he leaped up again. Strong gusts of wind were whirling by me now and then and I could hear them fade away in his direction. Maybe they made him nervous. Something surely did. He lay down again, the third time, but got up again and appeared to be giving up and leaving. He moved out in the open, walking steadily, head out and down, with his mouth open. His head came up and he paused a moment on the skyline, then dropped out of sight. I was glad that I was a good quarter of a mile away or I would have been feeling guilty by now, thinking I was the cause of his going away thirsty. As it was, he would probably go around the hill into the canyon where there was real shade and come back when it was cooler, as we had seen them do at Nevares.

I waited until dusk and was ready to go when there he was, just as I thought he might be—the old ram, coming back over the hill in the evening! He dropped down nearly to the sheer dry falls, then browsed, watching, taking his time now—waiting for ewes to come in, probably, poised on the edge of the 200-foot cliff above the spring. He seemed to be expecting others.

He looked down over the edge—and I could hardly believe what I was seeing—for he crouched down with his front feet out and inched down over the edge. Fifteen or twenty feet down I could see what appeared to be a ledge only 3 or 4 feet wide. He backed up and I thought he had changed his mind, but he was just looking for another place. Again he crouched on the edge with his front feet inching over and down! I heard myself saying, "Go on around, you old fool! You've got lots of time!"

I remembered seeing rams' skulls up on cliff faces just like this one, and now I was about to see one made. He backed up again, but he was not going on around the way he had done at noon—he went back toward the falls, still looking, still determined to go over! This seems to be the time of day that bighorn like to dare the devil. When humans can scarcely see to walk on level ground, they choose to scale cliffs, or jump over them! I looked at my watch—just 7:20—when he crouched farther down than ever—then over he went—at least five times his own height—no jump—just a sort of push out and let go— straight down, and folding flat to the ground when he landed—no bounce. No nothing for a second or two—then a tense, slow rise— then stock still for a count of 10. He didn't have a foot to spare—he couldn't bounce, there was no place to bounce to, but off—and down seemingly in the same fashion for another hundred feet. I couldn't tell whether he was hurting somewhere or just summoning up all his resources for the next plunge.

Then he moved a little but still stood there as though he might be feeling a little weak in the knees. I know I was.

It was getting darker as he started moving again! There was no way out there—except over the edge.

This time he bounced once about 10 feet down, and off, and down another 10 feet—and onto a trail crossing the face of the cliff!

He was in no hurry now, ambling along the trail a few feet, stopping to look at the sunset or whatever. He didn't seem to need a drink very badly. Perhaps he had come back to spend the evening and wait for the ewes to come in.

At 8 o'clock he still had not gone to drink, and I could barely see the top of his horns where he stood on the last crag before going down to water.

The above incident is reported in full in the hope that it will lead to a better understanding of the background of such activities, the conditions under which such things happen: The terrain, the weather, the temperature, the time of day, the objective of the effort, the amount of energy expended, and above all, the role apparently played by my own activity in disturbing the acceptable conditions of his watering there, impelling him to take a shortcut.

In any case, the evidence of this report will do little to detract from the widely held belief that the bighorn's ability as a mountain climber is probably unexcelled and has contributed substantially to its survival to the present time.

Fighting

Fighting, per se, finds practically no place in our data to date. The "fighting" of the rams in rut will be discussed fully under "Fighting With Other Males."

The negligible contact that the present-day Death Valley bighorn may have with predatory enemies has not been witnessed by us, precluding any description or evaluation of the bighorns' prowess in that field.

Their evident indifference to territorial claims is seldom pushed beyond a token defense. On November 18, 1956, in the Big Wash, the resident band of nine ewes were joined by six strangers, and we had an opportunity to see how strange bands reacted to each other when they met.

Kinky (a 5-year-old ram) ignored the two younger rams but became immediately interested in one of the ewes, who eluded him. But some of the ewes showed more animosity to each other than the rams did, cracking horns like rams are supposed to do.

One of the young rams came up to the older one and they rubbed noses and scratched each other's heads with their horns.

We went back to our truck to get cameras and lunch. We could hear horns crashing up the ravine and hurried back to find the entire band of 15 placidly bedded, chewing cuds.

Bighorn in Death Valley seldom have been observed actually fighting over water, food, or a resting place. The extent of a typical conflict of these proportions is indicated by the following observation made near Badwater on February 21, 1955: One ewe turned out to be a tyrant who would not make her own bed but roused the others out of theirs. Even the old matriarch was displaced, two or three times, pointing up the idea that she ruled only by example and was not "boss" of the band.

There never seems to be more than halfhearted resistance to this tyranny, the "displaced person" occasionally turning and presenting her horns for butting. The two seem to be rather cautious about it, carefully adjusting their respective pairs of horns against the other until the position of contact suits both, then the push begins. This usually is no more than a rocking back and forth two or three times,

not even moving the feet, then relaxing, raising the heads and looking about for several minutes, lowering the heads, adjusting the horns,
pushing back and forth, etc. Occasionally, one apparently pushes too
hard, and the other will suddenly shift a hind foot back and lunge
with enough force to cause the other to give ground. Once or twice
this has ended in a short chase, which in itself usually ends in the two
calmly feeding side by side for a few minutes, then returning to rest,
neither one apparently feeling concerned over what started it.

Rest

Rest, for the bighorn under certain conditions to be described, seems
to vary substantially by age class and sex.

The newborn lamb rests more than any other, with the length of
rest periods growing shorter and the interval between growing
longer as the lamb grows older. The ewe that is under pressure of
milk production seems to eat longer and rest less than dry ewes. Rams
under rutting pressure are likely to be observed resting more than ewes
or lambs. (See "Growth, Behavior, and Care of Young" and "Reproduction.") All age classes and sexes rest more when range conditions
are good, and under normally acceptable conditions all bighorn
apparently rest all night. The actual time per individual daytime rest
period ranges from the few seconds of a young lamb during travel
and play periods to an occasional 4 or 5 hours when a band is over-
stuffed or overtired.

Their manner of resting varies, although what controls the variation
is not known to us. They may go into a standing rest on a certain
point one day and lie down in the same spot on another. The smooth-
ness or roughness of the terrain seems to have no effect on their
decision. The standing rest position is almost identical to the trained
stance of prize domestic animals on exhibition, with the front legs
forward and the front feet higher than the back feet, hindlegs extended
to rear. This position seems nearly as restful as lying down. This
manner of resting is more commonly seen when animals are alone
but does not seem to be associated with nervousness or fear in the
sense that resting on foot may be safer than in a prone position.

The majority of daytime resting or, as they are commonly referred
to in this region, siesta periods, are spent lying down. Usually all
four legs are folded under the body, the forequarters lowering first,
then the rear, followed by a slight roll to one side to shift the weight
directly from the shoulder, the belly, and the hip to the ground. The
neck and head are usually erect and in balanced relaxation above the
body, but on some occasions, possibly from severe fatigue, the head

is thrust forward and rested on the muzzle and the tip of one horn. Some brooming of the horns may be caused by this position.

Bighorn do not always prepare a bed before lying down, but if they do it is accomplished by two or three or half a dozen pawing strokes of a front foot, apparently designed to remove some of the large rocks and to loosen the remaining surface of the site. The objective of this effort appears to be the formation of a shallow oval basin from 2 to 3 feet long and 2 or 3 inches deep, depending on the size of the animal involved. The desired cradling effect of the basin is further achieved by the manner of occupancy. An observation on December 3, 1956, in the Big Wash threw some light on this. We watched Old Mama bed and saw again how the basins are actually formed. We had often wondered how with three or four pawings they did so complete a job. Now we saw that they didn't. The pawing was actually preparation for the basin "forming," which was accomplished by a series of shoveling effects with the knees, hocks, and hooves as she settled into the ground thus loosened.

Basins are apparently not always desirable or deemed necessary. A ram observed for 3 hours on July 8 at Willow Creek lay down repeatedly with no preparation of any kind, and at Badwater on no occasion did all six animals prepare a bed. Usually only two or three actually made a basin. They were observed many times to lie down for a half to three-quarters of an hour on rocky fans with no effort at bed preparation. And on March 31, 1956, at 8 a.m. we "found the band bedded on top of Red Mountain, lying on huge boulders in the sun." They must have found this comfortable for 5½ hours, because it was 1:30 when "all began to rise and stretch."

While they may choose a spot on the sunny side of a slope in the winter, they seek the shade in the summer, with all the expected variations in between. Above Raven Spring, on September 3, 1957, a 2-year-old ram, Slim, was hot and wanted to lie down, but the rocky side of the canyon facing us had no level spots or soft ground. He found a place that was still in the shade, however, and after standing there for about 15 minutes, just sank down on his folded-up legs. He looked as though he was lying on a bundle of sticks. It must have been as uncomfortable as it looked, because 20 minutes later he was up and feeding among the rocks—only for 10 minutes, however, and this time he used better judgment. He fed to the base of the rock formation and found a good bed at 11 o'clock. He rested, with only shifts to get out of the sun, until it reached him at 12:30.

The variation in both the manner of rest and the nature of beds was further illustrated in the same area on August 25, 1957, when two big rams, The Hook and Skinny, had a time of it with 6-month-old Marco, who had gone on ahead and found himself a cozy nook in the shade, and after much pawing, turning round and round, lying down and getting up, had settled himself for a nice rest while the others rested down below. But Skinny saw him, and no sooner was he settled than big Skinny went up and routed little Marco out of his bed. It had hardly been big enough for the lamb, but Skinny was stubborn. He pawed and turned and scraped his skinny backside on the rocks and with much up and down and wriggling finally got himself settled and tried to relax. But not for long. The Hook had been watching him just as he had watched little Marco, and now it was his turn to move. The nook was not big enough for Marco or Skinny, and The Hook was bigger than both together. Did he have a time wedging himself down on the narrow little ledge! He never was comfortable but he stuck it out, half up on his "elbows" the while, until Little Ewe went by. The Hook was up and after her in a flash, and Skinny was in again, and again trying to feel as comfortable as little Marco had looked when he was lying there.

Meantime, Marco had gone on up about 200 yards to another small cave he seemed to know about and went in completely out of sight, finally alone as he seemed to want to be.

So the nature of the beds appears to vary according to the season and the current activity of the animals involved, occasionally highlighted by competition for particular sites.

Security, however, is probably the governing factor in the choice of a bedding location, whether for a brief moment of the day or the full hours of the night. Here we come again to acceptable conditions and their variations according to the experience of the animals involved.

Traditionally the bedding bighorn has been pictured as always scaling the heights of inaccessible peaks beyond the reach of all predatory enemies before he finally relaxed to rest.

The lack of a sense of security presumably offered by the proximity of precipitous terrain to watering and feeding grounds is commonly accepted as the controlling factor involved in the absence of sheep in certain areas. This may sometimes be true but certainly not always. The first Furnace Creek band on December 28, 1955, bedded down at 4 p.m., not on a high point but down in a canyon. And on November 18, 1956, a band of 18, with some of the personnel of the first band, bedded for the night in a shallow ravine a mile out on flat Paleomesa.

As discussed under "Herd Leadership," this bands' apparently imperturbable sense of security might have been a reflection of the attitude of their leader, Old Mama, who had no apparent fear of anything at that time and tended to bed anywhere that night or fatigue overtook her.

With the advent of her lamb, this mutual laissez faire between her and us came to an end. The old conditions of freedom and proximity were no longer acceptable to her, and renewed distrust set a greater distance between us. While she still took an occasional daytime siesta in the wash, at evening she reverted completely to the classic tradition and sought the inaccessible and secret bedding site which seems a prerequisite to the security of a ewe with a newborn lamb. Any effort on our part to follow her to her night beds met with increased anxiety, and she would continue to climb until she finally reached some point beyond the range of our observation. Later we found single beds on the mountain a mile and a half above the feeding grounds, on narrow ledges at the foot of overhanging cliffs with but one avenue of approach apparent. Ewe and lamb sign filled in the probable picture.

After 6 weeks of this wary existence, Old Mama's sense of security was bolstered somewhat by the appearance, on March 13, 1956, of the second Furnace Creek band, and night bedding on the mesa was resumed.

On March 16 on the edge of Paleomesa less than half a mile from the road, our field notes record, "they went up to the crest cliff and gave us good shots until sundown, then bedded right there for the night, the first time since lambing that we have known them to bed in sight of the road."

The next morning "I went up to the crest ledge to study sign from last night's bedding. Hit jackpot—62 beds used this year, 22 fresh, countless older beds of previous years, or generations. This is ancestral territory. It is odd that of all the bedding that has been done here we have not seen it before—but the camouflage is ideal, with rocky gravel slopes extending on up from the crest ledge where they bed."

While beds may be found almost anywhere in bighorn habitat, the factors of security and comfort in varying degrees, seasons, and circumstances lead the experienced observer to expect to find more beds in certain types of terrain than in others. Day beds, as has been illustrated, may be found in washes, on hillsides, along old trails and old roads, or anywhere the impulse to lie down may overtake a bighorn; but more beds seem to be found on promontories, especially above watering places, at the foot of shaded, north-facing cut banks, on the brow and at the foot of cliffs in summer browsing areas, and in shallow caves along trails to water than anywhere else.

Sanitation

Sanitation presents practically no problem to the bighorn since it seldom seems to spend two consecutive nights in the same place, thus holding excretory accumulation to a minimum.

The Death Valley feeding and watering conditions and the bighorn adaptation to them constitute a natural aid to sanitation, for between them they produce a quantity and quality of waste material which reduces still further what small problem they might have had.

Under normal conditions the bighorn utilization of forage materials for both food and water leaves a relatively small and dry amount of waste, deposited in groups of pellets of an infinite variety of sizes, shapes, colors, and number of pellets to the group. Once deposited, the sun and wind usually complete dehydration of the waste so rapidly that almost no odor is apparent to humans.

Urination

Urination seems to present the bighorn with no more of a problem in sanitation than does defecation under normal conditions. We have no observation of the commitment of either directly into water supplies. Many bighorn water sources, however, are located at the foot of cliffs and in other types of terrain where excrement deposited above the water is subsequently precipitated into it with concomitant fouling. However this seems to create no unacceptable condition for the bighorn because they continue to drink there.

Whether the fouling of water sources by droppings and urine is a significant communicator of disease among the Death Valley bighorn is not known. (See "Diseases and Parasites.")

Urination frequency is as variable as that of defecation and probably for the same reasons, depending primarily on the quantity and quality of food and water ingested and the nature of the circumstances surrounding ingestion.

When four of the original Badwater band returned on February 12, 1955, we observed an unusually high incidence of urination, in contrast to an earlier remarkable absence of it (only 12 incidents of urination from 6 bighorn in 8 days). Now within 3 hours we observed six incidents from four sheep.

This excessive urination continued all day. By nightfall there had been an estimated 20 incidents, sometimes a very small amount, as though not quantity but some other characteristic of the urine might be causing it.

After 4 days the incidence of urination returned to what appeared to be a normal of three observations per day.

In Furnace Creek Wash on January 7, 1956, we noted that in a band of seven, urination was very infrequent, three instances in 1 day. Two days later the picture had changed to the point that even during siesta they would rise to urinate repeatedly, which seemed most unusual.

Under average acceptable browsing conditions in dry weather on dry forage, no observations of urination may be recorded for days or even weeks if the weather is hot as well as dry. This does not mean that there is no urination but that it is so infrequent as to make is easily missed. This is perhaps more easily understood when compared with the infrequency of human urination under similar conditions.

During our 30-day observations at Nevares in the summer of 1957, with daily maximum temperatures running in the 120's, we each drank well over 2 gallons of water per day with an average urination interval of 12 hours.

The bighorn have no habits of elimination which we recognize as being designed to protect them from the effects of physical contact with excreta, such as those commonly associated with dogs and cats. On the contrary, we have recorded many incidents of sheep rising in the night, defecating and urinating in their beds, and lying back down in them. Excretory density increases with proximity to water sources and tends to reach a maximum where the sheep stand to drink. In general it would appear that it makes no difference to the bighorn when or where elimination takes place. This contrasts rather sharply and unfavorably with the Death Valley burro which is, popular opinion to the contrary, surprisingly clean at the waterhole. (See "Competitors and Enemies.")

The potential of urination as an associative agent in sign reading will be explored under that heading. The possibility of its being a factor in bighorn communication will be considered under "Signposts."

Communication

For the purposes of this report we have divided the means of communication into two groups according to the manner of employment. How applicable this division will continue to be as the study progresses is not known, but it is useful at this stage to think of bighorn communication in terms of being either voluntary or involuntary, dynamic or static, active or inactive. And since a communication to be complete must have a receiver as well as a transmitter each means must be considered in two parts: the method of transmission and the method of reception; that is, the sound must be heard, the touch felt, the odor smelled, and the action seen.

The largest and most dominant of the two groups, the voluntary-dynamic-active category is headed by the voice, snorting, stamping, and "clonking" involving four methods of transmission, with the ear and the sense of hearing as the common receiver.

Voice

Since it is possible to observe a band of bighorn constantly for days or even weeks at a time without hearing the sound of a single bleat from them, many observers have concluded as Seton (1929, p. 558) put it, "The Bighorn is one of the most silent of animals. The lambs up to 6 months old often bleat exactly as do the domestic kind; but I have never heard any sound from the old sheep except a loud snort or 'snoof.'"

Present evidence indicates a variation in the use of the voice both by age class and sex and by season.

On February 21, 1956, at Furnace Creek Wash, our notes record that a 3-week-old lamb "got lost (couldn't see its mother) twice today. Both times bleated several small bleats. This is the third time, third day, this has happened. Mother stops eating, listens, looks, decides nothing really wrong, never answers, goes on eating. Lamb eventually finds her without help." And of the same band when the two lambs were about 6 weeks old, March 16, "Once today mama missed them and climbed a 4-foot ridge in wash and gave three guttural calls, and both lambs came from the creosote [bush] full tilt. This is the first sound we have heard from the adults this year."

It was not until about 5 o'clock in the evening of April 10, when her lamb was 10 weeks old, that "Old Mama seemed to suddenly realize that (she and her lamb) had been feeding in shadow for some time. She abruptly raised her head almost with a 'double take' effect and scanned the horizon all around. She looked at the lamb and gave one of her rare, muffled, squeezed-sounding, gurgling grunts which passes with her for a bleat. The lamb as usual responded instantly by going to her. She took off across the wash to the north and in 20 minutes had crossed the eastern extremity of Paleomesa and disappeared into the canyon behind Red Mountain." Old Mama's voice as described above should not be considered characteristic of all adult bighorn ewes.

The "bleat" of adult bighorn tends to be deeper than that of domestic sheep and sometimes so vebrato as to be almost comical. In general, the "bleat" of the adult ram is probably somewhat deeper than that of the ewe, but we have observed no evidence of the two sounds close enough together for actual comparison.

The lamb's voice is the expected appealing complement to the general concept of the lamb's personality and is probably used more before weaning than during any other period of its life. As in most young animals, its primary instinctual drives are at least partially expressed by "voicing" its demands for food and protection from its mother and, to a lesser degree, its social demands from playmates.

Once the lamb is weaned, its voice is no longer useful in securing food but is still employed in the quest for security by calling for help when lost. Young animals sometimes appear to be engaging in a mutual exchange of distant identification and recognition with no other objective in view.

There is probably a correlation between the frequency of voice use and population density or, more specifically, the number of sheep in the band. In the Desert Game Range in 1953 we found bands of 15 to 20 ewes, with lambs not uncommon and with the urge for identification and recognition between mothers and offspring frequently and loudly observable.

Returning in our jeep truck to Joe May camp in the Desert Game Range on a moonless night in March, we came directly upon a large band of ewes and lambs bedded among the Joshua trees on a knoll at the edge of the wash. We shut off the lights and motor and listened for 15 minutes to a veritable din of anxious bleating, calling, and answering, which gradually subsided into quieter and plainly recognizable tones of recognition and reassurance, then finally silence when the last anxious mother touched her lamb in the dark.

Later the same week we watched a "babysitting" break up with a less anxious din of high and low voices as the lambs dropped off the cliff into the dense ground cover of the wash. Here the ewes waited where they were, head high, looking and guiding by call as the lambs bobbed about through the brush, calling in return and locating their mothers with surprising efficiency.

In the low-density, small-band population of Death Valley where more than two nursing lambs are seldom seen together, the problem of identity and the development of recognition by voice between ewes and lambs has seldom been observed. On March 16, 1956, when the new band joined Old Mama and her lamb in Furnace Creek Wash, the lamb, never having seen other sheep before, became confused and tried to nurse each animal as it came to it, even the year-old ram. Its mother watched for some time and then made one of her rare vocal efforts which brought the lamb to her at once.

Probably the most dramatic use of the voice by the Death Valley bighorn is the challenge of the rams in the mating season.

Our first introduction to this was on July 9, 1955, at Willow Creek, when a 2-year-old ram "called" to other sheep across the canyon as he made his way down the cliff toward them. This was probably one of his first efforts, and we did not recognize it as the "challenge" he apparently was trying to make.

The much overworked word "apparently" is used to emphasize the hesitancy with which we approach the semantic barrier which arises at this point, and to remind us that we do not speak the bighorn language and that we can only guess what a sound or sign may mean after we have observed the manner of its transmission and reception and the subsequent reaction to it. Even then, positive interpretation must be withheld until repetition has established empirical authority for conclusions.

Another case in point was recorded of a band of five on Paleomesa on December 1, 1956, and has been described under "Curiosity." This was the behavior of the 9-year-old ram, Tight Curl, when two prospectors began descending Pyramid Peak from their claim about 1½ miles away. His repeatedly uttered nasal growl was used to communicate his uneasiness.

In both the above incidents we have recorded a transmission by rams in the presence of ewes but eliciting no observable response from them. The young ram at Willow Creek seemed to be trying to communicate with the other sheep; the older ram on the mesa, on the other hand, appeared to direct his communique to the approaching prospectors and both his growling concern and the prospectors were ignored by the four ewes with him.

The question arises as to whether these reactions are due to the difference between the general nature of rams and ewes or to a difference in personal experience of the animals involved. The possibility of both factors being present is suggested by an observation made on a captive ram ("The Old Man" in our horn-growth photos) at the Desert Game Range on January 16, 1957. This observation includes not only voice but introduces movement, the sense of touch, and possibly the sense of smell as factors in communication.

When we were here on our last year's trip this ram was so "spooky" that it took me 2 days to get two rather poor closeups to show his horn development. At that time he and the two captive ewes seemed determined to keep the greatest possible distance within their fenced enclosure between themselves and us.

This year the ram had a different approach. His belligerence toward anyone who ventured inside the compound had been increasing year by year, earning him the local nickname of "Old Nasty," but this was the first time that he had challenged me right through the fence to "put up my horns and fight like a ram." As a matter of fact, you would think by his actions that it was the middle of the mating season, he was so willing to fight with anybody or anything.

The foot-thick almond tree in one corner of the small compound took a beating all day long. Standing about 20 feet from it, he would rear sideways on his hindlegs and with his head cocked on one side, his forelegs hanging almost crossed before him, he would advance to within about 10 feet of the tree; then, with a sharp increase in speed, his forequarters would drop toward the ground, his neck would arch, his head would come down, and he would lunge squarely into the tree, striking with all his speed and weight an instant before his forefeet touched the ground. It struck me that he seemed to be trying to show me what he would do to me if I would only come inside. If I remained motionless for any length of time, he would forget about me and wander off until I moved, then back he would dash until he was about 20 feet away, and then up he would rear on his hindlegs and sidle toward me with a walleyed stare down the side of his nose that would have been most discomfiting had there not been a strong fence between us.

He usually dropped to the ground a few feet short of striking the fence, although I knew that sometimes he didn't. I was trying to take a movie of this business by holding the camera a few feet out in front of me and guessing at having him in the frame as he advanced. This allowed me to stand 2 feet back from the fence in case he decided to make good his threat.

This he finally did, and with such force that the woven wire gave sufficiently under his weight to inflict a blow so painful to my thigh that I could hardly walk for almost an hour.

The day was very cold and windy, and at one time I was lying down close to the fence behind a mesquite thicket when he saw me and immediately and rapidly approached to within a foot of where I lay. Here he stood motionless, head down, staring fixedly at me with one eye about a foot from mine. After a few moments of this I became curious as to what his reactions might be if I slowly put my hand through the fence and took hold of his left horn.

He never moved a muscle until I began to push against his horn. He then arched his neck slightly and pushed against my pressure until I reversed the process by pulling instead of pushing on his horn. Rocking slowly backward and forward he pushed when I pushed and pulled when I pulled. This went on for possibly 10 minutes until I finally tired of it and stopped, whereupon he stood stock still for a moment, then leaned forward, proffering his horn for another round.

Later he approached me again while I was standing by the fence and once more we began a friendly tug of war. While this was in progress, Biologist Devan and a visitor came up, and on seeing that I had hold of one of the ram's horns, Devan called to me to hold on to him and we would examine his pelt to see if the wool could be seen at the base of the long winter-coat hair.

The ram became very uneasy as they approached, and by the time they reached me to offer assistance it was all I could do to hold onto his horns with both hands. As a matter of fact, it became all that two of us could do to hold him, especially as others came running up to see what his hide felt like.

When everyone had felt his winter coat, looked down his ears for ticks or excess wax, and administered such other indignities, he was released, and this time he left the vicinity as far and as fast as possible.

I didn't see him any more that day. The next morning when I went out to see him he eyed me suspiciously from 100 yards away and gave out that same warning blow through the nose with which Tight Curl had signaled the approach of strangers.

Here is a picture of a frustrated ram, in the absence of another ram, seeking an outlet for his drives through contact with a substitute species of animal. Evidently the conditions of the engagement were satisfactory up to the point of being detained against his will and subjected to disturbing, unfamiliar activity contributing nothing to his satisfaction.

Both his initial overtures and subsequent reaction would appear to reflect not only the fundamental nature of the ram but his personal experience as well. It might be argued that the entire incident reflected frustrations of captivity, but that it might not have been entirely so is indicated by an incident which occurred in the Red Amphitheater during the rutting season, October 29, 1957. It is included here in full as it was reported to us on that day by one of the participants, Geologist James McAllister. His field notes of that date are as follows:

While I was taking notes on planetable at 11:45 a.m. a ram came around the N. side of the mountain from the west. Paced later, about 200 feet. I heard it before seeing it. It saw me, facing me attentively for a long time.

For the first time in my life I heard a mountain sheep make a sound. First, light and short bronx cheer, several times. Then in short snorts. Bronx cheer developed into a slowly vibrating deep b-a-a-a.

It approached slowly about 50 feet. After more watching, it slowly butted a sage bush. Between buttings—or series of buttings—it would stop and look over at me. It advanced 25 feet further to a creosotebush which it butted at, slowly and deliberately tangled branches in its horns. It nibbled some creosotebush and advanced around below me, circling about one quadrant. It stood about 50 feet (paced) away from me, down a slope a long time. No more butting. Finally it headed back.

I had a good look at it without frightening it. I got up and followed it. It went back around ridge. It let me approach within 100 feet.

All this took 45 minutes (11:45 to 12:30). He circled behind the ridge and headed for Pyramid Peak.

Here again there seems to be no doubt that a ram, this one wild and uninhibited by captivity, was trying to communicate with a man. Repeated observations of parallel activity between two rams as a preliminary to a joust indicate the probability that this ram was extending the same invitation to McAllister.

It is not necessary to assume that the ram mistook the man for another ram; it is just as likely that he was simply seeking to fulfill his complete destiny as a ram, which includes the satisfaction of an urge to hurl himself into a headlong colliding contest with an opponent—preferably another ram, but lacking that, anything of a comparable size that moves, and lacking that, a tree, or a boulder, or the solid wall of a mountain, all of which we have recorded repeatedly.

"Clonking"

"Clonking," the reverberating crash of a lone ram's horns against a solid object, serves as a communication in that it reaches the attention of other lone rams who often seem to accept it as a challenge and seek him out to offer contest. The action is voluntary, but whether it is intended as a communication is not known and so remains unclassified.

Stamping

Stamping, smelling, and other actions were observed and reported by Park Naturalist Don Curry during Regional Biologist Lowell Sumner's second Death Valley bighorn survey in 1939 (Curry, 1939).

Some information on the rutting season of the bighorn and the habits of the male during that period was obtained on November 15, 1938. The writer was engaged in planetable mapping just south of Natural Bridge Canyon, in the Black Mountains. I had set up the planetable on one of the small gravel hills that flank the steep front of this portion of the mountains. The exact elevation, as taken from my map, was 764 feet, or approximately 1,000 feet above the valley flat. My assistant was holding a stadia rod approximately one-fourth of a mile distant and up the slope from me. He apparently startled some sheep which were across a deep canyon to the south; and both he and I were attracted by the sound of rocks rolling down the steep, 30° slope. At that time the sheep were at least half a mile from me, by actual measurement. (In the intense stillness that often obtains in Death Valley it is not unusual to have one's attention attracted to sheep a mile or more distant in this manner.) Pearson later reported seeing at least two individuals. One or more fled up the mountain slope, but a large ram started downslope, towards me. He ignored Pearson's presence, although he was much closer. Situated on the top of a hill, and bending over a planetable, I may have appeared vaguely like another ram. At least I am in hopes that it was the animal's eyesight, and not some other sense, that caused this misapprehension. The fact remains that the ram, impelled by curiosity or pugnaciousness, traveled all the way down the steep slope, out of sight into a narrow canyon below me, then up a tributary gulley to the top of the ridge and not over 100 yards from my position. He paused many times in this advance to gaze long minutes in my direction, immobile except for his dilating nostrils when he sniffed inquiringly. Occasionally he would give a hoarse, questioning blat, which I imitated to the best of my ability. The sound was voluntary and vocal; and from the animal's actions I would say that it is a definite inquiry or challenge, rather than an attempt to clear the nasal passages of parasites, as has been suggested elsewhere.

Watching the animal through the telescopic alidade, I had an excellent opportunity to study him. As I recall, he had eight or nine annular rings on his horns; and he was in perfect coat and condition. He was evidently in rut. The glands on his face below the eyes were running, and he showed every indication of being ready for a fight, tossing his horns and occasionally stamping or pawing the ground with a forefoot. He stayed on the ridge for about half an hour, during which time I advanced slowly and he retreated a few steps at a time, keeping about 75 feet between us. Finally he was satisfied that I was harmless and of no interest to him. He then dropped down a small tributary leading to Natural Bridge Canyon, passing directly below and within 25 feet of me but ignoring me altogether.

It may have been my attempts to imitate his call that made him so curious; or perhaps he never before had encountered man.

This is an excellent and enlightening report, but the purposes of this discussion would not be fully served were it not suggested that here again it is not necessary to assume that the ram mistook the geologist for another ram or that he was definitely impelled by "curiosity or pugnaciousness." Further, the report suggests that the ram's actions were an effort to determine the man's intentions toward him, that he decided the man "was harmless and of no interest to him." This is one interpretation but it also seems possible that the ram actually had hoped to engage in a fight, rather than to avoid one.

Exact interpretation becomes more probable when both the transmission and reception of a communication can be observed within the same frame of reference. A geologist's reception and reaction to a ram's challenge to a dual is not likely to throw much light on the ram's original intent or the content of his message because of the geologist's unfamiliarity with the medium of communication at hand, the bighorn "language."

To what degree a human understanding of this "language" could develop is not known, but comparison of the above observations with our repeated observations of opposing rams in their preliminaries to butting bouts in the field reveal too many striking similarities for coincidence.

We have, for example, many observations such as these notations at Nevares on August 27, 1957:

7:51 a.m. A mature ram is at Old Spring. At first I thought it was The Hook but the eyes make him look more—yes, he has turned around—Tan Rump!

Drinking again now—again, 10 seconds and something spooked him!

8:17. Well, I'm sure of it now, what spooked him is "clonking" somewhere. I've been thinking I heard it, somewhere to the north, 3 or 4 times.

8:20. Tan Rump thinks he hears something up the mountain now—

8:37. He has moved north of a clump of arrow-weed this side of the old blind—and is butting it!

9:10. Tan Rump has slowly worked his way up to The Saddle.

9:30. I hear a sheep bellowing, believe it or not! Or more, it sounds like Tight Curl's "blowing through his nose" last autumn. Tan Rump is looking—I see him coming—on the run.

9:35. I had lost the new arrival behind The Point, but he's here now. A ram—and incredible as it seems he not only sound likes Tight Curl—he unmistakably is Tight Curl! And on the prod—whop! He and Tan Rump are at it in The Saddle!

This was the first of many observations we were to make of the ram's use of the voice in challenging other rams, seen or unseen, to contest. Here too, was a ram "butting a sage bush," apparently stimulated to do so by the "challenge" of another ram.

On September 6 in The Notch above Raven Spring at 9:10 a.m., we heard two "blowings," and there was Tight Curl again.

He looked to the south, and, as he looked, his back arched in a spasm. Then he started rapidly toward the springs, and we saw then that Brahma and her lamb were feeding on the thistles at Round Pool.

They saw the ram coming and went on with their eating. Tight Curl gave Brahma the rush and got a cold shoulder in return. Then he, too, decided eating was a good idea and turned away and began to eat grass as vigorously as Brahma and her lamb were eating thistles.

So the "sounding," "bellowing," "blowing" may be a mating call as well as a challenge to battle.

By 11:20 that day we were hearing "clonks" steadily from high on Nevares Peak where Tight Curl had been chasing Brahma. She had eluded him and taken to the shade, and the "clonking" we heard was caused by him in his gestures of frustration—he had a cliff backed up against a mountain and was "blasting" it again and again! He banged it 15 or 20 times before he appeared to give Brahma up and took off for greener pastures.

By 6:15 that evening, however, a younger ram, Low Brow, had drunk from Raven Spring and was leaving via The Saddle when we heard a "call" and at once spotted a big ram running northward from The Narrows. There was Tight Curl again, and ahead of him, dropping into Red Wall wash, was Brahma and her lamb. Low Brow heard Tight Curl's bellow and immediately set off at a gallop to overtake them.

Hearing

In general, the systems of communication so far discussed depend on auditory reception. No extensive tests or experiments have been conducted to determine the quality of bighorn hearing. What little evidence we have, however, indicates a healthy, normal condition at least equal in sensitivity to ours. We have no evidence in Death Valley sheep of hearing impairment by ticks, as has been suggested by observers in other areas.

Touch

Touch as a means of communication is difficult to evaluate because transmission and reception involve the same sense and are expressed by the same means under intimate circumstances where other factors may be at work. One of the commonest examples observed, the "nursing touch" of the mother ewe just before walking away from her nursing lamb, may combine the sense of smell with the sense of touch because the contact is made with the nose. The common nuzzling of mothers for their lambs probably involves both systems, as does the identification-recognition activity which follows the age class segregation of "babysitting."

The stiff foreleg upthrust of the ram used on other rams in the preliminary to jousting and on ewes as a persuasion to mating is apparently more of a signal than a blow because no retaliatory action, or shrinking, has been observed.

Movement

Movement seems to serve in both a voluntary and involuntary capacity as a medium of communication. The change of posture and manner of walking in the "traveling look" of the leader is probably involuntary but usually is responded to by the rest of the band by cessation of browsing and an assumption of more or less the same posture and manner as the leader. The same is apparently true of a fear reaction; the retreating band will stop if the leader stops and will watch her closely for signs of her evaluation of the danger. If she relaxes and appears to dismiss the danger, the others usually follow her example.

Running seems to serve as an involuntary communication when the reason for the running is not readily recognizable to the rest of the band. The four-footed, drumming bound, however, seems to be responded to by all as a voluntary warning of danger.

Appeasement

The gesture of appeasement is widespread among animals. The bird may crouch to the ground with quivering wings outspread, and the dog may roll on its back with its throat and belly exposed. The bighorn holds its horns back from the fighting position and down on both sides of its neck by thrusting its nose forward, turning its head on one side, and advancing slightly sideways with mincing, quick, short steps, and an almost ludicrously placating manner.

This gesture may be employed by one ram toward another during the joust and result in a temporary cessation of tilting. It is often used by a young ram meeting an older one on the trail; and it is almost universally employed by all rams in their initial approach to ewes. But probably the most striking use of it we have seen has been between ewes. On July 1 at Nevares two small bands met near the spring, and the ewes "stuck their noses far forward, crouched, and slunk" past each other.

Showing Rump Patch

Showing the rump patch is a purely involuntary signal of location to other animals. The bighorn cannot "flash" its rump patch in the manner described for the antelope, and we have no evidence to suggest its voluntary use in any way. However, the involuntary gleam of white in the sun may be of importance in getting rams and ewes together in the mating season.

Other specific forms of movement, touch, and so forth will be discussed under "Reproduction."

Vision

The vision of the bighorn has assumed legendary proportions. Eight-power binoculars are often used in comparison with it. We have no way of determining the quality of their vision beyond the most rudimentary experiments and observations. On January 19, 1956, while watching a band of eight about $1\frac{1}{2}$ miles away through 12x glasses, we determined by repeated trials that they could see a wave of the hand although they were barely discernible to the naked eye.

The fact that they have good vision is too well known to warrant general discussion. We have seen ample proof of this in distant vision and in the close vision associated with the incredible surefootedness of the species. (See "Play" and "Climbing Ability.") There is some question, however, involving their intermediate vision suggested by a seeming inability to recognize well-known objects within certain limits. Under "Response to Humans and Equipment" in this report, several instances of this seeming inability are recorded in detail. Much more work would be necessary to determine the cause of it.

Sense of Smell

The sense of smell of the bighorn has been variously described in degree from acute to nonexistent. Acute can be a relative degree;

compared with the average human sense of smell it is acute; compared with the average canine sense of smell, it is not. On the other hand, no evidence points to its nonexistence; the lack of reaction to the transmission of human scent on a close wind does not necessarily indicate a lack of reception of the scent. Without exception, the bands involved in our prolonged observations have become indifferent to indications of our presence, whether by sight, sound, or scent, as long as acceptable conditions obtained. (See "Response to Humans and Equipment.")

The urination of a ewe and what seems to be some sort of olfactory analysis of it by a ram apparently plays a part in establishing the presence or imminence of oestrus in the mating cycle. The suggestion that the closely related sense of taste is also employed here has been considered.

That their sense of smell is developed enough for tracking of other sheep to a limited degree has been indicated repeatedly but not conclusively. For example, we have seen a lone ewe wander to certain outstanding but unfrequented points in the area to be traced (apparently) to the same spots by a ram an hour after she had disappeared. The route followed was not along an established trail and was traversed by the ram with head down and nose to the ground, much like a dog on the scent of a rabbit.

Lambs frequently will tarry at a spring for some time after the mother has sought shade out of sight on the mountainside. Occasionally the lamb has followed a most circuitous route, around the point of ridges, across boulder-strewn washes, turning back and leaping from the same rock to rock that its mother did and eventually finding her in her shaded resting place.

This type of behavior has all the appearance of the utilization of the sense of smell. What confuses the picture is the fact that they do not always follow this pattern. Sometimes a lamb will, on realizing that its mother is out of sight, give way to panic and run back and forth from one high point to another, employing only its eyesight and hearing in its effort to find its mother. Lambs lost during the rut-run have never been observed using their sense of smell to locate their mothers. Nor do adult sheep separated from the band seem to employ it successfully, apparently relying entirely on vision for the final solution.

According to Einarsen (1948), sheep have interdigital scent glands, but we have no data on their use, either on a voluntary or involuntary basis.

Signposts

The establishment and maintenance of "signpost" areas seems to be common practice among the rams and this custom sometimes is casually observed by the ewes and lambs. We have observed two types of bighorn "signposts" in Death Valley, the commonest being "urination." How the first ram decided to urinate in a certain spot is not known, but once he has, it appears to be common practice for every other ram passing that way to stop, sniff elaborately, advance a step or two, and urinate at length in or near the same spot. The second in popularity seems to be the "bush-beating signpost," which, when once chosen, may eventually end in the complete destruction of the shrub or even the tree thus favored.

Almost all phases of communication will be further developed in the succeeding discussions of this report.

Reproduction

Males

Rutting Period

The rutting period per se begins slowly in late June, increases in intensity rather sharply through July, maintains a fairly high level through September and October, and gradually declines through November to subsidence sometime in December. Our latest record of copulation is December 23, although sporadic activity has been recorded in January, February, and March.

The beginning of the season is signaled by the breaking up of the winter ram bands and the appearance of single rams along the trails, near the springs, or traveling temporarily with the ewes themselves.

While several rams may be observed together in an area during the rut, we have no record of two or more teaming up for the season as has been suggested by others.

Feeding Behavior

Feeding behavior appears to be substantially modified during the peak of mating activity. The older rams were observed to eat very little, yet, despite the increased expenditure of energy, they reached the end of the season in excellent condition. The younger rams (up to 3 or 4 years) ate more than the mature rams yet responded to the rigors of the season by some loss of weight and general signs of fatigue.

Distance Traveled

The distance traveled during the rut has not been determined, but two positively identified rams, Tight Curl and Rambunctious, were first observed near Travertine Point in Furnace Creek Wash in the spring and autumn of 1956; in upper Echo Canyon in January and February 1957; and at Nevares Spring in August 1957. This represents an airline distance of 12 miles, and both rams were headed north from Nevares toward Indian Pass 7 airline miles farther.

Attention to Females

Attention to females appears to vary in detail with the individual but some general behavior can be summarized:

Mature rams seem to show no persistent interest in ewes either before oestrus or after, only during.

Young rams from a few weeks up to 3 or 4 years of age tend to harass ewes to some extent whenever they come in contact with them. Copulation sometimes occurs under these circumstances, which may contribute to the length of the Death Valley lambing season. During this period the young rams usually defer to the older rams without contesting the field in any way.

Rams have several approaches to ewes during the rut, but some are more common than others. Probably the one most generally used was first recorded at Nevares, August 15, 1957. Our field notes read:

12:45. When I arrived from Navel Spring, Buddy had had a ewe and lamb "staked out" in the shade of a cut bank about 300 yards up Nevares Wash since 11 o'clock.

She's old, or sick, maybe both, Buddy says. And skinny—I can see her head from here where she rests in the shade. Reminds me of Old Mama. Buddy says she isn't sure it isn't Old Mama. I haven't seen the lamb yet.

1:00. The old ewe has come out in the sun, and it is not Old Mama. This is a typical Nevares type ewe. Large body, long neck, and high horns. She is lame, and old, I don't know about sick. The lamb has come out. About 5 or 6 weeks old, fuzzy, no horns, brownish and not gray like its mother. It has gone back into the shade. It definitely is not ready to travel. Its ears are held at an odd angle which should help in future identification. Mother goes back in shade and lies down.

1:30. Buddy left to see about supplies at headquarters.

2:00. I have been glassing the entire area ever since Buddy left—and again a sheep is standing at Old Spring! Out of nowhere, just standing there, already having drunk his fill, a huge ram, looking very much like the one at Navel yesterday. I thought at first it may be the same one. Then I realized this one is darker, and his horns hang lower on his head. He has gone down to the big boulder across the grass and vegetation below Round Pool and is pawing a bed. He's down, but not enough in the shade, I'd think.

2:10. He's up and heading this way. I have set up both movie cameras and the still camera with the 500-mm. lens, all under damp cloths to keep them cool.

He's moving steadily across the spring area with a most purposeful manner. If he keeps coming, or going, he will find the ewe and lamb. He acts as though he already knows they are there.

I got some good movie footage and slides as he crossed toward the cut bank where the ewe is still lying. I think I got a good shot as he saw her in the shade, broke into a fast trot, and rushed her to her feet, rose in the air and disappeared behind the bank as he tried to mount her, with no preliminaries whatever.

I don't know whether a new lamb is on its way just yet or not, but by this ram's manner he intends to see that one is if it isn't already.

They are back in sight now, and I am reminded of Fred Jones' account of rams knocking each other's testicles with their front feet. The ram is knocking at her flank in the same manner.

He is now standing behind her, and with steady persistence nips at her flank. She turns her head with a slight toss every time he does this—and eventually it assumes the characteristics of a dance.

The lamb is lying in sight, flicking its ears and ignoring the whole thing.

The ram tries again to mount and the ewe slides out into the sun, where she soon begins to feed again. The ram watches her for a moment from the shade, then paws out a bed and lies down. The ewe feeds for 10 minutes, returns to the shade, and all three are lying down. It is 2:30. Temperature, 110°.

I have watched for half an hour for fear I'll miss something. All I've seen is half an hour of cud-chewing.

3:00. They have repeated the business of the ram getting up, rousing the ewe, trying to mount, she moving away, the head-bobbing deal, now and then the strike with the rigid foreleg by the ram. Eventually she is out in the open again, feeding. The lamb changes position and lies down again. The ram follows the ewe into the sun, but only for a moment.

4:00. All are lying in the shade again.

4:30. Nothing has happened except I've just got eyestrain from watching.

4:40. The ram is out in the open after the ewe and she is running with a remarkable display of energy and agility for one who seemed so old and decrepit an hour ago. I don't see the lamb. The ewe stops now and then and seems to be remembering that she already has one child, and where is it? But the ram keeps pressing her, shoving into her flank, nipping at her flank and striking. She runs in a circle and seems to be trying to see her lamb. She slides out from under the ram and heads for the mountains—without her lamb.

4:50. She and the ram have dropped out of sight in Nevares Wash and I am trying to find the lamb. Here it is, just out of the shade where it has been resting all afternoon, looking around for its mother, who is still out of sight.

4:55. The ram and ewe are gone. The lamb is running across from Nevares Wash toward the second canyon to the north and goes out of sight alone, one canyon too soon!

5:00. At the site of the 4 hours of bedding and mating activity I can find two beds, two pellet groups, both adult; no sign of the lamb at all, two urine spots. This in 4 hours. Temperature, 115°.

More spectacular but somewhat less common is the exhausting and ritualistic "herding" sometimes engaged in by a ram and a ewe for several days before culmination. This was first observed at Nevares Spring on August 17, 1957, and again on the 18th.

We were still not certain what part this "herding" played in the mating pattern when on December 2, 1957, we got a report of two rams "playing" on a fan 5 miles below Badwater. Our notes of December 3 read as follows:

7:50 a.m. Spotted two bighorn running toward mountains through desert-holly sheep-head high. Glasses showed not two rams but one young ram (1½ to 2 years old) and, of all things, none other than our old friend from the Badwater band of December 1954, old Droopy herself! Spooky as ever and looking not a day older.

They ran to about a quarter of a mile from the highway and then stopped and watched me for awhile; then they began to feed on last year's annuals.

8:30. They have fed half way back to the road and are standing watching me. I have taken some record shots in this poor light.

8:35. They have both bedded about 100 yards from the road, and this seems like a good time to change film but there is still some to run.

9:00. The sun has reached them. I'll finish the two rolls nearly done and change film while they are still in siesta.

This young ram [Paleface] is "herding" Droopy. That is the "playing" reported last night. I got about 5 feet of one of their less vigorous efforts.

9:15. They have disappeared. While I was changing film I heard rocks flying, and over my shoulder I saw the most exciting "run" and "herding" display yet! Lee Shackleton is here watching now. He said that they were over half a mile north of here when he saw them last night. He was much surprised to learn that Droopy was not a ram.

They are "running" again, but too far away and in shadow.

9:50. The young ram has "herded" Droopy into a small ravine. After standing about her for awhile he is now lying down.

9:55. She is lying down.

10:00. The sun has reached his bed but not hers. If they were both in good light it would make a perfect illustration of the "herding" idea—the ram always trying to stay above the ewe or between her and wherever she wants to go. Or seems to want to go, because we have noticed before (and here this morning) that the ewe will often outrun the ram, then seem to wait for him to regain his position. Perhaps this is a ritualistic sort of thing, as most of the rams' fighting seems to be. Last summer when Knocker was herding Longhorn in 116° in the shade, we thought she stopped to rest, perhaps. But today is so cool, 60° at 10:15, that certainly the weather can be discounted. It begins to look like Droopy could get away if she wanted to!

10:20. The ram has stretched out his head and is resting and sleeping with the weight of his head on his muzzle and right horntip. This could certainly contribute to brooming of the horntips.

10:30. He is up, stretching, urinating. Now he is going down to Droopy. He strikes at her with front feet. Droopy leaps up and without further ado is off full tilt to the north with His Orneriness hotfooting it after her.

10:36. They are now feeding in a draw on some plant I can't see from here.

10:55. He began "herding" her and has been at it until just now at 11:30. I would estimate they have completed about a 2-mile "run."

11:50. Droopy made a run for shade but didn't make it; so, at 11:55, she lay down in the wash.

12:10. They are both lying down, both in full sun.

12:25. Now they are up and feeding. Droopy got up first, probably because I walked out of her sight and she had to get up so she could see where I was going and what I was up to. This happens quite often—often enough, in fact, that we realized long ago that it is better to stay in sight at all times if you want continual observations. Sheep get uneasy if you get out of sight for a moment, and sometimes we have found them gone when we reappear, perhaps running in a sudden panic generated by simple uneasiness in the beginning. Then one of them kicks a rock or sneezes and away they go.

1:15. They have been out of the wash on the first terrace at the foot of the mountain for some time.

After some good "runs" on terrace, they have been out of sight in ravine since 2:50.

3:20. I finally decided that they might have gone up the ravine and I had better move up with the jeep truck and equipment until I can see directly into the ravine. So I packed up all the cameras, slammed the truck doors, started the engine, and looked up to find them standing on the ridge again, come up to see what the noise was all about. This is the fourth time this has happened today. Their hearing must be o.k.

3:35. Sun has gone down behind the Panamints. Ewe and ram are feeding quietly in the wash 200 yards away. Now he's after her again.

3:50. The sun is still showing on Daylight Pass. Temperature, 67°.

4:05. The moon is up. This "herding" business has taken a new slant. I am quite sure that it is a game of some sort or ritual. In any case, it is voluntary on both sides. Again and again Droopy has been in a position to elude Paleface and really get away, but she never takes advantage of the opportunity. Instead, she has, once or twice, not only waited for him to catch up but retraced her steps until he saw her again.

He has now "forced" her all the way down the fan over half a mile to the highway by a series of short jabbing runs at her, which are not designed to reach her but to frighten her only—like running at someone and stamping your foot and shouting "boo." As a matter of fact, he sometimes gives the equivalent of a "boo" in a sort of snort. He drops his head low to the ground, nose out, ears back, takes one or two very slow crouching steps, then a sudden lunge toward her, but never to her. She obediently dashes away a short distance.

Now, since sundown, he has pushed her thus to the edge of the highway and out on it, while he himself patrols the berm, and will not let her off the pavement!

4:20. He suddenly seemed to say "that's enough of that," turned, and, head down and out, began to walk rapidly away toward the mountains. Droopy immediately picked up her cue and followed at a trot.

Now he starts something new. He pretends not to see her, but if she starts to go by him on the right side he quickens his pace and gets directly in front of her. She tried the left side with the same results; so from right to left and back four or five times; then suddenly he whirls and lunges at her. She whirls away for a few feet and stops. He stands, head down, glaring at her for a moment, turns his back, and away he briskly goes, she after him, and the whole process is gone through again.

As they near the ledge at the foot of the mountain they burst into breakneck speed and round and round they go. Who started it, or who is "chasing" who, is not really apparent. This finally breaks up when he leaves the chase and leaps up to the top of a 10-foot ledge and stands, head low, looking down at her. Here again her voluntary participation becomes apparent, because she now deliberately places herself directly below him, and the maneuvering begins: She to ascend the ledge, he to block her.

The last I could see of her she was lying down, placidly chewing her cud. He was still standing 10 feet above her on the loose ledge looking down at her. Suddenly the ledge began to crumble under him, and she got up and moved from under the falling rocks. He, however, was completely unperturbed, just spread all four feet out a little and rode down the small landslide until it stopped; whereupon, he simply relaxed where he stood. She lay down again a few feet away and I left them there chewing their cuds in the moonlight.

On the next and third day of activity, their behavior followed the same pattern as the day before, but with minor differences:

When the ewe approaches the ram and he her, face to face, she will start to run to the right past him but he heads her off, turning in always and intercepting her attempt to pass him on the left, back and forth with incredible agility and stamina.

As it grew darker, he reverted to the "leading cut"—going away from her but never letting her go past him or off in a direction of her own choosing.

It began to appear that he either knew where Droopy wanted to go or he was "leading" her and she deliberately following, because he would turn suddenly and walk briskly into a ravine or up on a ledge at right angles to their general direction of travel. She invariably followed.

At one point we thought that they had bedded down, and we were preparing to leave when a change took place. It was so dark we could scarcely see them with the binoculars, but Droopy suddenly took the lead and at a breakneck speed struck off across the nearly perpendicular face of the mountain to the north, with the ram about 10 yards behind her. Showers of falling gravel and boulders followed them both. Long after we could no longer see them, we could follow their progress northward by the sound of the rolling rocks and small landslides they loosed in passing.

By 5 o'clock the sounds were dwindling to a point where it appeared that even they were being slowed down, if not stopped, by darkness, and finally no sounds at all. The moon rose and we came home.

Finally on Nevares Peak on September 15, 1958, we got a definite indication of the objective of this unique behavior.

A mature ram known to us as Black-and-Tan persisted in his "herding" of the ewe, Brokeoff, until it netted him a completed copulation.

Their physical satisfaction from copulation didn't seem to last for more than about 15 minutes, however, during which time they just stood resting. Then they began again the same violent expenditure of energy involved in "herding," up and down the mountain and across the face of cliffs.

Actual copulation, after such a prolonged courtship and a vast expenditure of energy, was surprisingly brief.

A description of copulation, as well as another premating "technique," was recorded earlier on Paleomesa, November 19, 1956, when, as dawn broke, I watched mating activity in a band of 14. The mating was between a new ram which had joined the band the night before and none other than the leader of the band, Old Mama, herself.

Old Mama was quite aggressive, butting and shoving at the ram and then whipping around and nudging him with her hind quarters. He, in turn, stood with his head and neck across hers, and from time to time he would strike upward at her flanks with stiff foreleg. When he landed a sound blow this way, she would squat and emit a small amount of fluid from her vagina.

The actual copulation was brief, the ewe standing with head held forward, the ram mounting, and after two or three movements of adjustment, one long thrust forward, and then slowly sliding backward and off.

Copulation seems more likely to occur when only one ram is "pursuing" a ewe. Our observations indicate a tendency for two or more rams to become sidetracked from their amorous pursuits by the call to arms, and it is not uncommon for a third ram to appear and make off with the prize while the lusty antagonists try to prove to each other which is the better ram.

By constantly traveling back and forth from one spring to another during the rut, the rams, in effect, may increase their ratio to resident ewes by more than two to one. (See table 8.)

The varying results of this temporary imbalance has been recorded many times. A typical incident took place at Navares Spring on September 5, 1957:

5:15 a.m. Temperature, 82°. No wind. Thin clouds in the south.

I have been watching the ground to see if I can determine how early as well as how late sheep may travel. It seems to me that bighorn can travel by 5 a.m. at this time of year. Judging by the darkness of evening in which we have both seen and heard them, they can travel until 8 p.m. Longhorn was traveling across the mountain from the Red Saddle the evening of August 27 at 8 o'clock. The ground was just about equally discernible to me in both instances. I could not see a sidewinder on it, for instance, but I could see a large rock or a ditch well enough for walking.

6:00. It is light enough that I just saw without glasses a white rump patch moving on the point—no animal, just a patch. The 12×50 binoculars reveal the ram Nevares II starting across the mountain at Saddle level above the springs. He walks freely and rapidly, as usual not browsing. He is seen eating very little these days.

6:10. The quail are stirring.

6:15. Nevares II is heading for the upper Needle's Eye.

6:20. The sun hits Telescope Peak.

6:23. Nevares II is gone, high up on the Needle's Eye. Temperature, 80°.

6:28. Three sheep are running at Old Spring—a ewe, Full Curl, and Tight Curl. This is the full-tilt run that means business. I don't see a lamb. They are making a complete circle of the entire spring area. Tight Curl is hottest after her. I can see his mouth open, his tongue out, head forward and down, and I can hear him pant and puff! Full Curl is waiting back a way. Now he cuts in as they pass! She heads for Long Spring, grabs a mouthful or two of water. And here's another ram—Nevares II is back! So there she goes— looks like Little Ewe—with three rams in full chase. She heads this way. Nevares II drops out. Full Curl miscalculated. He cut across and she turned this way, and so he's far behind! Tight Curl forced her up the point about half way, and she turned back across the mountain. Full Curl didn't see this so he went hotfooting it up Nevares Wash while the chase went the opposite direction behind him.

6:45. How can they keep this up? She has found the Black Pool and is snatching a quick gulp. Tight Curl does, too, and Nevares II catches up. They head toward Old Spring.

Full Curl is coming down from the Saddle with another ram! This is the long-absent Toby. He and Full Curl take a moment out for a quick clonk and fall in after Tight Curl. The ewe heads for Old Spring, and as she and her four rams approach it another young ram is spooked out of the spring!

They all mill around above the spring and I can't tell who is who in the whirl, but I can see a lamb on the fringe of things. (This ewe lost her lamb in the chase. It came in to water alone on the 7th, but it came again with its mother on the 9th.)

I have gambled on pictures of this. I don't know whether the light is good enough, but I have to try.

They seemed to be leaving the springs and heading toward the Notch, so I thought I might get close enough to identify the new ram; but this was a mistake.

Just as I arrived above Raven Spring, I found that the ewe had switched and was coming back above me. And then the whole band spooked and headed at breakneck speed straight up the mountain.

I, of course, retreated, since interference with their activity is something we always try to avoid. I got the 12×50 binoculars here at camp in time to see some of them go over the Second Ridge into Nevares Canyon. Almost immediately Nevares II came back and headed south behind the First Peak. Then Tight Curl reappeared and headed east up Second Peak, from time to time looking back and down into the cayon where Full Curl and Knocker were evidently still at it. Tight Curl's mouth is still open and his tongue is out.

7:15. All is quiet at Nevares Springs.

7:25. Half a mile away and 2,000 feet up, Tight Curl is approaching the summit of Second Peak and is silhouetted beautifully against the rising sun. Nevares II comes across on the skyline from the south and they hassle awhile on the mountaintop until 7:45 and they leave. All is still now.

Then I hear a last good clonk from the canyon and I wonder: Is it possible that 3-year-old Knocker is so eager to know about life that he takes on Full Curl?

All quiet again.

8:20. The shadows are shortening faster now, racing silently up from the valley floor. It is 92°. I will try to catch up on my notes before it gets so hot that sweat soaks the paper whenever I touch it.

10:30. Just after Buddy arrived to take over the second "watch," I heard "sounding" in the north. I called Buddy's attention to it and heard it again, the distant foghorn sound of a big ram "calling." The glasses showed him standing on the rim of Fuzzy Canyon, half a mile to the north, and (even at this distance) also revealed him to be Broken Nose.

He came on down, posed for pictures on the point, and went on down to

Long Spring for water and feed. On his way south, he stopped and seemed to be drinking at a place where I didn't know there was water. He went on south and eventually out into the South Wash. When he was far enough away that I couldn't disturb him, I went down and checked where he had seemed to be drinking—and he had been. A small round pool, about 12 inches across and 8 inches deep, was still full after all his drinking.

12:30 p.m. He has gone out of sight up the wash.

1:00. A young ram at Old Spring already has had a drink and is working north. This is Knocker back again; so he had been sidetracked by all the excitement this morning.

We watched him work slowly toward The Saddle when we suddenly realize there is a big ram above him hurrying along at a great rate—Broken Nose! We thought he was a way down the South Wash, somewhere. We look ahead. What is he after now? There it is, just about to enter The Saddle, a ewe and lamb—Dark Eyes and Light Neck! They've obviously already drunk, their sides tight as ticks. How did we miss them? It must have been while we relaxed for about 10 minutes to eat a sandwich. Knocker apparently came in with them and drank with them and hung around just long enough for us to spot him before he followed them away.

1:15. They are through The Saddle and going steadily northward without stopping even to nibble at holly. Last time, on the 2d when Dark Eyes was here, she and Brahma gobbled up thistle and *Bebbia* for over 2 hours. Today, nothing.

1:45. She and her lamb and Knocker have dropped over into Fuzzy Canyon, but the "Nose" seems to have folded up in the shade somewhere along the way.

4:00. Temperature 106°.

6:00. Buddy was trying to spot three bluish birds flying toward the springs when she spotted instead a big ram going up the First Ridge. It was Tight Curl, last seen early this morning going over the Second Peak! He didn't come down to drink but climbed, tongue out, almost steadily until at 6:30 he went back over the crest of First Peak. Temperature, 102°. (Official temperature, 111°.)

It has been suggested that fewer rams would be desirable: That the four- or five-ram relay chase unnecessarily exhausts the ewe; that lambs are lost in the chase, thus contributing to the mortality rate; that hunting would have reduced the ram ratio and maintained a "better balance of the sexes"; that controlled hunting should, therefore, be considered desirable in sheep areas that are not in the National Park System. This point will be discussed further under "Status for the Future" and "Recommendations for Protection."

Fighting With Other Males

Fighting with other males is a much publicized but little understood phase of bighorn life history.

There is a real question as to whether their dramatic butting bouts are fighting or are simple contests of skill and stamina with little real antagonism involved.

The evidence of this report points strongly toward a ritualistic emphasis on the interpretation of the activity and suggests the need for much more observation and study before definite conclusions can be drawn about the part it plays in the propagation of the species.

Certainly it has nothing to do with the premating collection and maintenance of a "harem," or ewe herd; nor does it seem to result in the elimination of one ram from participation in mating activity with a certain ewe. From our observations, the "fight," "joust," "contest," "clonking," or "brain busting" appears to have no objective whatever except the satisfaction of some deep-seated urge aroused by the mating instinct and demanding and receiving an outlet for its own sake, whether it is with another ram, a bush, a tree, a boulder, or a mountain.

This subject has been discussed to some extent under "Communication" and "Play" and will be treated in its initial stages under "Growth, Behavior, and Care of Young."

The concept of deadly enmity between rams, with a "battle to the death" upon meeting, could scarcely be further from the truth. Rams' reaction to one another varies with each individual: Some challenge and are accepted; others neither challenge nor accept one extended to them. Under no circumstances is it necessary that a ewe be present to precipitate a struggle.

A contest may be heralded by a vocal challenge, as described under "Communication," but it may not.

A series of encounters is included in this report, chosen from many to illustrate, as completely as possible, the scope and complexity of this behavior pattern.

Rams seem to be uninterested in a contest with an inferior opponent. One instance of a young ram badgering a mature one into a duel has been included under "Attention to Females," but the usual reaction of an older ram to the young was well illustrated in Box Canyon near Deadman's Curve on March 23, 1956. Our notes read as follows:

Just before sundown an old ram, apparently spooked by my slamming the truck door, rushed out of the wash and up the rocky slope below and north of Deadman's Curve. He was a full curl, slightly potbellied, and very spooky. He worked his way into nearby Box Canyon, wary and suspicious. He apparently could smell the others there, yet when one of them suddenly appeared he turned and ran pellmell out of the canyon, then stopped, turned back, and cautiously retraced his steps.

He stopped 50 feet from the first ewe. Both stood, heads up, looking. The two lambs came, curiously staring at this ram whom we named The Stranger. Then came the young ram. He at once stood and walked on his hindlegs around the old ram, whose indifference to him could not have been greater.

They have met on a steep slope in the last rays of sunset, a quarter of a mile away, but I could hear the young ram blowing as he walked and could see him slant his head as he sighted for the rush. The Stranger seemed not to see him or his antics until he came to earth with his forefeet and lunged. The old warrior then casually turned his massive horns enough to catch and hold the force of the young ram's charge. He was ready, by force of habit perhaps, braced for it, and gave not an inch. Neither did he take one. The young ram strained against him, plowing deep into the talus, blowing mightily through his nose. Getting nowhere, he backed off, repeated the entire maneuver, rearing, circling on his hindlegs, charging. This was repeated three or four times in 15 minutes. It was like a drunken youth trying to pick a fight with an old prizefighter who has just dropped in for a nightcap.

The lambs both stood together and close by, like two children watching a street brawl on the corner. Once, while the young ram circled, a lamb came forward, nose out, and the old ram touched noses with it.

Suddenly after 15 minutes of badgering The Stranger, the young ram seemed satisfied with the situation, turned away, and began to feed.

The old ram seemed suddenly to catch the scent of Blondie, who was 30 feet above him. His nose went out, and up the hill he went, but she flipped out and away. He trailed her hopefully for several minutes and then got side-tracked by New Mama. She, too, repelled his blandishments, turning, as it were, a cold shoulder to him. All seven of the band were doing likewise. He stood there for several minutes staring at seven white rump patches moving slowly away. He took the hint and turned away down into the bottom of the ravine and climbed slowly up the other side of the canyon to the skyline.

Not only younger rams, but mature smaller rams are also ignored. To illustrate, on August 23, 1957, at 9:25 a.m., two rams came around Needle's Eye trail. One was Roughneck. The other had an outstanding blemish on his right shoulder and was much smaller than Roughneck, although he appeared to be about the same age. Our notes describe the meeting:

Roughneck has drunk for about 2 minutes and is all through, but the new one is nervous, moving around, and has now gone to the new pool at Old Spring and is almost standing on his head to drink from it. Apparently he gets in the water with both feet, as a habit, because he did the same thing while beside Roughneck.

Roughneck has finished drinking and is now going back up the mountain. The new one looks up at him but drinks more, again on his head. I've never seen anything like this. I wonder if that blemish on his shoulder causes this, by forcing him to bend his knees to drink. I can't see his forelegs at all. He reminds me of a bear cub I once saw at Crater Lake with his hindfeet on the rim of a garbage can and the rest of him hanging down inside. This is a strange way of drinking, like a little lamb. (We've seen this three times.) Now when he raises his head and stands up, I see that this new ram was on his knees! His appearance makes the count total 16 rams, 11 rams, and 9 lambs so far at Nevares Seeps since August 11. [Ewes and lambs remained unchanged but rams totaled 27 by September 10.]

Buddy arrived at 9:45, and we have named the new ram Little Joe, because he reminds us of a small belligerent man we once knew by the name of Joe, who had a chip on his shoulder for everybody. This Little Joe has a chip both literally and figuratively. He is constantly picking on big Roughneck, who doesn't want to do anything but rest in the shade.

Little Joe really charges him in the side or on the rump or anywhere it's handy. Roughneck acts bored and irritated by this, but not angry. Once or twice he has obliged by presenting horns, and we hear the familiar woodblock bang again.

They both finally found shady beds, Roughneck first; and then Little Joe made him get up and give him his and go find another for himself.

They and I snoozed until 11:10 when Buddy called me. They were on their way north, Roughneck in the lead by a hundred yards as though he were trying to shed himself of this nuisance, Little Joe, who was hurrying after him as though he weren't about to be shed.

Potential contestants often meet without combat or contest, even during the peak of the rut. A typical illustration of this indifference occurred on September 7, 1957, when two big well-matched rams approached Navares Spring about 4:30 in the afternoon. Tight Curl came trotting across Nevares Wash from the north, went directly to Raven Spring, and without hesitation dropped to his knees and proceeded to quench his considerable thirst in five 30-second drinks before he stood upright again. He then ambled over to Long Spring, where he knelt in the tall grass and was drinking again when Flathorn rounded The Point, saw Tight Curl, and immediately "blew" him a challenge and started rapidly toward him.

We rushed to get our cameras ready for the onslaught. It was still 112° in the shade, and so we soaked several towels, hung them over the cameras, and rushed down to the ledge for action.

Flathorn stopped 10 feet from Tight Curl, who stood immobile, watching. Flathorn turned to one side and began thrashing his horns in a *Baccharis* bush, but Tight Curl was unimpressed and turned away, pretending to eat. As Flathorn approached him he actually began to eat, ignoring Flathorn's growling shoves. Tiring of this in a few minutes, Tight Curl suddenly walked away a few feet into the shade of a mesquite tree and lay down. In a few minutes Flathorn followed him, and we had two of the best "fighters" we knew lying side by side in the shade.

Excessive heat seems a reasonable explanation of the lack of belligerence between Tight Curl and Flathorn, but it is more difficult to find an explanation for Mahogany's reaction to The Hook on the morning of September 9, 1957.

Mahogany's singular indifference to my proximity early that morning has already been described under "Response to Humans and Equipment." Normally wary and shy as any other ram we knew, he had calmly walked past me on the trail as though I were a boulder which he saw there every day. Now as I watched from camp with the big fieldglass, he lay on the trail, chewing his cud, shifting his big red body slightly now and then, flicking an ear, closing his eyes and pointing his nose skyward occasionally, the very picture of relaxed ruminant well-being.

At 8:30, with the spring area still in shadow and the temperature still only 98°, I heard The Hook's first call from far up in the hazy recesses of Nevares Canyon. Mahogany rose quickly but, to my surprise, looked only briefly toward the call from the canyon. Instead, he turned around in the trail and almost immediately lay down again.

The calling of the distant ram persisted and grew louder, but if Mahogany heard it he showed no sign, facing away from the approaching challenge as though it did not exist.

It was 8:45 when I saw for the first time that it was The Hook whose call was being ignored. As he leaped into view and paused ("posed" may be a better word) for a moment against the sky, I caught a glimpse of the jagged end of the broken horn which gave him his name. The carriage of his head, the lithe grace of his entire body, and the dramatic quality of his stance all told who he was.

The Hook was as different in personality from Mahogany as the classic rogue of literature differs from the hero. He was unpredictable, slender and fascinating to watch, with a flair to his every move; whereas, Mahogany was beautiful in a massive and solid way which made the observer feel, without reason, that he would always do what a bighorn was expected to do.

Now as The Hook came plunging down the mountain toward him, Mahogany rose majestically to his feet and turned to face his challenger. But as The Hook, with raised hackles and lowered head, began a menacing approach to him, Mahogany in a most unheroic manner calmly turned away and lay down again. The Hook continued his approach, however, and virtually knocked his reluctant opponent to his feet. Then head to rump and rump to head they shoved each other round and round, "blowing" and "growling" mightily. As was to be expected, Mahogany turned suddenly and began to walk away. The Hook accepted this move at its face value, and he, too, started to walk in the opposite direction.

But instead of rearing to his hindlegs for a charge as our hero would be expected to do, Mahogany again started to lie down. This seemed to infuriate The Hook, who whirled and charged him anyway, catching him half down and knocking him over on his side. The Hook then bounded lightly away a length or two and turned, awaiting expectantly for a retaliation—which never came. With incomprehensible good nature, Mahogany shook off a cloud of dust and lay down again! The Hook leaped forward furiously, pounded Mahogany on the rump with a front hoof, then on the shoulder. He lowered his horns and bore down on Mahogany's belly, but Mahogany just lay there and actually began chewing his cud.

This appeared to be beyond toleration for The Hook, who danced around to the front of Mahogany and leaped into the air, landing astraddle the prostrate ram, wrong end to. This brought Mahogany to his feet beneath The Hook in a whirling confusion which ended with both rams on their sides in a cloud of dust. The Hook leaped up and squared away for a charge, but again none came. Again Mahogany lay down. He just did not want to fight. Over and over again The

Hook would rouse him to his feet and wait for an onslaught which never came. Finally with magnificent anticlimax, The Hook roused him once more and with superb contempt lay down in Mahogany's bed. Impassively the big ram pawed another bed, lay down, yawned, closed his eyes, and pointed his nose into the first rays of the morning sun, and silence reigned on the mountain. The 9 o'clock temperature was an even 100°.

Half an hour later, with my attention momentarily diverted by a lizard on a waterbag, The Hook vanished and I never found where he had gone. Mahogany had the mountainside to himself for another half hour; then at 10:30, in full sunshine and 102° of temperature, he got up from his bed and climbed briskly through The Saddle and into Nevares Canyon as the morning haze was lifted by the heat waves rising beneath it.

Actual full-fledged bouts between rams is seldom observed for two principal reasons. The first of these is one of time and place, a combination of hot weather and inaccessible terrain. The bouts increase in intensity as the mating season advances into late summer when few observers are willing to spend enough time in the back country to be accepted by the bighorn as part of the scene. Until they are thus accepted, the second reason—the natural wariness of the bighorn toward the introduction of strange elements into his surroundings—will continue to obtain; that is, observers will continue to disrupt his normal activities to the extent that he is likely to retreat beyond the range of observation before engaging in an activity which cannot be carried on with divided attention. During 1955 and 1956, we had made many observations of rams together during the season of the year when "fights" were supposed to take place, but always their attention was occupied almost entirely by us as long as we were in sight of them. Our following them only increased their wariness of us.

It was not until the summer of 1957, when we "sat it out" for 30 days a quarter of a mile from the Nevares Seeps, that we finally created acceptable conditions for the making of these observations. We were there for 10 days, from August 10 to August 20, before the rams turned their gaze from us beneath our distant mesquite back to each other and these amazing contests began to take place. Between August 20 and September 10, we saw innumerable hassles, with much shoving, sharp "infighting," and "right upper cuts" with the stiff foreleg, but only eight times were these preliminaries climaxed by the measured walk away from each other, the simultaneous whirling turn and rise to the hindlegs, the astounding upright run toward each other, and the incredible precision and force of the blasting lunge.

It is doubtful if the human body would survive one such concussion, by comparison with the ram, whose bouts may range from one strike to the most spectacular contest of our records when Tabby fought Full Curl to a total of 48 blasts in one day.

A typical single-strike contest, complete with preliminaries and post-bellum maneuvers, began before sunrise at 6:15 on August 20, 1957, when two 7-year-old rams, Roughneck and The Hook, came trotting single file down the Needle's Eye trail toward the Round Pool. The Hook apparently caught a movement on the mountain because he stopped and, with his head far back, stared upward toward Middle Peak. Roughneck came directly on down to the pool. Our notes describe what happened:

I can see the slight roughness all over Roughneck's neck, shoulders, and back, but he is in fine shape. He is going back up. He meets the other ram, who "ups" to him. He whirls, hitting The Hook on the shoulder with his rump and goes on around. He lowers his head and pushes against The Hook's neck. The Hook stands with his nose straight up, and Roughneck rubs his horns up and down his neck.

Then, suddenly, they back off about 10 feet apart and hit—and I have heard the loud crack we've read so much about. You know what it is when you hear it. It sounds like rams meeting head on!

Too dark yet for pictures.

6:25. Dark Eyes and her lamb (what The Hook stopped to watch) came on down to drink, and Roughneck drinks again with her. The one bang seemed to be just a gesture. The Hook is standing up there, just looking. Now he sticks his nose out and again comes slithering toward them. He passes the ewe and goes to Roughneck and shoves him in the rump with his shoulder. Then, he suddenly mounts the other ram! He slides right off again.

This seems to be part of the mating behavior pattern. Roughneck didn't even stop drinking. The Hook dropped off and walked away without drinking and started toward Round Pool.

6:35. While The Hook was off drinking by himself, Roughneck started working on Dark Eyes, who promptly took to the hills on the south trail toward the Needle's Eye.

6:40. The Hook has overtaken them. Roughneck saw him coming and stopped and stood with his head sideways, his nose out. The Hook turns his head sideways, with his nose out, and they slink rapidly toward each other. They bypass each other's horns and manage to hit jostlingly, a shoulder against a hip, whip around and stand noses together and straight up.

Now Roughneck breaks the pose after 10 seconds, starts back toward the springs. The ewe and her lamb go on through the Needle's Eye. The Hook just stands there.

The above was scarcely an adequate introduction to the incredible encounter of the following day, August 21, 1957, when, with the temperature 88° at 5:30 a.m., I found a large dark ram lying down by an old blind at the foot of the mountain, above Old Spring. I saw that he was mature, and in the dim light looked like old Mahogany. As the light grew brighter, I wondered if his horns were heavy and broomed enough for Mahogany.

6:25. He has scarcely moved until now, when he stretched his head forward and 'laid it on the ground with all its weight on the tip of his right horn and his nose, or muzzle.

6:28. He raised his head enough to turn it and rest it on his left horn and muzzle.

I wonder if this is one way of brooming horntips? It's the only time I have ever seen the tips of rams' horns touch the ground under any circumstances.

6:30. I hear rocks, and so does old Mahogany. He's on his feet. Here they come: A ewe being chased by a young ram. Can this be Knocker and, yes, it's Longhorn.

6:48. They are milling around near Old Spring. The young ram, as is the way with young rams, has more or less stepped aside for old Mahogany. Longhorn says all she wants is a drink, but the boys try to keep her away. As the light gets better I see that it is not Knocker, but Slim drinking. Now Longhorn gets her head down. Mahogany and Slim are nosing each other, and the poor girl is finally getting a drink. After 4 minutes the rams leave each other and Mahogany starts nudging Longhorn, but she finishes her drink now no matter how much head-tossing and lip-rolling and smacking he indulges in. It was 6 minutes of drinking for her.

6:56. The rams are pushing each other around. I hear rocks again. The sheep do, too—to their left and up the mountain.

7:00. Longhorn stops, looks up the mountain, but is now drinking again— 2 minutes this time.

The young ram is scarcely 3 years old. He is no bigger than Longhorn, but he is very aggressive. His horns are very high, with the same curve as hers. Her son? Mahogany twists his head nearly upside down and with a wriggling lip makes a quick pass at her.

Slim seems too young or something to have learned the "lip-flick" in his approach to the girls.

While writing that, I heard rocks and look up to find Slim standing alone. At 7:12, I find Mahogany and Longhorn 300 yards up the mountain. She is squatting to urinate which, of course, always ties a ram in knots of lip-curling and taking stances of various kinds, which allows the girls either to stand still a few minutes or take advantage of his trance to get a headstart.

They are "pointing" the mountain again, but I can't find anything yet.

7:20. Here he comes, another ram—a new one! Tall, thin, long-necked, three quarter curl, slender horns and very flat, the sharpest curl in toward the end. Slightly Roman-nosed. Slightly mottled on the shoulders and back. Noticeably high-shouldered and ewe-necked. Brown, not mahogany or gray. He is, in fact, the perfect Nevares-type ram. Mahogany, in comparison, looks like a Durham bull.

As the newcomer—named Nevares I—crosses toward the first saddle I can see that the mottled appearance was probably caused by late shedding as of last year. But he is putting on a remarkable burst of energy, almost trotting straight away from the spring, never stopping, ignoring Longhorn (who, I notice for the first time, has white eyebrows!) and Mahogany and hurrying toward The Saddle with the air of a man hurrying back to a sick friend.

7:40. He's gone. He came in at 7:20, did his drinking, and is over the ridge again in 20 minutes.

7:50. Mahogany has followed Longhorn over the ridge.

8:30. Half an hour ago I heard horn-banging over the ridge, so I grabbed a camera and got around there in time to see Mahogany putting Nevares I to flight. Little Slim nowhere to be seen. Of course, Longhorn was standing innocently by. I tried to get around to where the light would be good, but they spooked at seeing me in a different place. Longhorn and Mahogany went up the first ridge and Nevares I went to the left toward Nevares Canyon. I tagged along, thinking I might get him going over the skyline.

Before we reached there we met another mature ram on his way in. Too far away to recognize without glasses and I had none with me. He went down out of sight and I waited for about 5 minutes, when suddenly he appeared on the skyline, against the sun, right above me. Just about the biggest head of horns I've ever seen. I tried to get a silhouette of him but I'm afraid he was gone too soon. I started back and soon came out from behind that ridge and found all three big boys tagging Longhorn up the mountain. I came back to camp and the big glasses.

I watched them until Longhorn led them around the top shoulder of the First Peak.

9:00. Two of them have reappeared on the very top of First Peak and are banging horns on the skyline. The big glasses show these to be Mahogany and Full Curl.

9:10. I tried for a telephoto shot; I don't know—for the last 5 minutes they've been standing still, except for Mahogany constantly banging Full Curl in the belly with that rigid right which Full Curl seems not to mind at all. Temperature, 94°.

They have apparently given Longhorn to Nevares I. When they were all together these two would start hassling and Nevares I would sneak off with Longhorn.

9:25. Buddy arrived and with delight took over the watching of the two big rams, who were still upsing [striking upward with stiff foreleg, but not hard] to each other near the top of the First Peak. I need not have been afraid she would miss them, because they almost at once began to work their way down toward the spring, pausing continually for a squaring off and a series of maneuvers ending in a little brain-busting each time. We were so preoccupied with our first extended observations of the "battering-ram" business that we did not keep a blow-by-blow account of it.

Seeing that they were coming in (Mahogany for the second time) and that they might do some fighting close enough for pictures, I began setting up all cameras on hand in readiness, while Buddy kept the glasses on them. I made it just as the first ram, Full Curl, hit the spring area at 9:40.

They were here from 9:40 until about noon, feeding, drinking, fighting. We have spent the entire time with the cameras, and we hope to have good pictures of them, both movies and slides.

We are pooling our observations for details of this phase of behavior, however. It is difficult to keep notes during their activities because of the speed with which developments occur. We found that we were constantly trying to write something down, hearing something else happen, and looking at each other, asking, "What was that?" So, for the main description of the patterns they follow (and in this they do have patterns), we will depend on a dictated account, which was done while I watched and reported and Buddy wrote. This will be filled in by both of us as we see fit and appended to the end of these notes.

We were surprised and delighted that they chose to come to Raven and Long Springs and stayed on this side of the Nevares Seeps throughout the entire time. All the old rams have gone to Old Spring before, or to Round Pool.

We were most lucky that it was a cool day, maximum of 104° here and overcast, and cooler most of the time. We were able to work out on the brow of the point the entire time without discomfort to ourselves or danger to our equipment.

Although we have never seen Full Curl here before, he was not a newcomer. He knew where to go for water and led the way in and out, although this was Mahogany's third or fourth trip, his second today. He's older, probably 10 or 11, slightly potbellied but still with great vigor.

Mahogany follows about 50 feet behind him and waits until he stops; then he deliberately strolls up and with his muzzle lifts Full Curl's rump off the ground. Full Curl ignores this. It has happened three or four times.

Full Curl seldom uses the stiff right, but Mahogany loves it. He is constantly smacking Full Curl somewhere when he is in a "clinch" with him— maybe in the chest, the belly, the penis or the testicles, but in no case does it seem to be painful. Especially when it lands in the genital area, it is more of a lifting shove than a blow.

After tolerating it repeatedly for several minutes, Full Curl will often walk away to the proper distance and they both whirl and get set for a bang.

This nonchalant turning away fooled us several times early in the game. We actually thought the jousting was over, and we would try to get something done quickly and be prepared for their next round, only to hear the bang before we had scarcely turned away.

They do sometimes actually eat during these displays of indifference, which could account to some extent for the good condition of these rams despite these prolonged expenditures of energy.

At one time, after a particularly violent blast, Full Curl turned away and, apparently at some signal, Mahogany walked right up to him and side by side they proceeded a few yards to Raven Spring, where they stood flank to flank and drank for several minutes.

10:45. They began to travel north, up over the foot of First Ridge, across the main Nevares Wash and on north, Full Curl in the lead, Mahogany following, occasionally catching up to Full Curl and lifting his hindquarters from the ground with his muzzle. Full Curl seems to ignore this completely, and it seems to be friendly, to say the least.

12:15. They finally disappear to the right in the canyon north of Red Wall. We tried to catch up on our notes and I took a nap.

4:20. Buddy roused me by asking if I heard that bang. From then until 7:32 we watched an unusual match of skill and strength and, to an extent, deceit.

These two are evenly matched and seem to enjoy this brain-busting, and as far as we can tell enmity or antagonism is not part of it. Competition, perhaps.

This second series of encounters between Mahogany and Full Curl took place high up on the foot of Dromedary Ridge, at least an airline three-quarters of a mile from here, but the structure of the cliffs surrounding the arena was such that the hollow woodblock sound of impact reached us clearly. The 12 x 50 glasses allowed clear observation of every move, which otherwise would have been barely discernible to the naked eye.

Not being concerned with picture taking at this distance, we were able to concentrate on their behavior. We counted 20 head-on crashes in 1 hour, all of which we saw as well as heard from three-quarters of a mile away. And when they finally ambled over the upper end of Pink Ridge at 7:32, they showed no sign of pain or fatigue or ill will toward each other. They had sparred, waltzed, wrestled, and tilted for nearly 7 hours, as well as climbed several miles through the roughest terrain in the valley, and were feeling fine!

Here are some of the details of the behavior pattern during these contests. This one began on the crest of First Nevares Peak about 9 a.m., continued down the face of the mountain to the spring area. It was pursued there for about an hour and a half, then north along the trail until 12:15. There was a lull, as far as we are concerned, since we neither saw nor heard them until 4:20. Then they took it up on the black limestone slope in the shade of an east-facing cliff on Dromedary Ridge, and they had no respite until sundown, when they took each other by the horn, so to speak, and went over the skyline.

One bears down on the other's rump with muzzle, and at times will push a foreleg between the hindlegs of the other as if to hit the genitals. The other does not shrink from this blow and appears never to be hurt by it. In fact, the aggressor seems to "pull his punch" as it lands.

They may butt each other on the rump for some time, milling around and around, leaving churned-up earth for the sign reader. We call these hassle grounds.

They hold noses side by side, heads high and back, and seem to be pushing the sides of their faces against each other, not their horns.

Stiff foreleg is delivered from the front, side, or back, just as it is to ewes in mating activity.

After sharp jab at other's shoulder with tip of horn, both stretch up high in air.

Aggressive activities are interspersed with most casual browsing, or at least a pretense of browsing.

They sometimes nip each other in the flank in the same manner a ram nips a ewe in the flank in mating activity.

One ram will put his forehead against the other's side and push, causing the other to whip around.

One pushes with his forehead the fullness of the other's neck or his chest while he holds his head high in the air in obvious enjoyment.

They will stand nose to nose for 5 minutes at a time, eyes nearly closed.

Each puts his nose against the other's shoulder and turns around and around. (See fig. 51.)

With a shoulder to a rump and a rump to a shoulder, they may growl and "waltz" around and around for half an hour at a time.

They scratch on each others' horns sometimes; each in turn accommodatingly holds his horns steady for the other.

After cracking horns loudly, they stand away, noses in the air again.

The farthest away we have seen them walk from each other today is 30 feet when they come head on; usually it is from about 10 feet. On the other hand, they may knock horns at 4 or 5 feet, or just lean back in their tracks and lunge forward without moving their feet.

They stand away from other other, noses in air, sizing up each other. They may crash horns or they may just both forget it and start to eat, or one walk toward the other with a peculiar side-to-side motion of the head, which seems to be the signal for a clinch, which they do.

As the area in shadow increases, the scope of their activities increases with it.

Part of the ritual, which seems to be understood by both parties concerned, is the overly casual walking away on the part of one (figs. 52 and 53) after a certain amount of hassling to any distance he chooses, which may be anywhere from 5 to 30 feet. He will casually start to feed, while the other watches warily, sometimes with head up, sometimes with head almost to the ground, always watching the feeding one. This feeding will be broken by an incredibly swift whirl and leap into the air by the feeding one, which never fools anyone except the uninitiated observer. Sometimes the feeding will go on too long to suit the other, and he will begin a cautious advance. They may rise to their hindlegs on the whirl (fig. 54), tilt their heads and sight down their noses for several seconds, in situ, then simply drop to the ground again.

Elaborate pretense of not knowing what the other is doing, seems part of it.

The accuracy of the collisions is really remarkable, but it isn't 100 percent perfect. If they hit off center, both heads are twisted violently to one side. Occasionally they miss enough to catch their entire weight in the crook of a single horn (fig. 59), in which case they lunge past each other with one or the other of the horns sliding out of the crook over the tip. This could break off the tip, causing brooming. (Three days later when we again saw Full Curl, one of the participants in these observations, he had lost several inches from the tip of his left horn.)

This seems a much more logical explanation of brooming than the alleged use of the horns in digging for plants, which we have never seen. We did, in fact, pick up a newly split-off ram horntip in a churned-up area near Virgin Spring last year.

The rams generally do not stagger back from the shock and regain their balance or control of themselves, as might be expected from such a collision. They seldom lose control of themselves in any way. They do not, as a matter of fact, fold up at all. Their entire physical setup seems timed to the blow to such an extent that, barring a slip or a miscalculation, the recoil is under perfect control, and they come to the ground in perfect balance, braced for any next move the other might make. Usually there is none for a few seconds. They just stand there with noses up, heads back and eyes nearly closed. Mahogany and Full Curl showed no sign of shock or pain after crashing 48 times by count in one day.

The low blowing sound, or growl, seems to be part of a generally aggressive mood and attitude in one designed to shake the confidence of the other. When this happens, the ram seems to be utilizing every muscle in his body to make this sound. His neck arches, his head is held very high, nose tucked in. The muscles throughout his torso tighten, his back arches slightly, and he seems to stand on tiptoe and tower above his opponent. He then expels his breath, apparently through his nose, which, when coupled with seeing his threatening action, seems to be some sort of a growl but, when heard without viewing the accompanying action, sounds ridiculously like an old man snoring in the early morning hours.

On September 10, 1957, Tabby and Broken Nose blasted each other more than 40 times (we didn't start counting from the beginning) in 2 hours. The bulges of cartilage on the back of their heads at the base of their horns, which apparently act as shock absorbers, had increased in size as the contest progressed, and from time to time the lower jaw of each ram was held on one side as though it might be dislocated. Another collision or two seemed to correct this difficulty and the jaw would be held normally again. Their noses gradually became swollen and puffy from the tip to between the eyes, but we saw no blood either from the nostrils or the ears, as legend would have it. As is commonly the case, no ewes were present during the entire time, nor did they seem to be looking for any. When for some reason they both decided they'd had enough, they ambled into the mouth of Redwall Canyon and lay down side by side for a 10-minute rest before they parted company as casually as though they were unaware of the existence of each other.

We have had reports from other areas of rams teaming up for "the season," fighting their battles together against all comers and, at least tacitly, dividing the "spoils" between them. The closest we have come to observing this in Death Valley was on August 28, 1957. Full Curl had been in the Nevares Spring area since 6:57 a.m. when we noted at 1:40 p.m. that he had met The Hook on Slope Trail. Our notes read:

1:45. New ram [Toby] at Round Pool. A three-quarter curl, tannish, bump on nose, reddish "wig" on back of head. Horns seem to be completely symmetrical and unbroomed, whitish instead of yellow.

2:00. He's gone south and met The Hook and Full Curl. He's not sleek as they are, low hipped and rather high shouldered.

2:35. Toby (with the thatch on the back of his head) suddenly broke off relations with Full Curl and The Hook and walked off the slope into the South Wash.

For the last half hour they've been hassling on the Slope Trail. More or less same routine, except once when Toby and The Hook clashed, The Hook shot clear under Toby and, more or less on his knees, came out the back way. Whether Toby overshot or The Hook undershot the mark I wouldn't know. They both seemed a little surprised but squared off and made a better job next time.

During this interlude the two oldtimers seemed to center their attention entirely on the newcomer. Although they had been doing a lot of infighting before Toby came along, they stopped it entirely and seemed to take turns on him until he left. He was not licked by any means; he just lost interest after about half a dozen clashes in 35 minutes.

3:00. All three of them showed up in the cut-bank shade of the South Wash and resumed their tiffs there.

3:30. I went into the drainage below them and got close enough, I hope, for good pictures of jousting. The wind, however, was terrific and very hot and may have spoiled much of it. I could hardly stand up in it sometimes.

The films taken during this time recorded an unexpected maneuver, the simultaneous "strike" of three rams at once, repeated several times. Full Curl and The Hook, standing about 5 feet apart and 10 feet away and facing Toby, would rise and "sight" him, and he, taking it all for granted, rose and "sighted" them both, taking the full impact of each ram on a single horn.

On one occasion as The Hook and Full Curl stood shoulder to shoulder facing Toby, Full Curl rose to Toby who rose to meet him, but, as they both sighted and lunged, Toby suddenly shifted his aim to The Hook, who could do no more than take it while Full Curl stood on his hindlegs sighting an adversary who had already passed him for another.

The difficulty in determining the objective of this intense activity should now be apparent. Of the eight full-fledged bouts we have recorded, not in one instance has a ewe been present during the entire time. Death or even severe injury appears to be more accident than intent. We have no record of one ram seeming to "win" over another in the sense that one is beaten down or back and put to flight by another. Nor have we observed an instance of a "winning" contestant pressing a temporary advantage over another. When The Hook caught Toby in the face as he leaped up the bank toward him, he watched Toby with all the appearance of delight in the other's discomfiture, actually kicking up his heels in apparent glee when Toby finally gave up and went around and came up the long and safer way.

That some sort of sexual satisfaction is derived from the contests is indicated by the fact that it occurs only during the rut. It has been suggested that it may be vestigial behavior from an earlier race with a harem pattern, but our observations yielded no evidence to suport such speculation. This much is certain: The contests have no direct connection with the acquisition of a mate or mates. If a ewe is present when a contest begins, she has no effect on it or it on her. She is just as likely to wander off with another ram, unnoticed by the contestants.

Response to Young

Response to young by mature rams seems to be practically nonexistent. We have no observations indicating an interest in lambs of either a destructive or a constructive nature.

Younger rams, up to 3 years of age, appear actually to enjoy the company of lambs, but older rams have at most been observed to touch noses with a lamb on rare occasions or butt one out of the way on equally rare occasions with no affection or animosity suggested by either action. (See "Growth, Behavior, and Care of Young.")

Under no circumstances does the ram appear to share in the responsibility for the care of the young.

One attitude of the mature ram was recorded at Old Spring on September 6, 1957. Tight Curl had been browsing with Brahma and her lamb, Little Brahma, when from across the thicket Tight Curl got a "scent"; his nose went out, his head down, and his hackles up, and he slithered through the *Baccharis* and thistles, came around a big boulder to find Little Brahma on his knees at a clump of grass. Tight Curl plowed to a stop, his head flew up, and he looked quickly around and lost interest.

Group Activity

Group activity among Death Valley rams seems to be limited to the 4 or 5 months of late winter and early spring when they separate themselves from the ewes, lambs, and young rams and form the far-ranging bachelor bands, about whose function and specificity very little is known.

During this study we have been able to locate but three bands of rams during the off season, and the remoteness and roughness of the terrain in all three cases prevented us from maintaining the contact necessary for the continuous, daylong observations that form the basis for this report.

Females and Young

Response to Males

Response to males has been reported under "Attention to Females," since it seems impractical to attempt an illustration of one without the other.

In general, during the rut the female bighorn plays the part of the pursued, with passive compliance the culmination of the pursuit.

Out-of-season overtures from rams are likely to be met by a head-on presentation of lowered horns, which is usually accepted by the ram as final.

Occasionally a ewe will digress from what appears to be a normal passivity and evince a positive aggressiveness toward a ram.

Some evidence indicates a possibility that as the mating season tempo increases ewes not in oestrus with lambs still nursing try to hide out to avoid unnecessary harassment from the younger rams.

We have no data determining the length of the bighorn oestrus cycle or the length of time a ewe is responsive to the mating season, but the records of captive animals at the Desert Game Range show that the bighorn ewe can and does conceive during her second year. Gestation is believed to take from 170 to 180 days (Aldous, 1957, p. 57).

Selection of Lambing Area

The selection of a lambing area in Death Valley apparently presents an individual problem to each ewe each year she bears a lamb. Low-density vegetation and sheep population seem in general to preclude effectively the gathering of ewe and lamb bands that we found so common on the Desert Game Range in 1953. (Under "Food" and under "Water," see "A Factor in Bighorn Distribution and Survival." See also, "Introduction.")

One possible exception to this generality was recorded on June 30, 1960, at Quartz Spring in the Cottonwood Mountains. It may be significant that the habitat in which it occurred is as nearly comparable to the Desert Game Range habitat as could be found in the Death Valley region—an elevation of 5,200 feet in one of the few areas in the monument where Joshua trees lead up into the piñon belt. Here at 4 p.m. we found two yearlings "babysitting" with 12 lambs while their 12 mothers browsed the mountainside at varying distances. We were with them that night until dark and the next day until noon, when the exigencies of the burro research impelled us into another area. It is a single incident and the only one even suggesting the existence of a lambing area in Death Valley.

Pluvial and floral instability may prevent the annual return of even one ewe to the same lambing area, as indicated by our population record of Indian Pass since 1955.

We have been able to make but one prolonged observation of lambing in Death Valley, but that fact in itself suggests its unpredictability, the lack of permanent lambing areas, and an apparent tendency of ewes to remain solitary for at least a week or two both before and after parturition.

Our first observations of lambing were made at the Desert Game

Range in 1953 when the captive ewe at Corn Creek Headquarters gave birth to her fourth lamb, as described by O. V. Deming (1955). Actual parturition was not observed, but immediate prenatal and postnatal developments were carefully studied and photographed and have served as a field indicator to the present time.

Number of Young

The number of young is often confused by the tendency of lambs to run in pairs (Deming, 1955, p. 136), but we have no record of bighorn twins being born in the Death Valley region.

Birth of Young

The birth of young has not been observed during this study. However, we were able to maintain full-time observations on a pregnant ewe in the Furnace Creek area for 3 weeks before lambing and for 10 weeks afterward. This was in addition to the study of a captive ewe at the Desert Game Range in 1953.

Positive field determination of pregnancy is generally difficult and sometimes impossible, but the pregnant ewe at Furnace Creek, identified throughout this report as Old Mama, left no doubt of her condition when her unborn lamb was observed vigorously kicking from within, first on January 7, then on the 16th, and with disturbing violence on the 18th when she was on her way to the solitude of Pyramid Peak. On two or three occasions she leaped up from siesta and moved restlessly about as though trying to counteract the lamb's activities in some way.

Although she was apparently still about 10 days from parturition, her udder had been developing for over a week, but her genitals were not beginning to swell. She was restless and quite evidently trying to leave the band. She had the sagging potbelly with the sunken appearance in front of the hips which suggests pregnancy instead of overeating.

When Old Mama returned on February 2, she was still potbellied, sagging more than ever in front of the hips. By February 19, 1956, this condition was still pronounced: "Ewe still potbellied. If seen for first time now, she would be mistaken for pregnant ewe, not as a mother of a 3- to 4-week-old lamb."

Prior to this observation, a bloody residue of vaginal excretion had defaced the white rump patch somewhat; on February 25 she began to show signs of afterbirth complications; and on February 28 "a raw, red protuberance from her vagina" became evident. Later in the day, a "chunk of meat about size of first joint of finger" was found at her day-bed site. On March 1 it was noted that the "ewe seems to have no ill effects from chunk of meat dropped from vulva 2 days ago. One urination at 11:45. Action normal, urine clear."

Growth, Behavior, and Care of Young

Growth, behavior, and care of young has been unavoidably disussed to a considerable extent under "Play." A review of that section will complement the following material:

Care of the young is usually treated separately, but in the case of bighorn lambs the very nature of the care received slants the growth and behavior immediately toward self-sufficiency and independence, and so the two factors will be considered at the same time. The following data were recorded during the observations of Old Mama and her lamb in Furnace Creek, but they are so typical in nature that they are included here as a generality.

The lamb's first postnatal experience with its new world is with its mother's mouth—the soothing warmth of the cleansing tongue, the warm breath, and the low, gutteral grunts of reassurance as the lamb staggers to its wobbly legs and falls back to earth. In its efforts to retain this assurance, the lamb reaches up, searching uncertainly for the source of its comfort, and eventually, if all goes well, begins to nurse.

The mother nurses the lamb a few seconds at a time, touches its rump with her nose, steps over its head with a hindleg, and walks away. As time passes, the nursing periods become farther and farther apart as other food becomes more important to the growth of the lamb. (See table 9.)

The muzzle contact remains important. For the first days the lamb spends most of its time doing three things: Nursing, sleeping, and hovering around its mother's head in its first wavering patterns of emulation.

The mother nuzzles the lamb as it wobbles up to her but turns away when this inhibits her ingestion of food at a critical time. In its efforts to determine what its mother is doing, the lamb staggers out into the brush, gets its legs entangled, and falls over. Its first lesson in self-sufficiency begins then, because the mother ignores it and eventually it must thrash its own way out and back to its feet.

By the end of the first week the lamb puts its nose to the ground beside its mother's and its jaw begins an empty chewing. The ewe raises her head with a spray of *Bebbia* in her teeth and, as she chews it up and swallows it, the lamb looks up and chews. Again the ewe reaches down and again the lamb nuzzles in, but this time when the ewe raises her head with food in her mouth the lamb looks up and chews—on its first twig of *Bebbia*. Browsing has begun.

TABLE 9.—*Observations on nursing new lamb*

Date	Hour of nursing		Duration of nursing and remarks
	Morning	Afternoon	
1956			
February:			
3	11:00	....	Lamb nursed whenever ewe stood still until 4:35 p.m. Nursing time: from 15 to 50 seconds.
4	11:00	....	3 minutes.
19	....	12:30–4:30	Lamb tried nursing 3 times, but it nursed only once during the 4 hours.
21	10:00	....	15 seconds.
	10:37	....	10 seconds.
	12:00	....	5 seconds.
	....	12:10	Do.
	....	12:35	Do.
		4:32	8 seconds.
		4:45	4 seconds.
22	11:45	....	8 seconds.
		12:15	Do.
24	9:00	....	5 seconds.
	9:30	....	Do.
		1:05	4 seconds.
		1:30	10 seconds.
		4:08	4 seconds.
25	....	3:45	Do.
		3:55	Do.
		4:28	Do.
26	11:00	....	No time given.
	11:40	....	Do.
		12:45	Do.
		2:30	Do.
		3:40	Do.
28	10:00	....	10 seconds. Using both sides of udder. Only nursing in morning.
		2:05	14 seconds. First attempt rejected.
		3:12	Lamb and ewe bedded. Lamb rose, demanded food; ewe rose. 14 seconds.
		5:00	20 seconds.
29	10:20	....	11 seconds.
	11:20	....	14 seconds.
		1:10	16 seconds.
March:			
1	10:30	....	6 seconds.
	12:00	....	4 seconds.
		1:12	15 seconds.
		2:00	No time given.
13	....	2:30	Do.
14	....	....	Another ewe with her lamb about same age joined Old Mama. Both nursed about 8 seconds.
16	....	....	1 p.m. both lambs nursing.
17	....	3:26	12 seconds.
30	....	4:45	10 seconds.
April:			
8	....	1:30	8 seconds.
10	....	2:30	10 seconds.
11	....	2:45	15 seconds.

While the lamb is still less than a week old, two ravens flying overhead fill the mother with apprehension, and she eats nothing for 15 minutes, until the ravens are gone.

When an overeager observer approaches too close, the lamb immediately takes its place against the offside flank of its mother and, assisted by touch, follows it as one dancer follows another. At 2 weeks of age, it is learning to paw out its own bed, eats everything its mother does, tries to defecate when she does, is very curious about her cud chewing, and tries repeatedly to get some from her mouth for itself.

Lacking another lamb to play with, it tries to play with its mother, who for the most part ignores it even when it jumps up and down on her side while she rests.

The independence of attitude and action so necessary to desert bighorn survival is now beginning to be noticeable. The lamb now makes no effort to keep up with its mother in traveling. It walks along steadily, catching up with the ewe only when she stops to wait. If its mother calls, however, or if it gets lost, it runs to find her.

At 3 weeks of age its rump patch is beginning to look more like its mother's changing from a dirty yellowish brown to whitish yellow, and white by 6 weeks.

It is beginning to browse incessantly when not resting. Sometimes even when resting it lies down close enough to plants to eat without getting up. We've never observed this in adults.

We wonder if its "eating" gravel now and then is experimental or mineral ingestion.

The mother and lamb are browsing over a distance of 3 to 5 miles per day and climbing from 1½ to 2½ miles to bed every night. The lamb is always friskier at the end of the climb than at any other time. We watch it make its first 1-mile climb when it is no more than 48 hours old, and at the end of the climb it makes a wobbly run and jumps up on a flat boulder about a foot high, tries to kick its heels in the air, and falls off the boulder, gets up at once, and begins vigorous nursing.

The mother seems to pay little attention to the welfare of its lamb, but on one occasion she climbed a cliff which the lamb failed to negotiate, falling back to the base: "Ewe crossed quickly to more accessible spot when she saw lamb fall, leaned over and watched lamb intently until it crossed the falls and gained the top of the cliff beside her."

The mother seems anxious to be always well up the mountain for bedding by sundown. On February 22 at 4:48, the ewe suddenly looked up, looked around, looked up at Pyramid Peak as though surprised at how late it was, and made the most rapid exit and climb for bedding to date.

At 4 weeks of age the lamb is learning rapidly, eating or sampling everything it can get into its mouth. It shows great curiosity about telephone poles, runs its nose up and down, slowly tilting its head back while its eyes run up the length of the pole.

At 6 weeks of age it finds a playmate. A new band of five strange bighorn have come into the wash and apparently have "chosen" Old Mama as their leader. The lamb, being hungry, tries to nurse the newcomers one at a time, even the ram, until its mother comes and feeds it.

There is another lamb in the band, about a week older than Old Mama's lamb. They touch noses and become friends (figs. 37 and 38)—they "pal up" and separate only for nursing.

On March 27, 1956, we notice that one eye of Old Mama's lamb is badly swollen, and the next day it is swollen shut. It lies down as much as possible and eats practically nothing. Keeping up with the band is a great effort. Its mother, Old Mama, seems totally unconcerned.

Temptation is great to try to do something for the lamb, but we must watch without interference and may learn something of resistance to infection, recuperative powers, etc., as a part of survival.

The next day the lamb's eye is open but it is a very sick animal, lying down as much as it can and still keep up with the band. It scrambled slowly up out of the wash with them just below Pyramid Wash to get away from too many Easter week visitors.

On March 30, 1956, we lost the Furnace Creek band for several hours, during which time they crossed the highway on their way to the Big Curve, and one of the lambs was struck by a car. Eventually this was reported to me by a visitor who first asked what those animals were in Furnace Creek Wash. I told him. He said, "One was hit by a car just now." Another visitor had asked him for a gun with which to kill the animal to put it out of its misery, he told us, but he had no gun and didn't know if one had been found. The accident, he said, had happened "above where all the red rocks were."

I hurried to see what had happened. No sheep anywhere. No blood on the road. No body.

I finally found the band in the far curve of the wash above the Big Dip and went out to see who was missing. Old Mama's lamb! Old Mama herself was placidly feeding as though she had never even had a lamb. The other lamb was browsing contentedly nearby. Devoted mother and inseparable playmate both gorging themselves on *Stephanomeria*. Evidently one of their number being killed by an auto leaves no disturbing effect! Or did they not see the lamb struck and therefore not know what had happened? Or again, was the lamb all right somewhere and they knew it?

With this thought in mind, I went back to the Big Dip and the "red rocks" (where presumably the lamb was struck) and began to trail the band up the wash to their present location. About 200 yards above the Big Dip a rustle in the brush attracted my attention from my close scrutiny of the tracks at my feet, and there stood the lamb, lame in the right front leg, but otherwise unscathed!

For 2 hours the lamb rested, eating a little, sometimes on its feet, looking for Mama. The band was still up the wash in a curve but coming down, with Old Mama now looking for her lamb.

While they were 50 feet away, the lamb managed a hobbling run to Mama and nursed 10 seconds. The other lamb, seeing the cripple from a distance, rushed, gamboling, toward it, and being a little ram tried to mount it, knocking it over on its side. The band began to climb and by dark was up the mountain half a mile, the little cripple plugging along with amazing stamina, the other lamb once more sticking close by.

The next day it rained. The band vanished on Pyramid Peak, and we did not see the lamb until April 3. Old Mama's lamb was still with them, its pelage rough, still limping, but eating fairly well. There still seemed to be no concern for the handicapped condition of the lamb. At 11 a.m., the band began an unusually rapid trek south, traveling to within 200 yards of Deadman's Curve before stopping, a distance of nearly 2 miles. They paid no attention to the sick lamb, who hobbled painfully, doggedly, silently along, sometimes out of sight, once nearly a quarter of a mile behind.

At the curve the lamb was finally eating a *Bebbia* plant when the young ram came up and without warning charged the lame lamb, hurling it through the air 4 feet into a rock bed on its lame side. It took the lamb a few seconds of struggle to regain its feet. It stood with its lame right front leg in the air for a few moments, shook its head, sneezed, then went back to feeding, ignoring the ram but 2 feet away.

Ten minutes after the lamb had caught up with them at the curve, they started back to Travertine Point at the same fast clip, the crippled lamb again trailing desperately along behind.

On April 8 we note that "as evidence of improved health of the lamb, it has been, during siesta, getting to its feet now and then to pester Old Mama with playful butting, pawing, and that curious effect of seeming to try to take her cud away from her."

The other lamb was about a week older, and possibly because it was a ram lamb, it had been showing button horns since it was 8 weeks old. Both lambs were now chewing their cuds.

We could not find the band on April 9.

April 10, 1956. By 10:30 I had begun to think that perhaps bighorn observations were over in Furnace Creek Wash. At 11:40 I made one more survey of the upper wash, and far off to the south above the Big Dip I spotted a tiny, solitary figure standing in the shade of a *Chrysothamnus*. Just standing there watching me. After 15 minutes of glassing of the wash both above and below the lamb, I found Old Mama about a quarter of a mile above the lamb, browsing steadily on one *Stephanomeria* plant. This has become more and more the pattern of the entire band the past few days: much less travel, more eating.

2:00. Old Mama began to move back down wash, from time to time standing with head held high staring intently in lamb's direction. Intermittent browsing and travel brought ewe and lamb together at 3:30. A matter-of-fact meeting, no joyful demonstration; they were about 100 feet apart when I was sure they had seen each other, but there was no change of pace, just leisurely ambling, nipping at browse as they passed.

That evening at sundown when they went up to bed, the lamb was like a small dog "following" a hunter. It was all over the mountainside, choosing the steepest, roughest terrain it could find. It was apparently feeling much better, no limp, no cough, although its coat was still rough.

On April 11, 1956, the lamb rested almost all day. At 2:45 two ravens, one at a time, dived at it, which its mother ignored, but it leaped up and ran to Old Mama. There it forgot its fears and nursed 15 seconds, the first time that day, the longest in many.

We did not find them again until April 16 and 17, 1956. Old Mama and her lamb were in Furnace Creek Wash both days: Monday from 12 until 2, Tuesday from 11 until 1.

They did not appear until nearly noon, both days at the foot of the curve below Big Dip. The ewe looked gaunt on arrival and fell immediately to voracious feeding, moving but a few feet from one plant to the other. *Stephanomeria* and *Bebbia* again, with only occasional *Hymenoclea* and *Franseria*. She seemed to stay in the farthest reach of the curve, as though to insure less disturbance. The lamb, while it looked less gaunt than its mother, was quiet and browsed constantly also, with one nursing of about 8 seconds each day.

Old Mama seemed to watch the mountains more and more in the course of her last 2 days with us and never came near us or allowed us to come near her.

On both the 16th and 17th the lamb was actually the first to take to the ridge on the way out. It seemed almost prearranged. Old Mama would start feeding toward the edge of the wash, and as she approached within about 50 feet of it the lamb ran past her and on up the mountains perhaps 50 feet above her. While she did not seem to hurry, Old Mama nevertheless followed the lamb up the mountain on both her last days here, after having been in the wash for but 3 hours each day.

We never saw her and her lamb together again. When she returned to the wash 7 months later on November 17, 1956, she was alone. Nine out of 10 Death Valley ewes who have lambs in the spring are likely to be alone again before the year is gone. (See "Chief Causes of Mortality.")

We have observed lambs through the Death Valley summer at Willow Creek, Nevares Spring, and Navel Spring. At these elevations, survival through a summer is a serious business, with no time or energy for play—getting enough to eat and to drink takes all there is.

How long a bighorn ewe will nurse her lamb appears to depend on the individual and the circumstances in each situation. We have seen 7-month-old lambs nursing, while on the other hand Little Fuzzy had already been weaned for some time when he died at an age of about 1 month. But the bulk of our evidence suggests that Death Valley lambs are seldom weaned before they are 4 months old.

Some lambs, probably those raised alone by a solitary ewe, seem to prefer staying with their mothers throughout their first year and sometimes the second. A very common Death Valley "band" is a ewe, a yearling, and a nursing lamb.

But lambs brought up in groups tend to show an increasing preference for companionship of their own age. "Babysitting," with all the younger lambs left in the care of one or two older members of the band, becomes common. In all cases, however, an increasing individual independence marks the first year of the lamb's life. The following notations are cited as a fairly typical observation of this phase of development:

July 7, 1958. Buddy spotted a ewe and lamb in shade on the trail at left of Navel Spring. We decided to go in and inspect the spring for sign. This spooked the ewe and lamb into the open. Both were sleek and fat, but unknown to us. The lamb was about 7 months old, large for the size of its horns. No "hornprints" [blemishes, chipped areas, or other distinctive markings of the horns] available on either animal.

Buddy went up on the ridge south of the wash to watch while I went in and inspected the springs. The sign there indicated perhaps six or eight animals, no sign over a week or so old. Water good.

When I came back out the ewe and lamb had not gone far. As a matter of fact, the lamb had come back to its original spot in the shade, ignoring a rare call from its mother, and stood watching us for an hour. The mother, meantime, had continued out and up the trail to Paleomesa.

At about 1 p.m. the lamb left, alone and unhurried, on the same trail taken by its mother. It had one coughing spell en route but showed no ill effects from whatever caused the cough.

The growth and behavior of lambs seems important enough to this report to review, in toto, the following field notes:

September 5, 1958. Nevares Spring. At 9:30 three sheep are coming in very slowly from the south on the Slope Trail below the Needle's Eye, a ewe leading. This ewe has an almost half-broken-off right horn. Following her is a this-year's lamb and a yearling ram. It takes 7 minutes for them to complete coming in to Old Spring from the time they were first observed.

This is the worst looking trio [described in "Amounts Taken" under "Water"] we have ever seen: thin, sick, and wobbly. The yearling ram's coat is rough.

The ewe and yearling drink steadily for 5 minutes; the lamb does not finish when they do but continues drinking for 2 minutes longer.

The ewe and yearling ram fill out after drinking and no longer look so poor; the lamb is still very thin, shoulder bones very noticeable. The lamb is a male, the length of horns indicating he is about 9 months old, born last January or even December.

After drinking, they look around briefly; then the ewe leads them closer to us to graze on grass. Continuing study convinces us this ewe was not seen here last year.

They ate for half an hour, then the ewe and yearling ram started to leave. The lamb did not leave, but continued eating, then went back to Old Spring, drank 3 minutes more and ate at Old Spring for 5 minutes. The ewe and yearling waited for it a short distance above the springs. The ewe nibbled on desertholly a few times, the yearling did not.

The ewe then led up to the rugged rocks above Old Spring and was joined by the others, who acted as though they would have liked to lie down if there had been a level or comfortable place. The lamb found a small shelf, lay down, but didn't stay long. It made no attempt to nurse during this entire time.

At 11:30 they are each standing in separate bits of shade higher up against the cliffs. Our thermometer reads 105° in the shade.

1 p.m. The three sheep we have under observation have moved very little and are still resting up among the boulders. The lamb has lain in one spot of shade for about 2 hours. They seemed quite exhausted when they arrived, and it would be most interesting to know how far they had traveled. The rest they have been getting would not have been possible if rams had been around.

This drink, this food, and this rest may mean survival or nonsurvival for this growing 9-month-old lamb.

The ewe butted the yearling when they were down at the springs, and we cannot decide whether she was disciplining her own lamb who is still with her as a yearling (although she has a this-year's lamb), or if this might be a stray just going along with her and her lamb.

The sun is beginning to hit the lamb's head at 1:40. Will he move? His mother lies about 100 yards above him and the yearling just above her.

The ewe is in full sun at 1:50 and does not move out of it. The yearling, in partial shade, gets up and stretches. The ewe climbs up to check on her lamb below, who doesn't leave the full sun. She and the yearling stood in the same place, gazing in all directions, for 20 minutes; then she and the yearling went down past the springs without drinking into south Nevares Wash. Looking for the lamb, we discovered that it was he who led the way down into the wash.

After a few brief nibbles at plants in the wash, all three are in the shade of the cut bank at 2:30. The ewe's gray face and white nose is all that stands out when they are in the shade here, even with the big glass. Her broken right horn, dark at the clean break, is her most distinguishing feature for future identification.

At 3:10 the ewe got up and began feeding on wash plants in the shade of the cut bank. Inside of 5 minutes, she pawed a basin in the gravel and lay in the shade again. The yearling got up, tried a couple of bites of *Encelia,* lay down again, but at 4 he went over to a large *Bebbia* and began eating steadily. He was joined by the ewe and lamb. The dried *Bebbia* flowers seemed to be the most sought-after item. They were too far away for us to be sure, and since *Eriogonum inflatum* grows there also they may have been eating it at the times their heads were low.

At 4:25 they abruptly left the wash, following the ewe, and returned to the spring area, not to drink, but to browse on *Sporobolus.* *Andropogon glomeratus* was sought and eaten by the ewe only.

At 5:20 the ewe had also eaten *Cirsium,* a few bites of the branch tips of screwbean (*Prosopis pubescens*), black sedge (*Schoenus nigricans*).

Ten minutes later the yearling decided it was time to leave. The lamb kept right on feeding around the springs. The ewe continued eating *Sporobolus,* dried thistle flowers (*Cirsium*), and a few more bites of screwbean.

Although they were near the different seeps and springs, as far as we could tell they did not touch water.

At 6:30 they left the spring area, having been eating exactly 2½ hours. Both the ewe and the lamb ate the first dormant holly they came to as they started to climb above the springs. The yearling was attracted to some smaller plant that we could not see down among the rocks.

As darkness fell they were still at the foot of Nevares Canyon, browsing on dormant holly, the lamb 100 feet in the lead.

This day's observations, during which the official temperature was 113°, provide several significant points to review:

1. The length of time spent, first in drinking, then feeding, and finally in resting was so far above average that great thirst, hunger, and fatigue are indicated, suggesting that a relatively long time had elapsed without water and that a great distance had been traveled. This suggests abandonment of a former home area, and their physical condition suggests a causative factor of either food or water failure.

2. These sheep all appeared to be in the last stages of starvation and exhaustion. I remarked to Buddy that "Here are the poorest sheep we have ever seen anywhere, and this can't be just dehydration." Yet within half an hour the most remarkable recovery we have ever witnessed had been accomplished. The ewe and the yearling by that time showed no sign of malnutrition and exhaustion, and the lamb had recovered to a great extent.

3. The fact that the lamb had drunk 5 minutes longer and eaten with greater persistence than the others and still showed a slower recovery may be pointing toward the area of mortality, the limiting factor in the survival of the bighorn which has eluded us for so long.

4. The lamb was the effective leader of the band of three in that it was the first to water and the last to stop drinking; after drinking it sought out its own feeding grounds, forcing the ewe to follow it in browsing; the ewe and yearling went up the mountain at one point

but the lamb went calmly to Old Spring, drank and ate for some time while the ewe and yearling waited; during the first part of siesta the lamb preceded the others from shade to shade with the ewe eventually coming to find it; the lamb broke siesta and led them back for browsing in the wash before they all went into the shade for more rest; when last seen at dusk the lamb was once more in the lead by about 100 feet.

5. The ewe's familiarity with the area leaves no doubt that she had been here before, but the fact that we had not identified her before certainly indicates the inclusion of more than one spring in her home area and bears out last summer's observations that some ewes seem to have only one spring as the focal point of a home area, while others may have several.

The next morning at 7:15 a band of 15 came into water.

One ewe, Brahma, was leading 4 lambs and a yearling away from the springs 100 yards up the mountain where the yearling (a ewe) was left to "babysit" while Brahma went back to drink.

After the mating activity of 4 rams and 5 ewes at the springs had ceased and they were leaving, the lambs came back and drank.

At 3:15, Brokeoff (the ewe of yesterday with one broken horn) and her lamb and the yearling ram have come back and are drinking at Old Spring. This is the first record we have of a band coming in on consecutive days. Rams have often done it, but not mixed groups. Again, the fatigue of yesterday is emphasized and the importance of food at spring areas becomes increasingly clear, for they are now feeding as voraciously as yesterday.

Buddy reports their drinking time: 7½ minutes for all three.

3:50. After half an hour of energetic grazing, they are drinking again, the ewe and ram for 1½ minutes and the lamb for 2¾ minutes. The lamb, as yesterday, is eating and drinking more than the others.

At 4:05, the lamb again leading, they went across the wash and into the shade of the Cut Bank. They rested there until 5:30, when they began browsing southward on *Bebbia* and *Encelia*.

6:00. The trio is still out of sight in the South Wash, and no others are adding to this new record of 18 into water in 1 day.

Ranger Parr met us at home with the hindleg of a lamb from Quartz Spring that had died or had been killed very recently. The flesh was still red, bloody, and obviously fresh. Rangers Parr, Dragoo, and Hoover had spent some time trying unsuccessfully to determine the cause of death. Sign in the vicinity of the dismembered carcass pointed toward consumption by ravens and buzzards with some assistance from coyotes or bobcats, but so little of it was left that no clue as to the cause of death could be found.

Comparative measurement of the leg and foot indicate an age of about 3 weeks. The texture of the pelage and the indistinct markings characteristic of this age also suggest that this lamb might have been born as late as the middle of August.

The rangers reported heavy use of the spring by bighorn as well as burros.

Official temperature: 116°.

The separation of lambs from their mother by rams during the rut-run has been discussed under "Reproduction." It is mentioned again here in emphasis of the need for independence at an early age.

Our 10-day Death Valley Buttes observations of a band of 14, including 6 lambs, gave us our only data in the growth and behavior of a group of lambs, and much of it has been previously discussed under "Play" and in other sections of this report. Some points are worth summarizing in the present connection:

How much and when lambs play and learn from each other and their elders is substantially controlled by weather and available food and water supplies.

The adult animals are for the most part content for the young (up to yearling ewes and 2- to 3-year-old rams) to carry on their own play activities. The difference in play behavior by age class and sex apparently arises from the probability of ewes being pregnant by the end of their second summer. We have no record of young ewes over a year old engaging in play activity to any considerable degree, but rams up to 3 years appear to be especially prone to play.

February 11, 1958. Death Valley Buttes. 4:20 p.m. Two of the lambs, 11 and 9 months old, are practicing the stiff uppercut with the 3 year old, who demonstrates the technique with marked gentleness.

The 11-month-old ram just now reared, ran, and lunged at the 3 year old, who just took it with no real return. The 3 year old just stands and takes the little one's butts on the end of his nose—woops! He had enough of that and lets the little guy have a pretty good one. The little one bounced right back, though.

February 14, 1958. 3:30. We now have two bands—one composed of three ewes and one ram and the other of three ewes, six lambs, and one ram.

The six lambs seem unconcerned by the absence of the three ewes. If this were the only band of sheep we had ever observed, we might draw the conclusion that here are three sets of twins. However, none of the six lambs show any attachment for any of the ewes, nor the ewes for the lambs. When the two lambs were lost this morning, it was the young ram, four lambs, and only one ewe who went to meet them. The other three lay placidly chewing their cuds throughout. All of this is not clarifying the family-band tie relationship at all. Or if it is, it is directly opposed to most of our evidence to date.

When the band finally broke up on February 16, 1958, we again had two bands of a confusing composition. The leader, Brahma II, had gone out on the south side of Twin Sister Butte with both the 3-year-old rams and two other ewes, while three ewes and all six lambs appeared to be headed in the opposite direction, toward Corkscrew Peak.

So, there are three ewes and six lambs—two about 11 months old, two about 9, and two about 7 months old. Either the family-tie theory is being strained a little or we have three sets of twins!

These lambs are all content with the group as it is, and so are the three ewes still on the main butte with the two rams. Certainly suggestive that either there are twins or that the tie between mother and young gives way much sooner than we have suspected. If it happens this soon as a rule, the family certainly is not always a basis for band composition.

That adult ewes do not entirely give up their authority was indicated on February 10, 1958:

2:30 p.m. While grazing, one of the little rams began chasing the 7-month-old ewe until both their tongues were hanging out. Suddenly one of the mature ewes leaped in front of the little ram and knocked him back on his haunches, as much as to say, "Junior! I don't want to speak to you again about chasing the girls! A boy of your age!"

Junior, however, was not immediately submissive. He regained his balance, reared to his hindlegs, and sighted down his nose at the old lady with a great show of ferocity. The old ewe met his challenge head on, though, and he dropped back without lunging, turned away, and lay down.

So we have followed the development of the young up to the time when it appears that the female may reach adulthood through the onset of her first oestrual cycle, which may be at any time during her second year. The young male seems to retain his juvenile attachments, at least to some extent, through his third year, at which time he is likely to abandon his off-season activities with mixed bands and join the "bachelor" rams in their supreme indifference to the growth, behavior, and care of the young.

Structure

Size

This report will add little of its own to the present data pertaining to the size of the desert bighorn. Details of measurements of desert bighorn are contained in the statistics from the Desert Game Range (Aldous et al, 1958) and from Arizona (Russo, 1956). We have no reason to believe that the Death Valley bighorn are significantly larger than those measured and weighed in Arizona or smaller than those in Nevada.

One lamb at the Desert Game Range (Deming, 1955) measured 17½ inches at the shoulder when it was 32 hours old.

We have no other measurements of lambs, but a relative size is indicated by the fact that a male lamb can walk under its mother's belly when it is born, may weigh as much as she does in 1 year and twice as much as she does in 4 years.

The seven rams and five ewes from Arizona weighed considerably more and measured longer than those from Nevada, but measured less at the front shoulder. These morphological differences (table 10) also are present to some degree within the Death Valley population.

The Badwater sheep were relatively stocky, heavy bodied, and short necked compared with the rangy "ewe-necked," high-shouldered animals at Nevares; and those at Navel Spring ran somewhere between the two, the first band being stocky, the second rangy and slim, but not ewe necked. Some of these differences may be noticed in the photographs of the sheep, at the end of this report.

TABLE 10.—*Measurements of bighorn from Nevada and Arizona*

Bighorn	Weight (pounds)	Girth (inches)	Height at shoulder (inches)	Tail length (inches)	Total length (inches)
Nevada:					
37 Rams:					
Maximum	190.0	41.5	39.0	4.5	63.5
Minimum	127.0	37.0	31.0	2.5	52.0
Average	156.0	39.5	36.5	3.2	57.0
15 Ewes:					
Maximum	114.0	40.0	34.0	....	....
Minimum	74.0	33.5	32.0	....	....
Average	96.5	35.7	33.3	....	....
Arizona:					
7 Rams:					
Maximum	200.0	44.5	39.5	....	67.0
Minimum	143.0	39.0	34.5	....	60.2
Average	169.0	40.7	36.0	....	61.8
5 Ewes:					
Maximum	126.0	38.0	34.2	....	59.0
Minimum	101.0	32.5	27.5	....	53.5
Average	115.1	35.8	31.7	....	55.9

Horns

Horns appear during the third month, with some indication that they develop sooner and faster on males than on females. Close inspection usually discloses a thickening at the base of the male's horn in observable contrast to the consistent flatness of the female's horn; the female buttons normally appear in almost parallel extrusion, while an outward divergence is noticeable in the male horns from their inception. Young horns tend toward a gray-blue color during the first year, turning yellowish in maturity.

By the end of the first year, the casual observer is likely to confuse the yearling ram with adult ewes, but the experienced fieldworker will readily observe the thickness and spread of the rams' horns as well as the fact that the male curl is already in evidence. (See fig. 32.)

As the bighorn matures, no two sets of horns develop alike, varying with the individual animal as definitely as do fingerprints in man.

The variation in rams' horns takes place on a larger scale than in ewes' and is therefore more observable in the field.

To the field observer the "horn-prints" serve two main functions—as age indicators and as identification marks.

Something of the scope of the variation in Death Valley ram horn development is indicated by the measurements of six skull and horn sets collected during this survey as shown in table 11.

TABLE 11.—*Measurements of Death Valley ram horns, from skulls*

Annual rings	Girth (inches)	Length around outside circumference (inches)	Spread (inches)	Dry weight (pounds)
12	14.0	30.0	22.0	18.5
12	12.2	36.0	20.0	18.5
8	12.5	31.0	22.0	12.5
10	11.0	26.0	28.5	10.2
10	11.5	25.0	15.5	8.2
11	13.0	29.0	22.0	14.7

Ewe and lamb skulls and horn sets are seldom found in the Death Valley region, possibly because they are more easily consumed or carried away by carnivores or scavengers. Smaller skulls and leg bones have been carried out of our camp by ravens, coyotes, and kit foxes.

The one ewe skull collected is above average but relatively typical of the Nevares type as shown here:

Annual rings	Girth (inches)	Length (inches)	Spread (inches)	Dry weight (pounds)
9	5.7	12.2	16	2.2

The length of annual ring growth decreases with age, until the rings of later years may become quite indistinct wrinkles around the base of the horns of a 10- or 12-year-old ram. Photographs included in this report clearly show this decreasing growth rate with age.

Irregular annual variation in ring width suggests a correlation with wet and dry cycles and concomitant dietary fluctuations, or in extreme cases, sickness. (See fig. 31.)

Aging by annual ring count cannot be positive since the extent of variation in ring growth is not known. The method is more reliable with rams than with ewes, because the rings are likely to be much more clearly defined in the rams' horns. Figures 68 to 76 present fairly accurately the development of rings in a ram of known age. Figures 63 to 67 illustrate the less well defined ring development often occurring in ewes. The unique set of "horn-prints" of Droopy (fig. 6), on the other hand, would appear to indicate an age of 7 or 8 years with reasonable certainty. An illustration of relative horn development of both sexes at 6 and 18 months of age is shown in figs. 32 and 33.

Brooming of tips is almost universal in the Death Valley rams. Jones (1950) reports a complete lack of it in the Sierra bighorn. This suggests the existence in Death Valley of climatic or dietary factors not prevalent in the Sierra Nevada that render the horns susceptible to brooming under abrasion or impact. Jones saw no evidence of horns being used to dig for food, nor have we.

The manner of resting occasionally indulged in, with a horn point resting on the ground, as described previously, could contribute to brooming if the horntips were already dessicated by excessive sun and aridity.

Our evidence, however, indicates "fighting" as the principal direct cause of brooming. (See "Fighting with Other Males.") The type of miscalculation illustrated in figure 59 could end in the loss of a horntip.

It should be noted that the captive ram at the Desert Game Range, with no access to fighting rams, has no brooming. (See figs. 68–76.)

Track Measurements

Track measurements played a lesser part in our field study than had been anticipated, since positive classification of tracks by age class and sex has proven, except in extreme cases, to be of doubtful authority. Owing to the overlap in hoof size of the smaller rams and larger ewes, it is often impossible to know which has left the track. (See fig. 42.) The largest sharp track we have measured was 4 inches long. Allowing for spread of the matrix receiving the imprint, a male front hoof of approximately 3¾ inches was indicated. The average ram track measures about 3½ inches by 2½ inches for the front hoof (depending on the nature of the mold). Ewe tracks generally average about the same width as rams but one-half inch shorter. The hind tracks work out about the same for both sexes, being approximately 2½ inches long and 2 inches wide. The smallest lamb track we have measured was 1¼ inches long.

The weather, the nature of the soil matrix or mold of the deposit, the relative weight of the animal at the time of deposition, and the nature of the gait employed while traveling are all factors to be considered in calculating the possible variations in the track measurements of one animal, and they will be considered further under "Sign Reading."

Pelages

Pelages of Death Valley bighorn present a picture that is confused by the extreme variations of altitude, climate, foraging conditions and uncertainties as to the dates of seasonal shedding and pelage renewal. Note the smooth, even texture of the Badwater band throughout the winter at low, warm elevations and on lush forage. (See figs. 1 and 7.) Figure 19 illustrates the even, but typically long and dull pelage of sheep on good forage but at higher (2,000 to 4,000 feet) elevations. Figure 30 shows the heavy, rough, bleaching coat characteristic of the band of five which came into Furnace Creek Wash on March 13, 1956. The heavy pelage and excessive hunger suggested the recent abandonment of a high, depleted range. These sheep remained blond after shedding in contrast to the dark brownish gray of the original band of eight from the mesa.

Present evidence points toward a darker pelage during the summer than winter, although the interseasonal variations described above complicate classification.

Death Valley lambs are generally a bluish gray at birth, with occasional tints of brown and indistinct markings. (See figs. 34–36.) The rump patch gradually becomes more distinct but remains yellowish until the lamb is about 6 weeks of age, when the patch becomes still more distinct and a clearer white (fig. 61), with a distinct rump patch, and white leg-lining, the dark body color matching the mother's.

There appear to be some regional or family characteristics of coloration. The Badwater band of six evidenced a rich chocolate-brown color of adults and immatures alike, with no noticeable variation between even the 5-month-old lamb and its 4-year-old mother.

On march 2, 1955, this notation was made of a band of six in Echo Canyon:

We were immediately struck by the differences in shape and color of this band as compared with the Badwater band. Longer of body, leg, and neck to a noticeable degree. Paler in color without exception. Spring shedding had hardly begun, whereas it was nearly completed with the Badwater band.

A question arose: Why were all the Badwater sheep short necked, short legged, and thick bodied, and dark desert varnish in color, while these in Echo Canyon were all long necked, slim bodied, long legged, and uniformly gray in color?

The Natural Bridge band were rangy in build and light in color, but all tan, not gray or brown. Their faces and feet were lighter, too, almost white, and one resembled a palomino.

Are these bands formed, at least in part, on a family basis?

The Willow Creek herd within our observations have been uniformly dark with blackish tints and distinct white markings. (See fig. 47.)

On September 19 and 20, 1955, we photographed a band of seven at Indian Pass that ranged in color from dark mahogany to pale cream. A band of 18 Paleomesa sheep were so uniformly brown in color that identification beyond horn-print distance was impossible.

That entire bands in the same area may differ in color from each other was demonstrated in the Death Valley Buttes by the 1958 band of 14 cream-colored sheep and the 1961 band of 27, ranging in color from very dark gray to light tan.

The 28 at Quartz Spring, 1960, were all gray with 2 of the darkest we have seen anywhere.

Pelage is somewhat of an indicator of relative physical condition to the extent that systemic or glandular malfunction, regardless of the causative agent, is usually reflected in a rough, lacklustre coat. (See fig. 39.)

Many of the 1956 Nevares population had a mottled appearance, apparently caused by incomplete molt. We saw practically no sign of this in any of the mature ewes or rams in the succeeding years through 1960, but some of the younger rams retained "shawls" throughout the summer.

Diseases and Parasites

We have been able to accumulate practically no data on the incidence and type of sickness among Death Valley bighorn.

The cause of the symptoms of the Nevares sheep described above was never determined and apparently was overcome by the adult members of the band. It might, however, have contributed to the absence of yearlings in 1957.

We were unable to determine whether the poor condition of The Old Lady at Nevares was solely because of old age or aggravated by pathological complications.

Old Mama of Furnace Creek Wash had a sporadic cough and nasal discharge which seemed to affect her energy in no way. Her lamb, on the other hand, developed a severe cough accompanied by badly swollen eyes and considerable lethargy. The lamb was better when last seen, but on the following November when Old Mama returned to the wash she was alone.

The symptoms described above are common among Death Valley lambs but the cause or causes of the symptoms and their ultimate development are not known.

Lungworm (*Protostrongylus stilesi*) was established as existent in the Death Valley area by laboratory tests conducted by the California Department of Fish and Game on fecal deposits collected during the 1955 census.

We found no incidence of either warbles or ticks.

Adult skulls collected during this survey have been remarkably free from dental abnormalities, indicating a low incidence of *Actinomyces bovis*. One ram skull has upper canines.

Population Dynamics

Longevity

The only indication we have of the life expectancy of a Death Valley bighorn is the fact that the great majority of the skulls collected are from animals less than 1 year old or over 10, indicating the probability that if a sheep lives past its first year it can expect to reach its 10th. The difficulty of a lamb surviving its first year in Death Valley is indicated by the fact that we saw no yearlings at Nevares Spring in 1957, with no accurate lamb count for the year before. The 1957 lamb count of nine was reduced to eight by Fuzzy's death (see Cast of Characters and fig. 44), and we counted a survival of three yearlings for 1958. At Willow Creek in the summer of 1956, we had 12 ewes, 12 lambs, 4 rams, and 3 yearlings.

Of the 30 individuals observed in the Navel Spring area in 1956–57, only 3 were yearlings. The survival ratio of lambs is therefore indicated as being somewhere between 0 and 3 out of 10, with a suggestion that we may have something in the nature of alternating years in good and bad lamb crops and survival.

Herd Composition

Herd composition, with the exception of the off-season segregation of the "bachelor" rams, appears to be more coincidence than anything else. This may be a local situation brought about by the low-density ground cover and population of the Death Valley region.

In the Desert Game Range in 1953, we saw several bands composed solely of ewes with lambs. On one occasion we counted nothing but yearling ewes in a band of seven.

The above is not true in Death Valley. The only age class and sex segregation that seems to take place regularly is that of the mature rams between mating seasons.

The 1960 Quartz Spring band was composed of 12 ewes, 12 lambs, and 2 yearlings, which might be called typical of what we observed at the Desert Game Range. But we were able to stay with them only 2 days, not long enough to determine the duration of specificity in this instance.

Two mature rams observed in the same canyon with them on the second day did not actually join the original band. If they had, it would have made a more typical Death Valley band.

Both of the Death Valley Buttes bands had two rams among them;

616472 O—62——11

there was a yearling ram at Badwater, a 3 year old at Furnace Creek, and a 4 year old at Jubilee Pass.

The family influence on herd composition is probably positive but temporary. The Badwater band retained its specificity for 4 weeks.

On February 12, 1955, four of the six returned with Droopy, and the yearling was missing, and finally by March 20 the band of six was reduced to one.

There is some indication that these splits are into immediate family groups, but how general this pattern may be is not known. Family resemblance is often noticeable in small bands, but by no means can it be considered the rule. Juvenile attachments probably carry over and to some extent influence herd composition. Some bands seem to be held together by a leader and break up with her loss, but apparently the strongest factor involved is the general gregariousness of the bighorn, which would probably result in much larger herds and bands if the food and water of the habitat would permit.

Seasonal influence on band composition is pronounced only in the sense that the word "seasonal" is defined as meaning wet or dry cycles in its application to the habitat involved in this study. The wet and dry cycles may be highly localized and variable within a small area. A wet season was created in Furnace Creek wash by high-country rainfall in 1955 and 1956 at the head of the Furnace Creek drainage. This wet season lasted from October 1955 through 1957, producing sufficient forage to permit the bighorn to exercise their natural tendency toward gregariousness.

This had happened, with variations, on the alluvial fans at Badwater in 1954–55 and set the observational pattern for this study.

The Furnace Creek runoff produced an oasis of *Bebbia, Stephanomeria,* and *Eriogonum,* which in turn produced another unique opportunity to observe two bands of relatively sustained specificity and family resemblance that formed the basis for much of the life history of this report.

Finally, the early concentration of flowers on Death Valley Buttes in February 1958 gave us our only sustained observation of a band of bighorn in the Grapevines.

Good ranges may be produced by wet seasons at any time of the calendar year; and when food supplies will allow it, bighorn tend to form larger bands and stay together longer. (See "Food" and "Water.")

Poor ranges result in breaking down of numbers to smaller groups of one to three animals, thus reducing the travel distance necessary to gather a sustaining diet.

Prolonged drought tends to reduce the bands to smaller numbers by decimation as well as by fragmentation. (See "Food" and "Water.")

We saw no specific bands at Nevares during the entire series of sustained observations from 1956 through 1960, but we recorded many instances of bands forming as they neared the watering area and breaking up again as they left. Such temporary bands, observed but once and then for but a few minutes or even hours, has led to many misconceptions regarding the average size of bands to be expected in the field.

The longest record we have of band specificity is that of the seven Badwater sheep who remained under constant observation for 5 weeks from December 18, 1954, to January 24, 1955.

Some concept can be gained of the transitory nature of band composition within the entire herd by data gathered on Paleomesa between November 4 and 25, 1956:

On November 4, Old Eighty, Scarface, Bad Boy, and Whitey came down from the mesa into Big Wash for the first time since Old Mama led the band of eight up Pyramid Peak the previous January. By November 15 this band had increased to nine. On November 18 we were still observing this band of nine in Big Wash when Old Mama with two strangers came down from the mesa on the south side of the wash, and Kinky and five others came down from the north. By 2 p.m. we were photographing our first band of 18 bighorn in Death Valley. They bedded together that night and were still resting at 6 the next morning. But by 7:20 Kinky and eight others, led by a ewe unknown to us, headed north and disappeared toward the Hole-in-the-Wall; we now had two bands again of nine each.

We followed Old Eighty and her band to water on the 24th of November. On the way in they were joined by four strangers, including a mature ram who left at dusk. At dawn of the next day the old gray ewe, Pearl, her lamb, and a yearling preceded the others in to Navel Spring, drank and left by way of nearby Hanging Canyon. At 2 p.m., Scarface, Bad Boy, and a new 2-year-old ewe went into Navel Spring wash; Whitehorns and Old Eighty bedded down with two others in the box canyon; Little Whitey, torn by uncertainty as to which group to follow, finally made an anxious exit alone toward Deadman's Curve. So in just 1 week our 2-day band of 18 had disintegrated into small groups of 1 to 4.

This same pattern was repeated in January 1961, on Death Valley Buttes: On January 1 there were 9; on the 3d, 11; on the 5th, 13 began the day with 2 mature rams heading back to Corkscrew in the afternoon. Nineteen had gathered among the flowers by the 10th, but the next morning eight of these went over the crest and back into the foothills of Corkscrew Peak as two others appeared briefly at the mouth of Bebbia Canyon. By dusk two small bands were left, one of five and one of six. Eight were counted the next day and on the 13th, none.

These two accounts of several small bands appearing briefly as one in watering or special feeding areas illustrate the rule and not the exception. It has been observed repeatedly at Willow Creek, Virgin Canyon, Indian Pass, and at Nevares Seeps. Its effect on sign reading is discussed under that heading. Unawareness of this pattern can be very misleading in determinations of numbers and distribution, and its discussion will continue there.

Numbers

Numbers and distribution pose three common inquiries which no one can answer with certainty for the Death Valley area: How many are there? Are they increasing or decreasing in number? Where can they be seen? Answers to these questions can be no more than a recording of the development of our knowledge of the subject at the present time.

Census Methods

Beginning in October 1935, with a preliminary survey by Field Naturalist Joseph Dixon, efforts were made on a gradually expanding scale to count the bighorn of Death Valley in sample areas. From these samplings, estimates of the total population subsequently were derived. During Dixon's 1935 survey, reports by others of 30 and 42 animals were accepted for the Cottonwood Mountains at Quartz and Big Dodds Springs, respectively. From tracks and pellets Dixon estimated 21 additional bighorn at other springs in the Grapevine, Funeral, Black, and Panamint Mountains (Dixon, 1935). From this total of 93 animals seen, or inferred, from sign, covering less than 10 percent of the total bighorn range, Dixon did not attempt to derive a population estimate for the entire monument.

In September 1938, another incomplete survey by Dixon, Sumner, and members of the park staff, in cooperation with members of the California Department of Fish and Game, resulted in a total of 65 bighorn seen, or inferred from sign (Dixon and Sumner, 1939). Rains dispersed the animals before the survey could be completed, and no population estimate was made for the entire monument.

In July 1939, a second cooperative effort by the same group yielded 66 animals seen and 208 inferred from sign. Summer rains again dispersed the bighorn before the survey could be completed (Sumner, 1939). However, from sample areas covered, Sumner derived a total population estimate for the monument of 500.

In July 1955, a third major effort was made by Sumner, the park staff, and the present authors, in cooperation with the California Department of Fish and Game. This was the last and most comprehensive of the cooperative surveys. The number of sheep actually seen by the official census takers was 90. An additional 15 were seen by unofficial but reliable cooperators, making a total of 105 seen. The results of this 1955 census and of subsequent samplings by us are shown in table 12.

TABLE 12.—*Bighorn census surveys, Death Valley National Monument, 1955-59*

[Degree of use: *, less use; **, average amount of use; ***, greater amount of use.   N: No census taken]

Area	July 1955, Sumner and others		1955–59, Welles and others		1959–61 Welles	
	Number seen	Number estimated	Number seen	Number estimated	Number seen	Number estimated
Cottonwood Mountains:						
Tin Mountain	10	25	32	60	***0	60
Race Track Pass	N	N	2	4	*0	4
Leaning Rock	0	0	*0	10	*0	10
Quartz Spring	0	15	**3	20	***28	40
Saline Valley Road	N	N	7	7	0	7
Burro Spring	0	0	0	0	2	2
Goldbelt Spring	0	0	0	0	0	0
Cottonwood-Marble Canyons	N	N	**5	20	***5	50
Grapevine Mountains:						
Grapevene Mountains, general	1	N	**4	30	**0	30
Klare Spring	15	30	**18	30	**5	30
Deadman Spring	N	N	**0	30	**0	30
Corkscrew Spring	N	N	***1	30	***3	30
Hole-in-the Rock Spring	N	N	*3	3	*0	3
Death Valley Buttes	N	N	*14	14	***27	27
Funeral Mountains:						
Keane Spring	0	0	0	0	0	0
Monarch Canyon	0	3	**7	20	**0	20
Keane Wonder Springs	N	N	0	0	**0	15
Indian Pass	31	40	***23	30	**0	20
Scraper Spring	N	N	*1	10	*0	5
Nevares Spring	O	3	***47	47	***28	35
Echo Canyon	N	N	**15	15	**10	15
Navel Spring	4	12	***30	35	***15	35
Black Mountains:						
Lemonade Spring-Badwater area	10	14	***12	30	***0	30
Copper Canyon	N	N	**3	10	*2	5
Willow Creek	13	50	***37	50	***7	50
Virgin Spring	11	20	***13	30	***5	30
Sheep Canyon	N	20	**0	20	**0	20
Scotty's Canyon	0	3	**2	25	**0	25
Jubilee Pass	N	N	*7	7	*0	3
Panamint Mountains:						
Panamint Butte	N	N	*3	3	*0	3
Pinto Peak	N	N	*3	3	*0	3
Emigrant Wash	N	N	2	2	0	0

[Degree of use: *, less use; **, average amount of use; ***, greater amount of use.   N: No census taken]

Area	July 1955, Sumner, Welles, and others		1955–59, Welles and others		1959–61 Welles and others	
	Number seen	Number estimated	Number seen	Number estimated	Number seen	Number estimated
Panamint Mountains—Continued						
Tuber Canyon	0	0	*0	5	*3	10
Jail Canyon	0	0	*5	5	*5	10
Hall Canyon	0	0	8	8	*3	8
Surprise Canyon	1	10	*5	25	*7	25
Happy Canyon	3	6	3	3	*0	5
Pleasant Canyon	3	10	*5	5	*7	15
South Park Canyon	3	0	*3	10	*0	5
Lost Spring	N	N	N	N	***0	30
Galena Canyon	N	N	*2	8	*0	5
Arrastre Spring	N	N	6	12	*0	8
Six Springs Canyon	N	N	*1	4	*0	5
Johnson Canyon	N	N	*0	4	*0	5
Starvation Canyon	N	N	*0	4	*0	5
Hanaupah Canyon	0	0	1	4	***0	20
Death Valley Canyon	N	N	*0	4	**0	10
Trail Canyon	N	N	*0	4	*12	12
Blackwater Spring	N	N	***0	50	***0	50
Twin Springs	N	N	***0	50	***0	50
Total	105	261	333	800	174	915

NOTE:
   July 1955 "revised conservative estimate"—420.
   July 1955 "liberal estimate"—1,260.

These surveys suggest that more intensive and continuous observations at high concentration localities would, with luck, yield even better results.

An estimated total population figure is always open to question, and no matter what the figure arrived at or the method by which it is obtained it is likely to be challenged.   The 1955 estimate of 261 total for the population within the monument (table 12), the result of a concensus of field estimates made by the individual teams, was based on what they saw in their areas only.   This was an ultraconservative figure, derived from the questionable assumption that the census takers had a reasonable expectation of finding nearly half of all the sheep in the areas they covered.

However, our subsequent controlled experiments at Badwater, with many competent observers and a known number of animals in a known area, would lead us to believe that if a quarter of the total population in a given area were sighted we were lucky indeed. There the band of six climbed the rugged western slope of the Black Mountains and browsed and bedded at about 1,000 feet elevation for 3 days. This was the peak period of their publicity, and hundreds of observers, including park rangers and naturalists from other areas, came to satisfy their curiosity. As far as we were able to determine, not once during this period was the band located without our assistance. We ourselves kept track of them only by constant surveillance from the earliest streaks of dawn when they left their bedding ground until sometime after dark when we could tell only by sound where they had bedded down again.

By this line of reasoning, it still seems conservative to estimate the total population at 4 times 105, the number seen, which would be 420.

There is nothing to be gained by being either conservative or liberal in estimating the total bighorn population, but both approaches were used for purposes of comparison. Using the "liberal" approach, a compilation of all the known sight records of bighorn was laid out on the map to give theoretical limits of both vertical and horizontal distribution. These limits were then modified by considerations of known forage and water supply, suitable terrain, seasonal migration (if any), etc. National Park Service Engineer Lin Spaulding then computed this sheep range as comprising 2,100 square miles (70 percent of the total monument area). The areas marked on the topographic maps as covered by each field team were then computed to be 703 square miles, or 33 percent of the total possible sheep range of 2,100 square miles. By these figures, we arrive at a possible total of 3 x 420, or 1,260.

An apparently obvious fallacy could immediately be pointed out here; the 33 percent of sheep range that we covered included all the areas of high concentration.

It is quite likely that we did cover the majority of the high concentration areas, but we do not know. For example, Indian Pass in the Funeral Mountains, with the highest count of any area censused in 1955, had been left out of all consideration for 20 years preceding this last census. Borell in 1935 wrote: "There are very few, if any, sheep between Daylight Pass and Echo Canyon. This takes in most of the area now known as the Funeral Mountains." Don Curry, Acting Park Naturalist in 1939, wrote that he "had never seen sheep sign at Poison Spring in the central Funeral Mountains, although it is the only source of water for many miles in any direction."

On the other hand, we still do not know how many unmapped sources of free water may be known to the bighorn. These, if known, might add materially to the population figures. Several new springs were found during the 1955 census, notably Bighorn Spring, which was discovered and named by Lowell Sumner and Fred Jones. Our subsequent discovery of large populations watering at two uncensused major water sources, Blackwater and Twin Springs, provides another example that will be more fully described later.

Another difficulty in deciding whether an estimate is "conservative" or "liberal" arises from the fact that up to a certain point the poorer the conditions are for the bighorn, the higher their census reports are likely to be, because the animals that are surviving these adverse conditions of drought or malnutrition are more and more concentrated in permanent spring areas accessible to observation.

Rainfall appears to be the controlling factor in the normal low-density sheep population of the entire Death Valley region. During a year when general rains fall throughout the high-mountain country, vegetation is relatively abundant and nutritious; temporary water supplies in the back country such as tinajas, or "tanks," are plentiful; conditions are ripe for fertility, high lamb survival, and a low disease ratio.

For example, during the winter months from January 1950 until December 1954, we were able to find but one bighorn throughout the entire monument, and none was reported by visitors. High-country rainfall made it unnecessary for the sheep to use areas accessible to humans. In short, when everything points toward an optimum count, very few sheep can be found.

On the other hand, from December 1954 until January 1957, with high-country rainfall scarce and spotty, we were in almost constant touch with at least one band of sheep and occasionally two or three at a time. We saw more sheep and more were reported by visitors during this period than at any other time on record, and it was taken for granted that the population was increasing.

From January 1957, when the rains came, until July, the sheep vanished, but a dry summer brought good observations once more, at springs only, until a late rain again dispersed the sheep.

Thus, it has been generally accepted that the waterhole count is the most reliable method of census taking, but now we find that the most favorable conditions for a count are the most unfavorable for the sheep.

The waterhole count is still the best method we have, but it is likely to be more misleading than we had thought. The 1955 census, based on quick visits to springs, shows no sheep counted and no estimate of a population at Nevares Spring. Yet under comparable weather conditions between August 11 and September 10, 1957, when continuous vigils were kept, 11 ewes, 9 lambs, and 27 rams were counted there. It was assumed in 1955 that it was reasonable to expect to count no more than 25 percent of the total population in a 4-day vigil at a waterhole, but we now know that at the climax of a long drought, such as August and September 1957, the entire population may use the waterhole and be counted in a period of 4 days.

The majority of the 27 rams counted at Nevares Spring from August 11 to September 10 were travelers. They were counted only once or twice in 30 days, and could possibly have been counted several times at different springs in any 4 days of the 30-day period. How far these rams travel during the rut is not known, but 2 of the 27 we have seen repeatedly over 20 miles south of Nevares in the Big Wash area, and both of them went on north when they left Nevares after a stopover of but 2 or 3 hours.

We have made no attempt at a census since 1955. We counted 105 bighorn then, and we estimated four times that many. Subsequent observations make that figure seem ultraconservative to the point of inadequacy even when the variables described above have been considered.

For example, in 1955 we counted 4 sheep at Navel Spring and estimated a total population of 12. Between that date and September 1957, we made prolonged observations of over 30 individuals at Navel Spring, and 18 of these animals were in one band. It is true that several things had happened in the meantime: We had improved the water supply at Navel Spring from a bee-seep to 75 gallons. Contiguous areas had practically no rainfall for nearly 3 years, possibly forcing a temporary migration into the washes above Navel Spring where flash-flood runoff had produced a substantial growth of *Bebbia* and *Stephanomeria*. But probably most important of all, prolonged observations were carried out in the area for the first time.

Present data still are insufficient for a really good estimate of the number of sheep in the Death Valley region. No clue is offered as to whether the numbers are increasing or decreasing at the present time. However, increase and decrease have relatively little importance in the long range picture, since they undoubtedly vary a great deal with the wet and dry cycles normal to the region. Nevertheless, evidence generally points toward a relatively substantial and healthy herd in the area.

In review, the "liberal" population estimate of 1,260 bighorn computed from areas of known favorable range following the 1955 census seems more plausible now than it did then. A bighorn distribution map is shown on page 154, and results of census surveys are given in table 12. Since 1955 additional evidence on the side of more liberal estimates has accumulated: Sighting or positive signs of current use by bighorn have been recorded throughout the Panamint and Cotton-

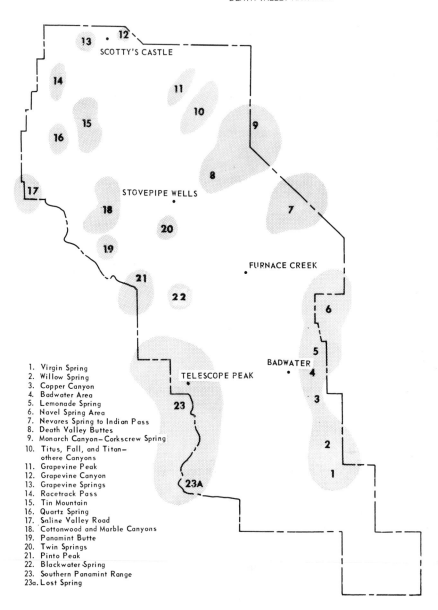

BIGHORN DISTRIBUTION

DEATH VALLEY NAT. MON.

1. Virgin Spring
2. Willow Spring
3. Copper Canyon
4. Badwater Area
5. Lemonade Spring
6. Navel Spring Area
7. Nevares Spring to Indian Pass
8. Death Valley Buttes
9. Monarch Canyon—Corkscrew Spring
10. Titus, Fall, and Titan—
    othere Canyons
11. Grapevine Peak
12. Grapevine Canyon
13. Grapevine Springs
14. Racetrack Pass
15. Tin Mountain
16. Quartz Spring
17. Saline Valley Road
18. Cottonwood and Marble Canyons
19. Panamint Butte
20. Twin Springs
21. Pinto Peak
22. Blackwater Spring
23. Southern Panamint Range
23a. Lost Spring

wood ranges on both the eastern and western slopes from Wingate Pass in the south to Sand Springs in the north, indicating a much higher density population for the region censused than was estimated in 1955.

Of still greater significance is the discovery that two previously uncensused water sources in the north Panamints probably are supporting two of the largest bands of bighorn yet recorded for the region. These new sources are Twin Springs and Blackwater Spring. They add approximately 200 square miles of high (1,000 to 6,000 feet) and relatively dense burro-free forage to the known bighorn range, and include practically all of Tucki Mountain.

An estimated population of 50 sheep for the areas surrounding each of these springs seems plausible. The size of the areas served, the food supplies, and the cooler climate are all factors comparing favorably with the Nevares Spring area, where 47 sheep were counted in 1957.

In general, the same can be said of a third area so far uncensused: Corkscrew Peak, with Corkscrew Spring at 4,000 feet elevation as the hub, probably supoprts another 30 or 40 animals.

On September 1, 1956, we saw six apparently resident bighorn at Monarch Canyon, which is exactly twice the number estimated in 1955. In 1956 and 1957, we saw at least 30 individuals water at Navel Spring and 47 at Nevares, 2½ and 16 times as many as were estimated in 1955.

The highly mineralized waters of the Keane Wonder Springs at the base of Chloride Cliff were blamed for the lack of bighorn sign there in 1955, when so little sign could be found that the area was eliminated from consideration in the final figures of the census. Annual surveys confirmed this view until 1959, when we found the area around Sulphur Spring had been "turned into a barnyard" during the previous summer, with sign indicating a population comparable in size with that of Navel or Nevares Springs.

To confuse the picture somewhat, however, the sign had been substantially reduced by November 1960, indicating much less use and suggesting the temporary presence of a drought-displaced population from another area.

Our rediscovery on March 14, 1960, of Lost Spring (4 miles south of Warm Springs Canyon) disclosed the existence of an uncounted but stable herd in the heart of the burro country between Warm Springs Canyon and Wingate Pass. (See "Wild Burro.")

At Quartz Spring, where no sheep were seen in 1955 but 15 were estimated, we actually observed 28 in one band on the first day of June 1960.

So we find that we have more home areas and more bighorn to the area than we thought we had in 1955. If the picture that has developed at Navel, Quartz, Lost, and Nevares Springs could be projected over the entire habitat, an estimated total herd of 1,000 would be conservative (and has been suggested). Present data, however, do not warrant an optimistic generalization.

If all the home areas of the Death Valley bighorn were substantially comparable with those studied in the Black and Funeral Mountains between and including Virgin Spring in the south and Klare Spring in the north, it would appear reasonable to use this region for projecting a total population estimate. The region in question comprises an area approximately 75 air-line miles long and 8 air-line miles wide—a one-story ground cover terrain completely free of predation, forage competition (except rodents), and relatively free of human encroachment. We have counted approximately 100 individuals in 3 contiguous areas of the 10 population centers involved: Lemonade, Navel, and Nevares Springs. This is an average of 30 sheep to an area and projects a not unreasonable total of 300 bighorn for the entire 600 square miles under immediate discussion. This represents a 33 percent increase over 200 estimated for the same area in 1955.

With the exception of Tucki Mountain and the Butte Valley-Lost Spring area, the remainder of the Death Valley habitat comprising the northern Grapevines, the Cottonwoods, and the Panamints, is dominated by high desert communities of drought-resistant conifers, presenting infinite possibilities of variation in the life history of the local bighorn populations.

The presence of mountain lions in the forested areas indicates the possibility of significant predation; exotic competition for food exists in all of these regions; mining activity, with a concomitant human usurpation of water and forage withdrawal is prevalent; poaching is believed to be common practice throughout these sections of the bighorn range; and deer-bighorn competition in the Grapevines and Cottonwood ranges is beginning to assume significant proportions. (See "Deer.")

All of these factors complicate census estimates, but since it seems imperative that an estimate of the population be made, this report offers the following figures as of January 1, 1961: The theoretical or "liberal" high of 1,260 for 1955 should be increased at least 15 percent by the new populations discovered since that time, which would bring the figure to 1,450. A wet cycle of 3 years could conceivably result in that many bighorn for a brief time. The actual maximum estimate is indicated in table 12 to be 915. For purposes of discussion, it is suggested that these figures be rounded out to 1,400 as the theoretical high, and 900 as the actual maximum. Deduct 30 percent for errors in censusing due to ram overlap and to provide for annual lamb mortality for a minimum of 662, or 600, to round out the minimum figure.

The above minimum figures take into account the fact that the best waterhole counts occur during July, August, and September, while the lamb crop is usually at a peak and rams may be counted more than once in their overlap of service at the springs. The minimum figure of 600 is believed to represent the average carrying capacity of the total biota when annual lamb mortality has restored the balance around January 1 of each year.

There is no evidence to indicate a perceptible general increase or decrease in numbers of the total herd. By February 1959 the sheep had responded to the autumn rains by dispersing to the outlying ranges not readily available to observation. Reports of sightings dwindled, and once more recurrent rumor had the bighorn dying out. History began to round itself out with autumn rains in November 1960. January flowers and bighorn were in the washes and on the alluvial fans, and bighorn were "on the increase" again in 1961.

Two types of density fluctuation must be expected: The annual appearance and disappearance of the lamb crop, and the intermittent but inevitable drought reduction of the entire range to a critical degree.

If a spring census were possible, the age class and sex ratio would probably be indicated at about 35 percent ewes, 35 percent rams, and 30 percent lambs. A winter count of the same population would indicate about the same number of ewes and rams, but the ratio would now be at 45 percent ewes, 45 percent rams, and 10 percent yearlings and younger.

To what degree prolonged droughts affect the general population is not known. (See "Food" and "Water" and "Chief Causes of Mortality.")

Distribution

Distribution is affected by the variability and fluctuation of food and water supply, but as indicated in the bighorn distribution map, bighorn tend to find their way to some extent into all areas of the region supporting bighorn forage. There appears to be no other natural factor of limitation. Left to his own resources, the Death Valley bighorn will apparently forage at any elevation in any season, below sea level at Badwater or atop Telescope Peak, summer or winter, as his demand for food meets the law of supply. A possible exception to this is indicated by the fact that we have never found bighorn tracks in the snow on Telescope Peak, which at least suggests a tendency to drop below the snowline when the snow is heavy. The absence of sheep or sheep sign at Doe Spring in the Grapevines is discussed under "Competitors and Enemies."

No food exists in much of the salt-flat area of the valley floor, but the rumor still persists that "bighorn cross it from one mountain range to the other."

In 1952, Ranger-Naturalist Richard Hartesveldt took pictures of bighorn tracks "about a mile out in the salt flats west of National Park Service headquarters." These he believed to be made by sheep crossing the valley floor, although coyote tracks have been misidentified as those of sheep under similar conditions. In October 1958, a ram was observed by the road crew "crossing the road 4 miles north of headquarters and heading out across the valley." Whether the ram continued to "cross the valley" is not known, since the crew moved on with their work. There have been other indications that sheep may for some obscure reason occasionally cross the salt flats to the other side.

That they do not do it regularly in any sense of the word is indicated by the fact that during the entire winter of 1954–55, when we were making the Badwater observations, we repeatedly checked the edges of the salt marshes from Mormon Point to Salt Creek, but we found no sign, old or new, of sheep crossing the highway and salt flats beyond at any point.

In the autumn of 1955, Geologist Charles Hunt began a 6-year mapping project focused on the salt deposits of the entire region. During the first four winters, he walked across the valley more than a hundred times at short enough intervals of distance to permit accurate mapping of every foot of the terrain, including all roads, and trails of all kinds. He found no sheep trails, no sign of bighorn ever having crossed the valley.

Here is a typical entry in our field notes: "December 5, 1955. The Hunts reported and delivered fresh sheep pellet clusters, black from fresh forage, found 1 mile southwest of Dinosaur Ridge, elevation 1,500 feet, about 5 miles northeast of Agueurreberry Point. No sign closer to valley floor (on the west side). Hunt has crossed floor 40 times, found no evidence of bighorn crossing, while coyote trails show plainly."

Ancient game trails indicate prehistoric use of such lower elevation springs as Travertine (in Furnace Creek, 1½ miles from the Inn), Texas (at the campground), and Cow Creek (at the Government residence area). During that time sheep undoubtedly ventured regularly into the salt flats as far as the mesquite habitat extended. We did not know until the summer of 1959 that some of these areas are still subject to periodic utilization. On August 28 of that year, I followed a 4-year-old ram through the heat waves as he headed away from Raven Spring, away from Nevares Peak, away from the Funeral Mountains toward the valley floor.

For 2 miles he walked steadily across the desert varnish of the mesas, then dropped down into the wash above Cow Creek Spring. There, to my amazement, I found fresh beds, tracks, and droppings of an entire band in the shade of cut banks, along the trails descending into the wash, and surrounding the *Bebbia* plants on which the sheep had been browsing. The sign showed the animals had stopped a hundred yards above the present utility area.

Human usurpation of water is a more prevalent factor in locally limiting the number and distribution of bighorn in the Death Valley region than is generally believed. The burro, on the other hand, has had less effect on the bighorn than it has had on the habitat in general. This will be discussed more fully under "Competitors and Enemies."

Field Identification

Field identification becomes an increasingly important factor in determining numbers, distribution, and movement of bighorn in the low density populations of the Death Valley region. The foreseeable future holds no prospects of success for any other method. Belt transects could be laid out by the dozen and yield no sheep at all. Trapping, drugging, marking, and the application of Lincoln's index involve a larger personnel than is likely to be available here.

There is probably no way of proving to the skeptical the practicability of field identification as a substitute for trapping and marking, and no effort will be made in this report to do so. Acceptance of the principle would carry with it the responsibility of practice, with a greater expenditure in the field of time, energy, and money than appears to be available in most bighorn study areas.

Figures 25 through 33 present a brief introduction to the method of development in field identification that was followed during the investigations upon which this report is based.

No two sets of horns are alike, nor are two single horns identical. Determining the difference between them may be as rewarding to the fieldworker as the precise determination of fingerprints is to the sheriff's office. An understanding of horn development as an indicator of age and sex is necessary for work with live bighorn in the field. Old horns and bones sometimes constitute the only sign of the former presence of bighorn, and are indispensable to the trained observer, who may find nothing to record except what the bighorn has left behind it.

Sign Reading

Sign reading as a science suffers from the fact that the average fieldworker has never proved to himself how wrong he can be. This conclusion is inescapable to anyone who has spent considerable time actually studying the sign left by known numbers of bighorn, of known age classes and sex, of known time and activity, and of known climatic conditions.

The importance of sign reading can scarcely be overemphasized in a barren region like Death Valley, where the entire population of bighorn may vanish into the back country for months or even years at a time and very few if any of them can be found for actual observation. Concepts of numbers and distribution, age and sex ratios, lamb crops and survival, forage conditions, and adequacies of water supplies are formed from the accounts of happenings recorded only by old bones, footprints, bedding basins, fecal pellets, and partially eaten plants.

The importance of accuracy in conclusions drawn from sign reading is obvious, and yet the need for training in method, or for testing the extent of knowledge of the subject is generally ignored. The margin of error widens as one false premise is drawn from another and the stockpile of misinformation reaches such proportions that facts become hopelessly buried beneath it.

A population estimate based on conclusions drawn by an incompetent observer from sign alone can be less than worthless—it can be extremely costly to a management program. The cost of man-hours wasted in gathering misinformation and the launching and carrying out of faulty projects generated by this blundering activity could be staggering.

Probably the most outstanding example of this is the case of the feral burro which will be referred to under "Competitors and Enemies" but must be mentioned here because of the probability that the incredible mass of misinformation about the wild burro that has been accumulated and disseminated through highly respected channels was initially the result of the misreading of sign at waterholes. The obvious abundance of burro sign and the apparent lack of bighorn sign in the vicinity led to a quick and specious conclusion that there was no bighorn sign present, that therefore bighorn did not utilize the water source, and that this failure was due to the fact that burros had somehow rendered it unusable for bighorn, thereby forcing them to abandon the entire area.

There are many springs in the Death Valley region today which apparently tell the same story—unless the observer has learned to look beneath the surface of the dust or gravel surrounding the water where the bighorn pellets have been inadvertently buried by the shuffling feet of burros milling about the water source during the night. The drinking, mating, fighting activity of a band of half a dozen burros can obliterate a 6-month collection of sheep sign in one visit to a spring. And when it is known that burros not only leave much more sign while watering but water three times as often as bighorn, it becomes increasingly clear why the sign is so often misread and misinterpreted.

The case against the burro was further heightened by a lack of knowledge concerning the discoloration of standing water by the chemical action of the soil supporting it.

During our reconnaissance for the 1955 Death Valley bighorn census, we made our first survey of "burro-fouled springs," and our failure to find any led to some surprising conclusions. We visited 45 springs which were in constant utilization by burros and found only one contaminated by defecation. With two observers on each side of Cottonwood Creek, we had walked its entire length and found exactly one incidence of defecation in the water.

It was there we learned where to look for bighorn sign at burro watering places. We found sheep tracks coming down to within 25 feet of the water, then vanishing in the loose earth which had been churned up by much shuffling of burro hooves. It occurred to us for the first time that the bighorn sign was underneath the burro sign and immediate investigation proved it to be the case; thus, the entire picture was changed.

At Rest Spring in the Cottonwoods, we found no droppings within 30 feet of the pool, but the water had been trampled in by burros and was a brownish urine color and had an odor that could be detected while standing above it. We assumed that here was an instance of water pollution and photographed it as such. We saw several other springs in the burro country bearing the same evidence and listed them accordingly. It was not until we began working in the Funeral Range, where there were no burros, and found springs with no animal tracks of any kind in or near them and yet found the water dark brown and with a strong odor that we realized that the "fouling" was coming from the ground itself.

Poison Spring in Indian Pass is a typical case in point. The water is brown and bitter the year around, but it is perfectly acceptable to bighorn. Caught there in July without water, we dug a small shaft above the established point of discharge, which filled with clear, uncloudy but exceedingly bitter water, and we drank it with no ill effects whatever—but we thought we knew why it had been named "Poison."

By the time the 1955 census was over, our lessons in burro-bighorn sign reading had progressed to the point that we wrote, "as far as his exact influence on the bighorn is concerned, we do not know enough to say." The first fact regarding our knowledge of burro-bighorn interrelationships had been recorded.

Some of the problems in the reading and interpretation of browsing sign has been discussed under "Food" and will be developed further under "Competitors and Enemies." The subject of sign is also discussed under "Water," "Trails," and "General Habits."

We must emphasize the necessity for study of sign reading by fieldworkers. Bighorn sign cannot be studied apart from the bighorn themselves. It is not feasible to expect an observer to be able to interpret the meaning of sign when he is not familiar with the type of activity producing it.

The "dance" described under "Play" could scarcely be envisioned from the sign unless a similar incident had been observed previously. We had often wondered how certain bushes and mesquite trees acquired such a devastated appearance until we became aware of the "signpost" aspect of their destruction. (See fig. 40.) Likewise, the churned surfaces left by the preliminary hassling of a ram bout had repeatedly left us puzzled until we saw it happening.

Usefulness of Beds

By the same token, the usefulness of beds as a definitive factor in sign reading appears to be more limited than was to be expected. The presence, number, size, placement, time and season observed, and weathering of beds contribute to estimates of population, herd composition, and activity but provide the experienced observer with only one certainty: Bighorn have been there.

The number of beds is not an accurate indication of the number of sheep involved. The Badwater band of 6 usually left but 2 or 3 beds behind them, but on one occasion the Furnace Creek band of 7 left 22 fresh beds on one site. Certain bighorn seldom prepare basins of any dimension, while others prepare and occupy several in one night. The suitability of some areas for bedding may cause repeated use of the same site, each use complicating the story to be read by the observer. We have never seen a band bed in the same place on consecutive nights.

The quality and quantity of soil available for bedding must be considered before conclusions are drawn. The crest of Paleomesa, a vantage point above Navel Spring, is covered with hundreds of beds of all conceivable sizes and ages along the ancient trails that contour the mesa ridges and the edge of cliffs towering 200 feet above the spring. The soil of the mesa is apparently ideal for both the preparation and the preservation of sheep beds and could contribute to an overestimation of the population.

The opposite is true of the rocky terrain above Nevares Spring, where a population at least as large and of as long standing as that at Navel has left practically no beds at all. The solid rock of the mountainside successfully resists all bighorn techniques of basin building and offers so few natural bedding sites that bighorn seldom spend the night within sight of the springs and, when they do, leave little but droppings for the record. The big ram Broken Nose on September 2, 1957, lay in one of the most uncomfortable beds on record for over 4 hours, and he left no tracks or basin and but one small group of small "lamb-size" pellets.

The term "vantage point" draws attention to the significance of placement—where the bed is located with relation to the surrounding terrain. The tendency of bighorn is to survey the watering area and surrounding terrain both before and after watering—before, to assure themselves that it is safe to water, and after, apparently to give their bodies a better opportunity to absorb the water ingested. And, of course, during the rut the promontories become important points of contact for both sexes.

In the summer, a fresh bed on the southern exposure of a promontory at an elevation of 1,000 feet is very likely a night bed; on a northern exposure it may be either a day bed or a night bed, as it would be on a southern exposure with sufficient elevation to reduce the temperature to a point of toleration for daytime bedding.

A typical observation was recorded at Deadman's Curve on March 22, 1956: "9:45. Temperature (shade), 78°. Ground temperature 94°. All sheep (band of seven) are bedded in the open wash in full sun. Apparently they like the 94°. They seem to have no feeling of insecurity there one-quarter of a mile from even a low ridge, let alone a cliff for escape." We have no record of bighorn bedding in low open washes either at night or in the summer.

During the precensus reconnaissance work in July 1955, we camped overnight to check a report of abundant fresh sign on the rim of Indian Pass, 1,500 feet above and a mile northeast of Poison Spring.

The approach to the rim looked hopeless: flat rolling hills almost barren of vegetation of any kind, no cliffs, no place for sheep. Sign of mining operations of the 1930's was everywhere.

But there was a change at the rim. In the vast canyon area there were many miles of dusty sheep trails bending down from the rim edge toward the springs below. The dominant vegetation was *Encelia* sp., much browsed. A quarter-mile strip on the rim disclosed three current bedding areas, yellow-dusty and rimmed with clustered pellet groups and "apple-seed" lamb droppings. There were three groups of 17 beds, 30 beds, and 24 beds, less than 100 yards apart. Other smaller groups were more widely scattered.

Let us consider this observation step by step: (a) The presence of the beds indicated the past presence of sheep. (b) The freshness of the beds (yellow-dusty) indicated use of the beds within the last few days. (c) More than 70 fresh beds suggested a relatively high number of sheep, certainly more than 2 or 3, probably at least 12 adults. (d) The relative size of some of the beds (as well as of the pellets) indicated several lambs, a probable minimum of six. (e) The placement on a high rim in full sun close to a water source suggested a lambing ground, which checked with (f) the season during which the beds had been and were being used. And finally, (g) the weathering of all the beds, both old and new, indicated annual use of the area, or a resident herd.

The usefulness of weathering in determining the age of a bed is modified by the nature of the terrain where the bed is made. Exposure to wind, water, and sun cause weathering, and the more protection a bed has from them the less the bed will change with time. Therefore it becomes obvious that a bed lying well back in a north-facing cave, protected from all three modifying factors, will look fresh longer than the one on the south-facing promontory fully exposed to them.

Examination of a fresh Death Valley bighorn bed will disclose dust as the denominator of freshness in most cases. If the exposed subsurface dust of a bed in the open has not been blown away or disturbed by the wind, washed back into the soil or gravel, packed down by rain, or crusted, bleached, or burned back to the color of the surrounding earth by the sun, it probably has not been there very long.

Scraping out a similar basin by hand and comparing the quantity, color, and looseness of the dust in both may be helpful, but it must be remembered that a sheep may have lain in the bed all night and packed it down. However, the manner of their rising usually disturbs the surface enough to make comparisons profitable.

All data point to many variables in "bed reading." During a dry winter with no rain, a low sun, and a hazy sky, a bighorn bed could remain "fresh" as long as no wind blew to remove the dust and fill in the basin with gravel and bits of vegetation. On the other hand, the "reading" of a bed can be made impossible in a matter of minutes by either rainfall or heavy wind.

Usefulness of Pellets

Pellets are probably the least understood and most misleading single factor in sign reading. There are so many factors, many of them still unknown to us, governing the distinguishing characteristics of pellet deposits, that definitive classification by age class and sex will not be attempted here.

Earlier in this study we shared with many other observers the comfortable conviction that the size of ram, ewe, and lamb droppings would naturally reflect a relative difference in the size of rams, ewes, and lambs, and therefore render field determination of age class and sex of unseen animals a reasonably accurate procedure. The largest pellets, especially those deposited in cowlike clusters, were by this concept ram pellets, the intermediate size, ewes, and the smallest, lambs.

As soon as we began in 1954 to follow the Badwater band and to collect and tabulate the pellets of sheep of known size, sex, and age, the smooth flow of misinformation from the old formula was interrupted. A long and enlightening series of lessons in sign reading had begun.

The first of our 16 interim reports contains these notes:

The Nelson bighorn leave remarkably few droppings behind them, apparently using up a great percentage of their food material. In 8 days, we witnessed less than a dozen occurrences of defecation, and most of these were unobtainable, owing to the inaccessible location of deposition. At, or near, the one known all-night bedding ground which we could reach, we obtained four distinct shapes and sizes of pellets.

At the Desert Game Range, Biologist O. V. Deming would accept as specimens only those pellets which were seen dropped and the age, sex, and condition of the sheep noted. Freshness is of great importance in dropping analysis; and since there is very little moisture left in them when fresh, there is no way to tell how old they are except by seeing them drop. The dark-brown to black exterior lubricant will dry in 10 minutes, and the entire pellet can be pulverized to dust, leaving no moisture, discoloration, and very little, if any, odor on the fingers.

Tabulation of piles of droppings as means of census seems to us to be most inconclusive, since at one site where we know six sheep had slept we found but two piles of droppings at the site itself. There were 5 piles along the entrance trail nearby and 3 on the exit, making a total of 10 in the vicinity.

The four distinct sizes and shapes would indicate four sheep of different ages. In many species of mammals, the size of the droppings increases with age. In the case of sheep, it would seem that an old ram would likely produce the largest of all [but this inference later was proven wrong].

By the time the 1955 census data had been digested and our fourth report written, these conclusions had been reached:

That the science of sign reading is still in its infancy has been emphasized by the occurrence at Klare Spring of 10 sheep watering and leaving no pellet groups; at Navel Spring, of 4 sheep watering and leaving 1 pellet group; at Willow Spring, over 400 pellet groups and an almost total absence of beds being left in less than 2 months' time. One lamb was sighted at Indian Pass, yet bedding sign indicated by pellet-group count that at least eight lambs were in one band.

The list of what we don't know about sign reading is too long for complete compilation here; but to emphasize the necessity of greater exploration in this field, I would like to approach a few gates for which we have no keys, as yet, to unlock.

1. The daily incidence of defecation is assumed by some to be about the same as in deer and domestic sheep, or around 14 times daily. However, the difference in the use of food in the acquisition and conservation of water precludes the validity of this assumption.

2. At Badwater last winter we found a great variation in the incidence of both defecation and urination, promoted apparently by the change in diet which circumstances fortunately enabled us to observe. If this variation is general, the implication of complication on this point is infinite.

3. The influence of certain vegetation at certain stages of growth on the color of pellets is positive but specifically undetermined. At Willow Springs

we found three distinct color groups—black, brown, and green. If we knew what plants in what stages caused what color, we would have had at least an aid in estimating the elevation and hence the distance the animals were ranging from water.

In case this hypothesis should seem farfetched, let me cite this instance, again at Badwater: When the band was first observed in December, feeding largely on relatively dry desertholly (*Atriplex hymenelytra*) and honeysweet (*Tidestromia oblongifolia*), their droppings were brown. The introduction of fresh *Physalis crassifolia* and *Euphorbia* sp. into their diet produced a nearly black dropping. Whenever they retreated into the Black Mountains for a few days, their droppings were brown again on their return. This pattern was repeated several times, until when the last ewe departed on the first of April, her exclusive diet of *Atrichoseris platyphylla* was producing a jet black, soft, flat petal-shaped dropping which was difficult to associate with ordinary sheep sign.

August 24, 1955, found us camping above Willow Creek in an effort to keep the spring under full-time observation. Seven weeks after the census, we found "sign plentiful, with a full complement of lamb sign now, where in July, sign showed 400 adult pellet groups to 8 lambs."

Our confidence in the old relative size formula for determining lambs was still unshaken. Still firm, too, was our conviction that relative brightness of pellet varnish was a dependable measure of the time lapse since deposition. This time-honored practice received its first setback on December 22, 1955:

We spent the day with a ewe and a 4- or 5-month-old lamb. The pictures we took identified her as one of the band later to be observed.

There was a very strong wind blowing all day, and from this we were able to make a valuable observation.

During the time the sheep were there, we stayed out of the wash to keep from "spooking" them. At the same time, we were anxious to show some friends who were helping us what sheep sign looked like and how much would be left by a ewe and lamb being very active in one area all day. The sheep left about 3 o'clock, and we went into the wash to study the sign in two or three marked areas. To our surprise, none could be found that looked less than a week or two old. The wind had filled in the tracks with gravel, dried and scattered the pellet groups, and disturbed browsing sign to such an extent that had we not just seen the ewe and lamb there all day we would have guessed that none had been there for several weeks. We found several adult pellet groups but no lamb pellets.

This was our first realization of how quickly and how much the desert winds can modify a story written on the face of the land.

On the morning of December 29 came the first of many opportunities to study the story told by pellet groups at bedding sites. A band of 5 had bedded down the day before at dusk, and by 7:30 that morning the 5 sheep had left 11 beds and 14 pellet groups, with nothing to indicate that one of them was a lamb.

The following day the band increased to five ewes and two 5-month-old lambs. A week later we were making a special effort with this band to "check variation in pellet colors, find lamb pellets if possible. Have not yet found any, although we have come across dozens of adult groups, some brown, some black. This variation is probably caused by their spending half time on green and half on dry food."

Although we intensified our search for lamb pellets, taking turns watching the sheep with glasses and trying to trace their course after they had passed by in the wash, it was not until January 15, over 2 weeks after they came into the area, that we "found lamb pellets for the first time. The absence of lamb pellets from these two continues to amaze us."

On February 20, after 3 weeks of constant daily observation of Old Mama and her new lamb, we noted that the "ewe's pellet groups are numerous, pellets large, squarish, and both black and brown by groups. This size and shape have been considered ram sign." We had been collecting droppings from this ewe for over 2 months, and comparison showed a considerable increase in size during that time.

Later the same day, "Buddy and I went up and down the wash, combing it for lamb droppings. Found some looking fresh, but big enough for a 6-month-old animal. Is it possible that this feed, making ewes' droppings so much larger than they were a month ago, is also making this lamb's droppings much larger than would be expected?"

The old formula was up for examination. Here were ewe droppings which we would have unhesitatingly labeled ram droppings had we not seen them fall. Questions began to multiply. What caused this change? Was it the type of forage available now? Was it because the ewe was old? Did parturition have something to do with it? Why could we find no "apple-seed" lamb pellets? Was it possible that a 4-week-old lamb utilized its food to such a degree that fecal deposits were so small that they could not be detected?

On February 25, we combed the wash all day for sign. Still no lamb sign of any kind, but we found fresh, wet, soft ewe pellets that I had seen fall 45 minutes before—Old Mama's, still extra large (ram size), and jetblack. These I placed in various places, in shade and out, exposed to the wind and sheltered from it, to check aging. So, belatedly, controls in the study of sheep sign had been inaugurated.

The exhausting task of keeping the lamb under constant fieldglass surveillance was finally rewarded on the 29th: "Lamb is a ewe. We finally caught a urination in good view. Nursed 11 seconds at 10:20. Several 'apple seeds' hung on lamb's whitening rump patch, indicating that (larger) pellets found in wash so far were of the older lambs of the previous band. At 10:25, we finally saw pellets in process of deposition. We now know why they have been so hard to find. Total of 5 in group. One-eighth inch in diameter, one-fourth inch long. Genuine 'apple seeds'."

The small number of pellets in the lamb deposit served as a reminder that the ewes' pellet groups seemed to be more numerous and to contain less pellets per group than previously. Why was this? The type of food? The type of activity engaged in at the time of deposition? Did age class and sex enter into it? Would the number deposited while moving along a trail be consistently different from the number deposited while browsing? Would the group left at a daybed differ from that at a nightbed? Was a physiological malfunction in evidence?

On March 2, 1956, by 2:10 p.m., we had counted 6 (browsing) pellet groups. They contained 50, 54, 64, 74, and 80 pellets respectively, all adult, but we found no more from the lamb for several days.

Old Mama and her lamb were joined on March 13 by a 2- or 3-year-old ram, three ewes, and a lamb about the same age as her own— 6 to 7 weeks. On March 17, we followed them up on the mesa. Along the crest ledge [a bedding area] we found droppings of all colors from white (bleached by at least a year's weathering in the open) to jetblack. Five groups were still wet at 12:30 (5½ hours after band left nightbeds, suggesting both an abundance of green in forage and cool and relatively damp atmosphere). We counted pellets in 46 groups: 41 adult, 3 young, 2 lamb (6–7 weeks, those with this band). The count per pellet group ranged for adults from 36 to 406, for young from 43 to 74, and for lambs from 70 to 174.

There were 7 groups with over 300 pellets on the edge of the beds, suggesting that after the sheep had an all-night rest the number of pellets greatly increased, for the average on the trail was something under 100.

It is a point of interest that of 46 groups only 2 of the young lambs' (apple-seed size and shape but brown) were found. It was becoming quite apparent that the ratio of lambs in a group (band) is not indicated by the ratio of the pellet groups.

On March 20, 1956, we counted pellets in 40 groups. The groups dropped while feeding averaged 128; daybeds, 175; nightbeds, 310.

On March 22, 1956, at 10:45, we noted that the seven observed sheep had taken an hour's siesta in the sun. We went to study sign and found five beds, three adult pellet groups, all nearly as large individual pellets now as Old Mama's have been and all very wet and jetblack. There was no sign of pellet groups of the two lambs, although they both bedded there. Individual count of each daybed adult pellet group: 105, 124, and 128.

By June 27, 1956, observations on pellet deposits in another area were cautious: "Nevares. Much use. Wet pellets indicate bighorn still in area. Examined all seeps, all used. Long Spring used the most. Large and small, black and brown pellets, big enough for rams, and small enough for lambs, some apple seeds."

Throughout the winter of 1956–57, we counted, collected, and compared droppings from known animals and of known times of deposition, and we were gradually becoming aware of a staggering number of modifying agents which could contribute to the condition of droppings before we found them in the field.

By now we had a constantly increasing number of "control stations" under observation. These "stations" were simply marked deposits of all types of pellets from known animals of all age classes and sexes, left in the field in as nearly all types of terrain as could be kept under observation. We noted the effects of protection from the sun and the lack of it; we checked the bleaching effect of rain in both shaded and unshaded terrain. We began to see a correlation between the rate of decomposition and the elevation of the area where the deposit was located. It became apparent that the type of food ingested affected the size and color of the pellet, as before noted; additionally, the amount and quality of "varnish" on each pellet appeared to be at least partially determined by the chemistry and growth stage of the plant eaten: thus, we began to see that pellets with the thick, black coating, generally associated with abundant green forage, retained their sheen and original color much longer than those with the thin, light-brown "varnish" often found in association with dry forage.

Associative Principle

The word "association" began to assume a new importance in dropping analysis, and eventually our entire concept of sign reading began to re-form into what we now refer to as the associative principle of sign reading. This means simply that any one factor in a sign picture acquires authority only from its association with other factors inherently present in every picture.

January rains released the bighorn from our "control" areas around permanent water supplies, which gave us 6 months in the field with not only the opportunity but the necessity of depending on sign only for the accumulation of bighorn data for that period. Our observations of droppings were beginning to reduce them to the auxiliary status which they occupy in the sign story today. Some of our notes of this period show the beginning development of the associative principle:

Echo Canyon. March 11, 1957. Found no fresh sign anywhere except by one *Hymenoclea* near Window Rock, where buds had been stripped from plants within the last day or two.

Plants are at the same stage as when bighorn stripped them for 3 or 4 days, but a month later than this last year.

There was plenty of water at tinajas (tanks), but no bighorn use since the rains of 9–10 days ago.

March 13, 1957. Monarch Canyon. No fresh sign now, but sheep had been in often until the last rain. Found where new *Stephanomeria* had been pawed up and eaten, setting time as not longer ago than a month or 6 weeks, since *Stephanomeria* was not growing before then.

March 16, 1957. Spent half an hour with pregnant Gimpy (lame ewe from Furnace Creek) in Red Amphitheater. She was feeding alone. Moved leisurely but steadily away across wash into mountains eastward. The wash was so hard we could not follow her sign. Owing to the natural cement in much of the soil of this area, the postpluvial crust is often so strong that entire bands of sheep can walk across it without leaving a track.

April 4, 1957. Checked Virgin Spring and on to where three sheep had been reported by visitors to have crossed the road in Jubilee Pass. We found tracks to prove that they were there as reported; followed them both north and south for half a mile. All sign indicated they were just going through, not feeding there. No pellets in groups, but strung along while the sheep were traveling.

June 13, 1957. Today we found two new patches of green farther up and back on the inner slopes of Corkscrew Peak. We could see no converging trails to them, but neither can you see any to Twin Springs on Tucki until you get above them. As a matter of fact, the rugged and rocky nature of the terrain surrounding both of these areas makes the study and evaluation of sign very difficult. Two years ago, before we had the experience of following bands of sheep and checking what we found in their sign with what we actually knew about them, I might have undertaken to estimate by the sign how many bighorn use these springs, but not today.

August 11, 1957, we found the ground crust at Navel Spring still so hard from the January rains that tracks mean little, but there are about 40 fresh pellet groups, mostly jetblack, suggesting that the sheep are feeding on green stuff somewhere. The pellets appear to be more than 2 or 3 weeks old, and so it seems likely that the sheep came first to water about the last of July.

An entry made later the same day in the Nevares area indicates a further maturing of the associative principle in sign reading:

Much fresh sign at Raven Spring and nearly dry. Old Spring a barnyard! Most gratifying to find work of restoring it not wasted. Round Pool hardly touched. One or two animals have used it but grass has nearly taken over. Long Spring shows some use, but nothing like last year and, surprisingly, seems nearly dry.

Apparently the sheep are not needing the local grass yet, for it has been hardly browsed at all. Or is this only utilized by rams later in season? It occurs to me that rams are the only ones we've ever seen eating this grass.

Highest ratio of lamb pellets to adults yet seen here. More like Willow Creek last autumn when we were seeing a lamb for every ewe. Two or three real apple seeds among them. Here again, pellets appear no more than 2 or 3 weeks old. No checking in the varnish. One pellet group was light brown and completely unvarnished, the first we've ever seen of this. Last year we found some only partly varnished and of course wondered if this is due to type of food eaten or to some deficiency in the animal's digestion.

In any event, we seem to have a good lamb crop, which of course makes us wonder where they were having them last spring when we were combing the Nevares back country for them.

Back at Navel Spring on August 15, 1957, we found more pale-yellow unvarnished droppings, both ewe and lamb, very much like those we saw at Nevares. We know now that such pellets are not peculiar to the Nevares area, at least.

Later the same day in the shade of Nevares cut, a ewe with a lamb was observed under intense mating pressure from a big ram for over 4 hours. After their departure, a close search of the area disclosed only two adult pellet groups, with no sign of the lamb at all. This occurred in almost identically the same spot where the year before on July 1 we had observed a ewe defecate eight times in 1 hour!

August 23, 1957. Raven Spring. I checked Tabby's (a 10-year-old ram) 4-hour siesta site and found one group of still-wet pellets, not ram size but lamb size! Small, light brown, and practically unvarnished. Yet there's none more healthy than he.

The next day three of the largest and most aggressive rams we had observed in the entire Nevares area scuffled for 3 hours at Raven Spring. After they left, I went to Raven Spring to check the sign. The three big rams did not deplete the spring in any way. But the pellets they left (one group we saw dropped by Full Curl at 7 p.m. still wet) were no bigger than what we have thought of as those of young animals, if not even lambs. Here is one of the most mature rams we have ever been personally acquainted with, and he doesn't leave the large "ram-size" pellets. Neither has Tabby, Mahogany, nor The Hook, and here we have pellets from them all.

September 2, 1957. Nevares. I just collected wet pellets left by (another big ram) Roughneck, 142 in group. Looks like from small ewe. Also from Mahogany's first bed, small long and brown, almost like Tabby's but varnished. Also small cluster from The Hook, looks like yearling. Around 150 pellets each group.

I count dozens of pellet groups which I no longer record because of their repetition. We have recorded around 180 counted groups. Day beds range from 80 to 200, but average about 150. Night beds, 200 to 450, average 300. Traveling, from 1 to 130, average 80.

Telling age, sex, or size of animals by droppings is at present impossible except in extreme cases. Young lambs are a little more accurate in that "apple seeds" so far have been left only by the very young, up to 4 or 5 weeks. The surprisingly small pellets left by the mature rams were like apple seeds but twice as large.

At 6:30 that evening the old warrior, Broken Nose, left The Saddle where he had been recuperating for 5 hours. An inspection of the site disclosed one small group of yearling-like pellets.

By now we were considering the possibility of the small size of the ram pellets being associated with the rutting season. We had seen some of these rams and checked their ram-sized pellets during the previous winter. We wondered if the smaller pellets could indicate a more complete utilization of food materials by the fully mature rams during the rut, which might at least partially explain why they remain so physically fit and yet seem to eat so little during the peak of the mating season. The younger rams, whose pellets remain relatively normal during the same period, seem to eat more normally, but some also evince definite signs of strain and fatigue by the end of the season.

October rains ended 1957 sheep observations abruptly but also presented us with one of our most valuable lessons in sign reading: With the exception of browsing evidence, all sign at Nevares in the immediate spring area began to disappear within a week or two after the rains; and by January 1958 practically none could be found except high up on the mountain where the angle of repose and lack of soil precluded water retention.

Tracks and droppings had completely disappeared, disintegrated by the action of ground salts being carried to the surface and impregnating the tracks and droppings through capillary action. The ground turned white and fluffy, and the outlines of tracks and trails first softened, then blurred, and finally disappeared. Droppings became encased in salt crystals forming rough ovals from a half to a full inch in length, containing the pellets which were eventually reduced to particles by the expansion of the salts and finally returned to soil as the salt crystals eroded away.

We now understood why Nevares Spring had been left out of the 1955 census effort, but the full extent of how far we might have been misled by this phenomenon is indicated by a notation made on December 1, 1955: "Survey of Nevares Spring area. Found complete reinvestment of bighorn of that area. From 20 to 30 bighorn using grasses and shrubs of area as well as water. No sign of past habitation, indicating this as first year of reinvestment since vacating of premises by Adolph Nevares and installation of gate to access." We estimated no population at Nevares in 1955, yet counted 47 individuals there in 1957.

The pellet story for this report was given a final fillip by the band of 14 bighorn luxuriating among the flowerbeds of Death Valley Buttes on February 11, 1958:

1:40. Found 3 bedding sites, each with from 20 to 30 beds. Some with no pellet groups at all. None with more than one. Pellets hard to find since none are glossy black, as we had expected after our Badwater survey.

Last night's bedding ground right where we last saw them had still moist pellets at 1 p.m. Of pellets from 14 groups, none were alike in size or shape, but all had two things in common: a greenish-brown color and a corrugated or striped appearance from end to end. Some do have actual corrugations in the varnish. Some are single and standard shape, others are in clusters from 1 inch to 1½ inches in diameter. There are too many of the latter for them to be all rams, so some must be credited to ewes. Nearly half of the groups found were in clusters of flat chocolate-drop-shaped pellets, and all were still moist. Those of a day or two in age were slightly hollow, as though a great deal of moisture had been drawn out by the sun, which gets sweaty hot up there in the afternoon. Green, striped bighorn pellets!

This much time and space has been devoted to the development of the specific study of bighorn droppings in the hope that through the illumination of some of the false concepts common to the study, some light might be shed on a true one.

Usefulness of Tracks and Soil

The associative principle must be applied to tracks as well as to the other elements of the sign picture.

Figure 42 illustrates some of the problems of determining how long ago a track was made and by how many animals. The fact that each animal leaves two sizes of tracks often is not taken into consideration by the observer, and he tends to double the number that should be estimated. In figure 42, the nature and placement of the matrix in which the print was left preserved the fresh look of these tracks for several years before they were finally covered by another runoff. This is true in varying degrees in many spring areas.

The opposite can be true as well. At Nevares Spring, for example, the self-rising nature of the soil often obliterates tracks as well as droppings in a few weeks.

The soil around Navel Spring, owing to the natural cement in the soil, will resist the imprint of a track completely if the ground has had time to set up after a rain. On the other hand, if the track is made during a rain or while the ground is still wet after a rain it will look fresh until it is finally broken up by other watering animals or covered up by another runoff.

In soft gravel it is sometimes impossible to tell what made a track unless some pellets can be found to further a diagnosis.

Sometimes, too, bighorn will step in the tracks of the animal preceding them, thus confusing the sign as to the number of animals passing.

When the band of 19 sheep on Death Valley Buttes was breaking up in January 1961, I watched 8 of them racing across the north wash toward Corkscrew Peak, but when I reached their crossing no amount of searching revealed more than the tracks of 4 animals.

Definite conclusions from signs as to how many animals did what and when are seldom made by workers who have taken the trouble to find out how misleading signs can be, and therefore how tentative must be the conclusions drawn from them.

Chief Causes of Mortality

The chief causes of mortality have not been conclusively determined. Evidence indicates the greatest age class incidence of mortality to be during the first and tenth years. (See "Longevity".) We have seen no sick adults, with the possible exception of The Old Lady, where old age made other diagnosis difficult.

Old Mama had afterbirth complications, a cough, a "runny nose," and old age to contend with, and yet she reflected no sign of ill health in her daily activity and was the leader (to our knowledge) of her fourth band when last seen on December 20, 1956. All evidence indicates old age as the chief cause of death in mature ewes and rams. Contrary to considerable data from other areas, loss of teeth in old age plays no significant part in mortality here. Collected skulls of old animals usually display remarkably sound dentition.

Accidents claim some lives. We find carcasses, particularly lambs, at the foot of cliffs, suggesting death by fall. However, it is also known that sick animals tend to bed at the foot of cliffs. We have never found a carcass soon enough after the animal's death to determine the cause of its demise.

In the autumn of 1954, a ewe with a broken leg was found by a visitor at Klare Spring and was reported to the National Park Service before we returned to duty for the winter. Park Service personnel found her dead, and they disposed of her without acquiring further data. In 1940 Sumner (1940) found at Bighorn Gorge the skelton of an adult ewe that had received a fracture of the right hind leg (metatarsal) a considerable time, probably several years, before its death. The fractured bone had fully healed, although in a bent and shortened position.

By far the majority of bighorn deaths occur during the first year, but the actual cause of death is not known. Poor condition appears to be accompanied by a cough, rough pelage, and increasing lethargy. We have not observed the last stages of this deterioration, but its ultimate fatality is attested to by the continued scarcity of yearlings.

The lambs' need of water and "emergency rations" in spring areas in hot and dry weather appears to be more urgent than in adults, suggesting at least a contribution to juvenile mortality by the harsh environment.

The probable prevalence of lungworm, with pneumonic complications encouraged by dietary deficiencies, should be included in mortality postulations.

Symptoms of trace element deficiency in domestic sheep of Australia, described by Anderson and Underwood (1959), are similar enough to those of the 1956 Nevares herd to justify an attempt to determine whether such a deficiency, especially of cobalt, is a mortality factor here. Through the efforts of Charles Hunt of the Geological Survey, U.S. Department of the Interior, and Lowell Sumner, the assistance of several specialists in the field was solicited for the project, but no conclusive data were forthcoming by the time of this writing.

Competitors and Enemies

Man

Competitors and enemies of bighorn seem to be few, with man heading the list.

Hunting unquestionably still is done in the Death Valley region and probably accounts for the absence of sheep in considerable areas of the monument. Once relatively dense populations are no longer seen in many of the areas where mining activity has continued over extended periods. This phase of bighorn life history has been discussed at length under "Response to Humans and Equipment."

Expropriation of water, the attendant withdrawal of range from use, and the heightening of fear through the presence of humans at the waterhole are components of a single problem arising from the multiuse designation of an area. This is described under "Response to Humans and Equipment" and will be discussed further under "Status for the Future."

Grazing of domestic stock has not entered the field of this study to a great extent. It never should. The presence of domestic stock within the boundaries of any area of the National Park System would seem out of keeping with the declared policy of preserving these areas as nearly as possible in their primitive state.

One item has come to our attention. The residents of the Beatty area bordering the Nevada section of the monument, who are familiar with the Grapevine Mountains, are unanimous in their assertion that no bighorn are ever seen on the eastern slope of the mountains, where cattle and goats were grazed for many years. Much further study would be needed to determine which aspects of this exotic occupation had eliminated the bighorn, or if they were actually eliminated.

Deer

Deer competition in this area may be as definite a limiting factor on numbers and distribution of sheep as cattle and goats were, or as burros were supposed to have been in the Panamints. In any case, the deer were much in evidence in the piñon-juniper zone of the Grapevine Mountains through the summer of 1960, and the bighorn were not.

During the summer of 1959, deer and sheep tracks in abundance had been "reliably" reported to us from that area repeatedly, and we verified the reports by a visit to the spring in November. What appeared to be both bighorn and deer tracks and droppings were spread in barnyard profusion throughout the spring area.

For 6 weeks in August and September 1960, we maintained a camp and a round-the-clock observation post at an elevation of 7,300 feet, a quarter of a mile above Doe Spring at the head of Phinney Canyon, which is 2½ miles southeast of Grapevine Peak.

However, our vigil there disclosed the rather startling fact that all the sign was being made by deer and there were apparently no bighorn in the entire Doe Spring area. At least no sheep came to the spring during our time there. Each morning we found some sign that looked like what we expected deer sign to look like and some that was indistinguishable from bighorn sign. In the earliest hours of morning we heard occasional snuffing and pounding as some animals apparently caught our scent and bounded away up the mountain. We finally saw two large bucks in the early dawn of August 7, but our presence even a quarter of a mile away was too disturbing to them and they left within a few minutes.

Hikes in the mountains around the spring showed well used trails leading toward it from all directions and fresh beds and pellets indicated constant use of the area.

In Deer Canyon (about 1¼ miles southeast of Grapevine Peak) we found the only evidence of overbrowsing that we have seen in the monument. Cliffrose (*Cowania*), *Ephedra*, sagebrush (*Artemesia*), and *Eriogonum* were all stubbed back, with pellets among them so thick that we could scarcely take a step without crushing some underfoot.

Members of the Strozzi family who used to live and hunt in the area tell us that there never were bighorn there, only deer. Sheep, they say, won't mix with deer. They also point to the Panamints, where there are sheep but no deer, and add it up to the same story in reverse.

At the Desert Game Range, Dr. Charles Hansen has found some indication that deer are relatively aggressive in their relationship with bighorn and in some instances drive them away from water and forage.

The extent or exact nature of this competition was not known in time for this writing. It would certainly entail much more study to determine whether the presence of deer in the pinyon-juniper belt of the Grapevine Mountains actually contributes to the absence of bighorn in any way. We found only four known bighorn forage plants there, *Cowania, Artemesia, Ephedra,* and *Eriogonum* (mentioned as browsed by deer), and it occurred to us that the lack of variety in the diet might also contribute to the apparent undesirability of the habitat as bighorn range.

There is some overlap of the two ranges in the Cottonwood Mountains, since both species are found there, but indications are that deer are scarce and confined largely to the oak belt on Hunter Mountain. Time has not permitted the gathering of any conclusive data in that area, and it would be especially difficult at the present time, since the bighorn has not only the deer to contend with but also burros, cattle, and horses which still ranged there in 1961.

Whether the fact that mountain lions are known to be in both the Cottonwood Mountains and the Grapevine Mountains can be correlated directly with the presence of deer is not firmly established but is certainly suggested.

We have not personally seen lion signs in the Panamints, but on June 4, 1955, the Clair brothers, mining in Pleasant Canyon for over 25 years, told us of having had an 8-foot lion near their camp for several nights in the previous March. To say the least, however, they are scarce in the region, a fact locally attributed to the absence of deer.

Recent archeological findings (Hunt, A., 1960) indicate the probability that deer have been absent from the Panamints for 1,000 years or more.

Why there should be a substantial population of deer in but two of three so nearly identical areas is not readily apparent.

Our brief sojourn in the deer country in 1960 can be considered no more than a reconnaissance. A full-fledged life history study should be made before any clear picture can be drawn of the part deer play in the ecology of the Death Valley region.

Wild Burro

The wild burro has been briefly discussed under "Food," "Water," and "Sign Reading" because its history in this region is inevitably correlated with these subjects in connection with bighorn.

While our own work here has been aimed primarily at the life history of the bighorn population in Death Valley, considerable data on the burro have been accumulated, some of it indicating significant gaps in the generally accepted concept of burro-bighorn interrelationships.

In an effort to fill in these gaps as much as possible, the National Park Service temporarily shifted the emphasis of our work from bighorn to burros for 4 months in the spring of 1960.

The results of that brief survey have brought about what has been described by some as a "new look at the burro" and certainly presents a new concept of the problem.

It has been long and eloquently contended by many biologists that burros have become one of the most inimical factors in the life of desert sheep; that they befoul waterholes by trampling and defecation

616472 O—62——13

until the supply is usurped completely; that by vicious attack they have driven bighorn out of some ranges; that without removal of the burros few sheep will ever again survive in the area (Buechner, 1960; Dixon and Sumner, 1939).

We have found no evidence to support any of these claims.

In 1959 we made the only wildlife water survey that has been made in Death Valley (Welles and Welles, 1959), and in 1960 we made the only actual field study that has been made of the Death Valley feral burro (Welles, 1960). Out of these surveys one fact emerges with overwhelming cogency: Some of the most substantial populations of bighorn in the Death Valley region are feeding in the same areas and watering at the same springs with burros.

Corroborating our own findings, Charles B. Hunt in a recent geological mapping of this area, checked every known spring on the Death Valley side of the Panamint Range. He told us he found no springs fouled other than by hoofprints in mud, although he found both burro and bighorn sign throughout the range.

In 1937 Chief Ranger Thomas Williams found an unmapped spring in the Panamint Mountains north of Wingate Pass. There was abundant burro sign at the spring, and he saw five bighorn on the mountainside. At that time it was believed that the burros would eliminate the bighorn from the spring. But when we rediscovered this spring in 1960 [now known as Lost Spring], we found both burros and bighorn still abundant in the area. [In the late summer of 1961, as this report was going to press, Park Naturalist Ro Wauer took three photographs confirming that, contrary to the dire predictions made by observers 24 years earlier, wild burros and bighorn still use this spring similtaneously and without strife. See fig. 77.]

For the sake of the entire biota, the burros must be controlled and their numbers kept down, and this the National Park Service is doing—though not because the burro is running the bighorn off the range or destroying the water supplies, for it is doing neither. An extensive program of live capture of burros to be used as pets and pack animals has been inaugurated and promises well as a control method.

Mountain Lion and Other "Predators"

There are mountain lions, coyotes, bobcats, and golden eagles in the Death Valley bighorn region, but no data point to significant predation from any of them.

In the summary of the interim report on our Nevares Spring observations of 1957 is this notation: "Predation seems to be almost, if not entirely, nonexistent here. There are coyotes, bobcats, foxes, golden eagles, and ravens watering regularly at Nevares Spring, but not once have we seen any interest on their part in the bighorn. They seem to be concerned exclusively with the smaller residents of the mesquite area. The only animal we have seen waiting at the waterhole for its prey is the sidewinder."

This picture was modified somewhat in 1959. A 5 o'clock in the morning of June 30, I arrived at our observation camp above Nevares Seeps for a dawn-to-dusk check. As usual no sheep had been in during the night, but at 7 three ewes, three lambs, and a yearling ram came in from the Needle's Eye, drank, and began to graze on the spring grasses. There had never been a less wary-seeming band in the area. We knew the ewes as Little Brownie, Little Ewe, and Dark Eyes, and their lambs ranged in age from 3 to 6 months. The yearling had identical marking and coloration with Little Brownie.

At 7:30 I turned away from my 16-power glass to pick up my notebook, and in so doing I knocked the glass slightly to one side. I immediately started to refocus on the sheep, but to my amazement they had completely disappeared, in a matter of seconds and with no warning, no sound—just gone.

While searching the mountainside for the band which had vanished, I discovered that another band had been approaching from the Needle's Eye but was now standing, staring in alarm toward Nevares Seeps 200 yards below them. This was old Brahma, her lamb, and a yearling. She had been the least wary of all the sheep in the area, but now she suddenly broke away and ran, followed by the other two, toward the perpendicular cliffs above Cave Rock.

Turning the telescope back toward Nevares Seeps I now saw the cause of their alarm—a coyote, a big red fellow, standing above Old Spring, looking up at the bighorn above him.

Now I saw the first band, working its way across the sheer face of the cliff toward Brahma, who had stopped at the foot of it and stood looking back at the coyote.

Here was a perfect example of leadership in action. Old Brahma was always the accepted leader in any band she was with and we had seen her with several in the past 3 years. Now, as the others sought safety on the face of the cliff, she stood gaging the danger— watching to see whether the coyote posed a real threat to their safety.

The coyote now crept forward about 10 feet and crouched down behind a 2-foot boulder and lay down with his gaze fixed on the mountainside. Very shortly Brahma made her decision and lay down too and, keeping a wary eye on the coyote, began to chew her cud. The others relaxed somewhat but remained on the cliff face, two of the lambs actually finding a projection large enough to lie down on.

THE BIGHORN OF DEATH VALLEY ✦ 179

The coyote waited for half an hour, then got up, yawned and stretched, and without a backward look trotted off along the north trail at 8:30.

It was 10 o'clock before Brahma finally led the sheep down, and even then their apprehension was so intense that they did not reach water until noon.

This was the only incident of this nature we have ever seen. It would seem to indicate that the sheep recognize in the coyote a possible danger to their lambs, but in actuality it must seldom materialize or we would have found some evidence of it.

That summer we watched three golden eagles circle slowly in and come to water at Old Spring, while a band of five bighorn, containing one 6-month-old lamb, lay in siesta on a point a hundred yards away, The sheep watched the eagles idly as they came and went, but no interest in each other was shown by either the sheep or the eagles.

Ewes with "wet" lambs show anxiety over large flying birds, but so do they of almost everything that moves in their vicinity at that time.

Of possibly greater significance is the fact that of the hundreds of sheep we have kept under prolonged observation, only on Death Valley Buttes did we find an adult ewe concerned over the presence of a raven.

Brahma II was up on the talus slope alone, bedded down about 100 yards above the others, when a raven swooped down to within 100 feet over her head. She leaped up and in evident fright hurried down to the others. This made me wonder if the scars on her shoulders, neck, and face could possibly have been the work of an eagle, and if so, whether she had interposed herself between it and her lamb, as ewes are reported to do.

Four days later on the 15th of February, I noted: "3:00 p.m. A raven has been circling and settled on a rock nearby. After a few minutes one of the ewes made a run at the raven, forcing it to fly. Here again, a different attitude toward big birds. Is it toward ravens as such or toward all big birds?"

Status for the Future

If the present comfortably optimistic statistics of the Death Valley bighorn population could be projected with undiminished clarity into the predictable future, this report would be justified in no other recommendation than to leave things as they are. Unfortunately, the picture grows dim with projection and things cannot be left as they are.

The opening paragraph of the summary of the 1955 census report reads as follows:

While the figures themselves look good there is no room for complacency in the picture. The census disclosed jeep tracks in every canyon. The pressure is increasing. Our own observations are buttressed by figures given in *Time* magazine, July 25, 1955, in an article ominously listed on the cover, "American Desert, the Air-conditioned Frontier." I say "ominous" from the point of view of preserving any part of the desert in its primitive state. One quotation alone will point out what I mean: "[since 1940] on California's Mojave Desert the population has soared from 32,000 to 147,000," an increase of 360% in 15 years.

The traffic counters on the monument highways and the jeep tracks in the canyons fit Death Valley into the picture, dominated by the probability that the population of the United States will be doubled in 40 years. ("From Mankind at the Flood," July–September 1955 issue, National Parks Magazine.)

If the present status of existing water and food supplies could be maintained with no more human and exotic encroachment of any kind the bighorns' future undoubtedly would be assured, but the pressure described in 1955 is increasing everywhere on the desert more rapidly than ever.

Four years ago dozens of lots could be bought for taxes in Beatty, Nev., 11 miles from the monument boundary; today none can. And a minor land boom is in progress at Lathrop Wells, 29 miles north of Death Valley Junction. Both of these happenings indicate the general trend in the desert.

The demand for accommodations at all resorts in the region has reached an alltime high. The overflow of campers during the 1958 Christmas holidays was unprecedented, with more campers in undesignated areas than at any other time on record with the exception of the Death Valley 49'ers celebrations. Today we find evidence of prolonged camping at Willow Creek, Virgin Spring, Rhodes Well (3½ miles northeast of Jubilee Pass), Navel Spring, and Daylight Spring (in Daylight Pass), to name only a few.

Three of these areas, Willow, Virgin, and Navel Springs, are ancestral and current strongholds of the bighorn, and the other two once were but have been completely diverted to human use, one by the

National Park Service on behalf of the visiting public and the other by mining interests.

Willow Creek and Virgin Spring apparently were divested of bighorn rights by prospectors during the depression and have but recently regained a semblance of their former populations.

The population of the Navel Spring area met distress during the summer of 1958 as described in our notes:

August 27, 1958. It was 119° yesterday. In the morning we went to see how much work has been done since yesterday. Navel Spring will never look the same. Some of the mesquites have been bulldozed out and the floor of the little canyon entrance to the spring has been cleared and leveled. Work not completed, evidently. Timbers for shoring piled around.

However, the two half-drums for the sheep were full of water, with fresh tracks of recent, but slight, use.

The two-car-wide newly graded road, visible from Highway 190, is an open invitation for anyone to drive up to Navel Spring, to camp beside the water, or to wait at the water to try to force the sheep to come close enough for photography.

Navel Spring is Government owned, but a private company has water rights there. This development represents a definite encroachment into the bighorn domain and emphasizes the general nature of the competition between bighorn and human use.

This construction work was being done within 100 feet of the only water available to the Navel herd, during several weeks of the hottest and driest part of the summer when access to water is imperative for lamb survival. A later report from one of the miners engaged in the work indicated that "for the first 3 or 4 weeks we saw about 75 head altogether. They'd come and stand up on top and watch and maybe they'd come on down to drink, real spooky, and maybe they wouldn't. And finally they quit coming altogether."

Navel Spring is the one permanent water source for the entire Paleomesa, Red Amphitheater, Furnace Creek, and Big Wash area, as well as the recently included Pyramid Peak extension of the monument boundary. If extensive visitor encroachment should complete the encroachment already begun for the purpose of diverting water for human use, the inclusion of Pyramid Peak in the monument for bighorn protection could become futile.

This fact is incontrovertible: We have in Death Valley no record of continued bilateral utilization of spring areas by both man and bighorn. What Adrey Borell wrote in 1935 must be repeated here: that he had "talked with many prospectors and miners about sheep and every one of them had the same answer: 'There were quite a few sheep when we first came here, but us just being here, what with blasting and all, we hardly see them anymore'." (Borell, 1935.)

On the 4th of April 1956, we talked with a Mr. and Mrs. Beaver, who for 3 years in the thirties had operated a mill at Virgin Spring. During the entire time, they "saw sheep on the ridges and mountains above the spring, looking down, but they never came to water."

And in 1958 at Navel Spring "after 3 or 4 weeks they didn't come any more."

Navel Spring is not an isolated case. During the progress of this survey, comparable developments have taken place at Keane Spring, Grapevine Mountains, Tin Mountain, Skidoo, and Trail Canyon.

Conclusions

The research covered by this report, though centered on the bighorn, inevitably points toward many interrelated fields of ecological investigation. These include the wild burro, the fluctuating and vulnerable water supplies of Death Valley, and the needs and aspirations of man himself.

Our work with the bighorn has been of sufficient scope to provide much data significant to an understanding of the Death Valley environment, and to its protection. However, it represents only the beginning of the work that can be accomplished. It indicates many additional lines of research that promise to yield useful results. Such research can lead toward management and interpretive programs designed to accomplish a twofold objective: (a) To help the bighorn of the Southwest deserts to survive mankind at the flood, and (b) to help mankind more fully to comprehend and enjoy the beauty of form and of desert adaptation presented by the bighorn and his way of life.

Our related wildlife water survey presents far-reaching opportunities for taking research findings off the shelf and translating them into a firm program of wildlife interpretation and management.

Further research will be required to determine the exact ecological impact of the feral burro on all the park biota. While our work has proved the burro to be much less of a villain with respect to the bighorn than had been feared in earlier years, it has not suggested that, from an ecological standpoint, he is a desirable part of the Death Valley biota. If, for example, a small herd should be maintained to provide historical atmosphere, a firm management program would be required to avoid serious ecological consequences.

The ecological role of the deer, in relation not only to the bighorn but to various desert shrubs, is a subject barely investigated so far. The condition of some of these shrubs under present deer-browsing pressure indicates in turn the need for a better understanding of the possible role of the larger predators in holding the deer within the carrying capacity of their range.

As in many other areas of the National Park System, more information will be needed to assure the survival of normal numbers of various predatory species in the region, particularly in centers of habitat occupied by inholdings.

Research accomplished over the past 8 years on the interrelationships between bighorn, burros, forage, water, and humans, has stimulated much interest. The information thus gained already is being reflected in interpretation and protection programs. Much more can be accomplished by following various leads opened up by this preliminary research. The resulting increased comprehension in turn helps to create attitudes of overall responsibility for conservation over and above individual interpretive and protection assignments.

Further research along the various lines indicated could provide additional material for the Service's regular programs of inservice training in conservation conducted for its personnel. Since the impact of human visitation will tend to increase each year, as forecasts of increasing visitation become reality, further research can provide much-needed periodic measurements and evaluations of this impact on the ecology, in turn making possible the necessary offsetting precautions.

In this severely arid region, water is the keynote of the research program, to which geology, archeology, botany, and zoology contribute and relate. Human occupation of Death Valley has resulted in the development of some new water sources, offsetting in part the usurpation of some old ones. Mining activities have been specially productive of both these results. An expanded research program should include studies of the various ecological effects of mining operations, with the objective of determining how these may be so carried out as to result in the least harm and to convey the maximum benefits to the natural biota.

The boundary of the monument does not afford complete ecological protection because it does not include the entire Panamint biota. The ecological difficulty of attempting to preserve half a biota is too well known to require elaboration of this point.

In view of the apparent inability of bighorn permanently to coexist with man at their ancestral watering places, it appears obvious that protection of the animals will require that all possible avenues be explored for preventing nonessential penetration of their domain by powered vehicles of any kind. Similarly, camping and some other forms of human use, if extended into areas where bighorn now range, would be inimical to their continued welfare.

The possibility needs to be taken into account that camping or construction near spring areas not already in such use could bring far-reaching consequences, for the withdrawal of a spring from bighorn use means not only the loss of water, but, as with Navel, Twin, and Blackwater Springs, it can mean the loss, along with each spring, of hundreds of square miles of bighorn range as well. Navel Spring is on the verge of no longer being an acceptable area for bighorn. Similarly, unless research can point the way toward effective ecological countermeasures, mill-site claims on Blackwater and Twin Springs could be the first step toward possible eventual extermination of the Tucki Mountain herd.

Obviously, further research needs and opportunities with respect to the Death Valley biota are sufficient to fully occupy an ecologist, or a team of ecologists, of broad experience in various related fields of wildlife research and management, for an indefinite period. However, in advance of this needed team approach, enough already has been learned from studies so far completed to materially enhance the effectiveness of the protection program for the monument.

The future status of the bighorn is inexorably tied to the attitude of man toward the natural world in which he lives. The nature of this attitude may determine the quality as well as the quantity of encroachment with which the entire world community of living things will have to contend—whether, as Aldo Leopold expressed it, man continues to consider himself the conqueror of the living world or attains the wisdom to become a fellow citizen in it, sharing with other creatures the rights and privileges of living. Death Valley National Monument and other units of the National Park System are regarded by many research workers as outdoor laboratories or classrooms where man can obtain, through the scientific study of these natural areas, a more complete understanding of America's lands and environments everywhere, and develop ways of living ever more harmoniously on these lands.

The present piece of research is but a first step in what is hoped will be a continuing, overall program of ecological investigation of Death Valley as an entity. But returning to the bighorn, our last recommendation is this: If we want to insure the future of the bighorn in Death Valley, we, the human occupants, must decide at what point we are willing to discipline our own ecological use of the valley; to what extent we are willing to share with other living things the privilege of enjoyment of the vast distances, the isolated oases, the miracle of a desert spring—curbing to some necessary extent the human tendency, normal elsewhere, to consume the environment, so that we may maintain the unique natural values of this area as a place of special enjoyment and of scientific study—a permanent haven for the bighorn and for ourselves.

Selected Bibliography

[Manuscript reports are on file in the office of the Superintendent, Death Valley National Monument]

ADOLPH, A. F. 1947. The physiology of man in the desert. New York, Interscience Publishers, Inc., 357 pp.

ALDOUS, M. CLAIR. 1957. Status of bighorn sheep on the Desert Game Range. First Desert Bighorn Council Trans., pp. 35–37.

—— 1958. Trapping and tagging of bighorn sheep. Second Desert Bighorn Council Trans., pp. 36–39.

ALDOUS, M. CLAIR, FRANK C. CRAIGHEAD, JR., and GEORGE A. DEVAN. 1958. Some weights and measurements of desert bighorn sheep. Journ. Wildlife Management, vol. 22, pp. 444–445.

ALDOUS, M. CLAIR, and FRANK C. CRAIGHEAD, JR. 1958. A marking technique for bighorn sheep. Journ. Wildlife Management, vol. 22, pp. 445–446.

ALLEN, REX W. 1960. Diseases and parasites of Barbary and bighorn sheep in the Southwest. Fourth Desert Bighorn Council Trans., pp. 17–22.

ANDERSON, A. J., and E. J. UNDERWOOD. 1959. Trace element deserts. Scientific American (Jan.), vol. 200, pp. 97–106.

ASCHMANN, HOMER. 1958. Great Basin climate in relating to human occupance. Univ. of California, Archaeol. Survey No. 42, pp. 23–40.

BALL, WALTER S. 1959. Wild burro legislative problems in California. Third Desert Bighorn Council Trans., pp. 11–13.

BARRETT, WAYNE. 1960. [in] Wild animals of North America. National Geographic Society, Washington, D.C., pp. 107–115.

BENDT, ROBERT H. 1957. Status of bighorn sheep in Grand Canyon National Park and Monument. First Desert Bighorn Council Trans., pp. 16–19.

BORELL, ADREY E. 1935. Bighorn report. 8 pp. Manuscript.

BROWNE, J. ROSS. 1864. A tour through Arizona. Harpers, vol. 29, pp. 689–711.

BROWNING, BRUCE. 1960. Preliminary report on the food habits of the wild burro in the Death Valley National Monument. Fourth Desert Bighorn Council Trans., pp. 88–90.

BUECHNER, HELMUT K. 1960. The bighorn sheep in the United States, its past, present, and future. Wildlife Society Monographs, No. 4. Wildlife Society. 174 pp. (Copies available from Executive Secretary, Remington Farms, Chestertown, Md. $1.50.)

BURANDT, VERN. 1959. Bighorn sheep patrol and protection problems in California. Third Desert Bighorn Council Trans., pp. 37–40.

CAHALANE, VICTOR. 1943. Meeting the mammals. New York, The Macmillan Co., 133 pp.

CLEMENTS, THOS. 1954. Geological story of Death Valley. Palm Desert, Calif., Desert Magazine Press, 52 pp.

CONTOR, ROGER. 1959. Bighorns of the Rocky Mountains. National Parks Magazine, vol. 33 (Feb.), pp. 7–9.

COTTAM, CLARENCE, and C. S. WILLIAMS. 1943. Speeds of some wild animals. Journ. Mammalogy, vol. 24, pp. 262–263.

Curry, H. Donald. 1939. Special report, bighorn sheep, Death Valley National Monument. Aug. 28, 1939. 8 pp. Manuscript.

Darling, F. Fraser. 1960. An ecological reconnaissance of the Mara Plains in Kenya Colony. Wildlife Society Monographs No. 5, Wildlife Society, 41 pp. (Copies available from Executive Secretary, Remington Farms, Chestertown, Md. 50¢.)

Davila C., Jose Angel. 1960. Sheep and antelope in Mexico. Fourth Desert Bighorn Council Trans., pp. 104–106.

Deming, O. V. 1952. Tooth development of the Nelson bighorn sheep. Calif. Fish and Game, vol. 38, pp. 523–529.

—— 1955. Rearing bighorn lambs in captivity. Calif. Fish and Game, vol. 41, pp. 131–143.

—— 1954. Government sheepherder. Desert Magazine, vol. 17 pp. (Mar.), 4–8.

Devan, Ged A. 1958. Daily movement and activity of the bighorn. Second Desert Bighorn Council Trans., pp. 67–72.

—— 1959. The use of the CO_2 Cap-Chur gun at Desert Game Range, 1958. Second Desert Bighorn Council Trans., pp. 50–52.

Dixon, Joseph S. 1935. Status of the bighorn sheep in Death Valley National Monument. 19 pp. Manuscript.

Dixon, Joseph S., and E. Lowell Sumner, Jr. 1939. A survey of desert bighorn in Death Valley National Monument, summer of 1938. Calif. Fish and Game, vol. 25, pp. 72–95.

Doudna, Wilbur. 1939. A record of observations made on the desert bighorn. Manuscript.

—— 1941. Observations on the desert bighorn in Death Valley National Monument, summer of 1940, 6 pp. Manuscript.

Duncan, Gerald E. 1960. Human encroachment on bighorn habitat. Fourth Desert Bighorn Council Trans., pp. 35–37.

Einarsen, Arthur S. 1948. The pronghorn antelope and its management. Wildlife Management Institute, 238 pp.

Elliott, Nelson. 1959. Effects of wild burros on range conditions. Third Desert Bighorn Council Trans., pp. 9–10.

Farmer, Garland R. 1959. Effects of radioactive fallout on bighorn. Third Desert Bighorn Council Trans., pp. 15–19.

—— 1960. Radioactivity in bighorn sheep. Fourth Desert Bighorn Council Trans., pp. 23–25.

Fredine, Gordon. 1957. The National Park Service and its wildlife program. First Desert Bighorn Council Trans., pp. 20–21.

Frost, N. M. 1942. Gestation period of bighorn sheep. Journ. Mammalogy, vol. 23, pp. 215–216.

Gorczynski, W. 1940. The aridity coefficient and its application to California. Scripps Institution of Oceanography, La Jolla, Calif., Reprint No. 5097, 7 pp. Mimeographed.

Gordon, Sydney Paul. 1957. The status of bighorn sheep in New Mexico. First Desert Bighorn Council Trans., pp. 3–4.

Grater, Russell. 1959. Recreational values of bighorn other than hunting. Third Desert Bighorn Council Trans., pp. 53–57.

Grinnell, Joseph. 1937. Mammals of Death Valley. Proceedings Calif., Academy of Sciences, vol. 23, pp. 115–169.

Gross, Jack. 1960. Progress of Mexican bighorn sheep life history and management investigations in the Big Hatchet Mountains of New Mexico. Fourth Desert Bighorn Council Trans., pp. 62–65.

GROSS, JACK. 1960. History, present and future status of the desert bighorn sheep in the Guadalupe Mts. of southeastern New Mexico and northwestern Texas. Fourth Desert Bighorn Council Trans., pp. 66–71.

HALL, E. RAYMOND. 1946. Mammals of Nevada. Berkeley, Univ. of Calif. Press, 710 pp.

HALLORAN, ARTHUR F., and O. V. DEMING. 1958. Water development for bighorn sheep. Journ. of Wildlife Management, vol. 22, pp. 1–9.

HAM, BENJAMIN. 1958. Physical disturbances caused by trapping. Second Desert Bighorn Council Trans., pp. 51–56.

HANSEN, CHARLES. 1960. Lamb survival on the Desert Game Range. Fourth Desert Bighorn Council Trans., pp. 60–61.

HAURY, EMIL W., KIRK BRYAN, EDWIN H. COLBERT, NORMAN E. GABEL, CLARA LEE TANNER, and T. E. BUEHRER. 1950. The stratigraphy and archaeology of Ventana Cave, Arizona. Albuquerque and Tucson, Univ. of N. Mex. and Univ. of Ariz. Presses. 599 pp.

HOCKETT, CHARLES. 1960. The origin of speech. Scientific American, vol. 203, pp. 88–96.

HUNT, ALICE. 1960. Archaeology of the Death Valley salt pan. Salt Lake City, Univ. of Utah Press, 313 pp.

HUNT, CHAS. B. 1960. The Death Valley salt pan, a study of evaporites. Denver, U.S. Geological Survey professional paper 400 B, p. 456.

JAEGER, EDMUND. 1950. Desert wild flowers. Stanford University Press, 322 pp.

———— 1950a. Our desert neighbors. Stanford University Press, 239 pp.

JENNINGS, JESSE D. 1953. Danger cave: progress summary. El Palacia, vol. 60, pp. 179–244.

JOHNSON, EDWARD L. 1957. Vision and mechanical injury in desert bighorn sheep. First Desert Bighorn Council Trans., pp. 38–42.

———— 1958. Physical and mechanical injuries. Second Desert Bighorn Council Trans., pp. 47–50.

JONES, FRED L. 1950. A survey of the Sierra Nevada bighorn. Sierra Club Bull., vol. 35, pp. 29–76.

———— 1960. The esthetics of bighorn management. Fourth Desert Bighorn Council Trans., pp. 47–48.

JONES, FRED L., GLENN FLITTNER, and RICHARD GARD. 1957. Report on survey of bighorn sheep in the Santa Rosa Mountains, Riverside County. Calif. Fish and Game, vol. 43, pp. 179–191.

JONEZ, AL. 1957. Status of bighorn sheep in Nevada. First Desert Bighorn Council Trans., pp. 12–15.

———— 1958. Hunting the desert bighorn sheep in Nevada. Second Desert Bighorn Council Trans., pp. 1–5.

———— 1959. Nevada 1958 desert bighorn sheep hunt highlights. Third Desert Bighorn Council Trans., pp. 20–23.

———— 1960a. The Bighorn as a multiple use animal. Fourth Desert Bighorn Council Trans., pp. 45–46.

———— 1960b. Hunting results in Nevada, 1959. Fourth Desert Bighorn Council Trans., pp. 76–80.

KELLY, WARREN. 1957. Status of the bighorn sheep in Arizona. First Desert Bighorn Council Trans., pp. 5–7.

———— 1960. Bighorn sheep management recommendations for the State of Arizona. Fourth Desert Bighorn Council Trans., pp. 41–44.

Kelsey, Harlan P., and William A. Dayton (Editorial Committee). 1942. Standardized plant names. Harrisburg, Pa., J. Horace McFarland Co., 673 pp.

Kennedy, Cecil A. 1948. Golden eagle kills bighorn lamb. Journ. Mammalogy, vol. 29, pp. 68–69.

—— 1957. Status of bighorn sheep on San Andres National Wildlife Refuge, Las Cruces, N. Mex. First Desert Bighorn Council Trans., pp. 31–33.

Kennedy, Charles. 1958. Water development on the Kofa and Cabeza Prieta Game Ranges. Second Desert Bighorn Council Trans., pp. 28–31.

Koplin, Charles. 1960. Information on tagging on the Desert Game Range. Fourth Desert Bighorn Council Trans., pp. 49–52.

—— 1960. New development on water requirements on the Desert Game Range. Fourth Desert Bighorn Council Trans., pp. 54–57.

Leopold, Aldo. 1933. Game management. New York, Scribner and Sons, 481 pp.

—— 1949. A Sand County almanac. New York, Oxford Univ. Press, 226 pp.

Leopold, Starker. 1959. Wildlife of Mexico, game birds and mammals. Berkeley, Univ. of Calif. Press, 568 pp.

Lorenz, Konrad. 1958. The evolution of behavior. Scientific American, vol. 199 (Dec), pp. 67–78.

McCann, Lester. 1956. Ecology of the mountain sheep. American Midland Naturalist, vol. 56, pp. 297–324.

McKnight, Tom L. 1958. The feral burro in the United States: distribution and problems. Journ. of Wildlife Management, vol. 22, pp. 163–178.

Merkel, Dalton E. 1959. Status of bighorn in California State parks. Third Desert Bighorn Council Trans., pp. 30–32.

Miller, Alden H. 1946. Vertebrate inhabitants of the piñon Association in the Death Valley Region. Ecology, vol. 27, pp. 54–60.

Monson, Gale C. 1955. Kofa Game Range waterhole counts. Washington, U.S. Fish and Wildlife Service, 18 pp. (Mimeographed.)

—— 1957. Status of the bighorn sheep on the Kofa and Cabeza Prieta Game Ranges. First Desert Bighorn Council Trans., pp. 26–30.

—— 1958. Water requirements. Second Desert Bighorn Council Trans., pp. 64–66.

—— 1960. Effects of climate on desert bighorn numbers. Fourth Desert Bighorn Council Trans., pp. 12–14.

Moore, Tom D. 1958a. Transplanting and observations of transplanted bighorn sheep. Second Desert Bighorn Council Trans., pp. 43–46.

—— 1958b. Immigrant on trial. Texas Game and Fish, vol. 16, pp. 16–19.

—— 1959. Handling and transporting desert bighorn sheep. Third Desert Bighorn Council Trans., pp. 47–49.

—— 1960. Progress in trapping and transplanting desert bighorn. Fourth Desert Bighorn Council Trans., pp. 58–59.

Muir, John. 1894. The mountains of California. New York, The Century Co., 381 pp.

Nichol, Andrew A. 1939. Special report, bighorn sheep survey, Death Valley National Monument, Aug. 5, 1939, 10 pp. Manuscript.

Ober, E. H. 1931. The mountain sheep of California. Calif. Fish and Game, vol. 17, pp. 27–39.

Ogren, Herman. 1957. Additional information on the status of bighorn sheep in New Mexico. First Desert Bighorn Council Trans., p. 34

OGREN, HERMAN. 1958. Sheep hunting in New Mexico. Second Desert Bighorn Council Trans., pp. 13–16.

OLIN, GEORGE. 1954. Animals of the southwest deserts. Southwestern Monuments Association, 112 pp.

PILLMORE, RICHARD E. 1958. Problems of lungworm infections in wild sheep. Second Desert Bighorn Council Trans., pp. 57–63.

PUTNAM, GEORGE PALMER. 1947. Death Valley handbook. New York, Duell, Sloan, and Pearce, 88 pp.

REED, JOHN J. 1960. Highlights of the 1959 Arizona bighorn sheep hunt. Fourth Desert Bighorn Council Trans., pp. 81–84.

RUSSO, JOHN P. 1956. The desert bighorn sheep in Arizona, a research and management study. Arizona Game and Fish Dept., Fed. Aid Project W–55–R, 153 pp.

SCHMIDT-NIELSEN. 1959. The physiology of the camel. Scientific American, vol. 201, pp. 140–151.

SETON, ERNEST THOMPSON. 1929. Lives of game animals. New York, Doubleday Page and Co., vol. 3, 780 pp.

SHADLE, DANIEL P. 1958. Arizona's catchment then and now. Second Desert Bighorn Council Trans., pp. 32–35.

SMITH, S. E., and J. K. LOOSLI. 1957. Cobalt and vitamin B_{12} in ruminant nutrition: a review. Journal of Dairy Science, vol. 40, pp. 1215–1227.

SPEARS, JOHN R. 1892. Illustrated sketches of Death Valley and other borax deserts of the Pacific Coast. Chicago and New York, Rand McNally, 226 pp.

SUMNER, E. LOWELL, JR. 1939. Preliminary report on the second Death Valley bighorn survey, summer of 1939. Aug. 14, 1939, 35 pp. Manuscript.

———— 1940. Special report on a winter investigation of Death Valley bighorn. Apr. 3, 1940, 30 pp. Manuscript.

———— 1953. Special report on status of wild burros and bighorns in Death Valley National Monument, 1953. May 27, 1953, 4 pp. Manuscript.

———— 1959. Effects of wild burros on bighorn in Death Valley National Monument. Third Desert Bighorn Council Trans., pp. 4–8.

SWANK, WENDELL G. 1958. The influence of trophy hunting on horn size of bighorn populations. Second Desert Bighorn Council Trans., pp. 17–20.

TEVIS, LLOYD, JR. 1959. Man's effect on bighorn in the San Jacinto-Santa Rosa Mts. Third Desert Bighorn Council Trans., pp. 69–75.

TIME MAGAZINE. 1955. The American desert. A new way of life in the United States. Issue of July 25, 1955, vol. 66, pp. 44–53.

VAN DEN AKKER, JOHN. 1960. Human encroachment on bighorn habitat. Fourth Desert Bighorn Council Trans., pp. 38–40.

VILLA, R. BERNARDO. 1959. Brief notes on the present status and distribution of bighorn sheep in Mexico. Third Desert Bighorn Council Trans., pp. 77–79.

VOGT, WILLIAM. 1955. Mankind at the flood. Nat Parks Magazine, vol. 29, pp. 109–110, 133–136.

WARD, F. N., H. M. NAKAGAWA, and C. B. HUNT._ 1960. Geochemical investigation of Molybdenum at Nevares Spring in Death Valley, Calif. U.S. Geological Survey professional paper 400–B, 3 pp.

WEAVER, RICHARD. 1957. Status of the bighorn sheep in California. First Desert Bighorn Council Trans., pp. 8–11.

———— 1959. Effects of burro on desert water supplies. Third Desert Bighorn Council Trans., pp. 1–3.

WEAVER, RICHARD, FLOYD VERNOY, and BERT CRAIG. 1958. Game water development on the desert. Second Desert Bighorn Council Trans., pp. 21–27.

WEBB, PAUL. 1958. Trapping on the Kofa Game Range. Second Desert Bighorn Council Trans., pp. 40–42.

WELLES, FLORENCE B. 1955. Bighorn-burro survey, Death Valley National Monument. Report II, 9 pp. Manuscript.

—— 1956a. Bighorn observations at Nevares Springs, Death Valley National Monument. Report VII, 18 pp. Manuscript.

—— 1956b. Bighorn observations, Nevares Springs, June–July. Report IX, 16 pp. Manuscript.

—— 1957. Supplementary field notes at Nevares Springs. Death Valley National Monument. Report XIII, 72 pp. Manuscript.

—— 1959. Photographing the bighorn. Third Desert Bighorn Council Trans., pp. 80–86.

WELLES, RALPH E. 1955a. Survey of the Nelson bighorn sheep in the Natural Bridge-Badwater area. Death Valley National Monument. Report I, 22 pp. Manuscript.

—— 1955b. Bighorn survey report, Death Valley National Monument. Report III, 15 pp. Manuscript.

——1955c. The Death Valley bighorn census, July 1955, Death Valley National Monument. Report IV, 61 pp. Manuscript.

—— 1955d. Bighorn Report V, Death Valley National Monument. 19 pp. Manuscript.

—— 1956a. The Furnace Creek Wash bighorn, Death Valley National Monument. Report VI, 70 pp. Manuscript.

—— 1956b. Bighorn field notes, Death Valley National Monument. Report VIII, 25 pp. Manuscript.

—— 1957a. Bighorn field notes. Death Valley National Monument. Report X, 58 pp. Manuscript.

—— 1957b. Bighorn field notes. Death Valley National Monument. Report XI, 35 pp. Manuscript.

—— 1957c. Bighorn at Nevares Springs. Death Valley National Monument. Report XII, 134 pp. Manuscript.

—— 1957d. Bighorn observations—Jubilee Pass, Willow Creek, Keystone Canyon. Report XIIIa, 14 pp. Manuscript.

—— 1957e. Status of bighorn sheep in Death Valley. First Desert Bighorn Council Trans., pp. 22–25.

—— 1958. Death Valley Buttes bighorn, Death Valley National Monument. Report XIV, 19 pp. Manuscript.

—— 1960. Progress report on current Death Valley burro survey. Fourth Desert Bighorn Council Trans., pp. 85–87.

WELLES, RALPH E., and FLORENCE B. WELLES. 1958a. Field notes, Death Valley National Monument. Report XV, 18 pp. Manuscript.

—— 1958b. The Death Valley bighorn report, Death Valley National Monument. Report XVI, 11 pp. Manuscript.

—— 1959a. The Death Valley bighorn project. Third Desert Bighorn Council Trans., pp. 58–66.

—— 1959b. Preliminary study of wildlife water sources in Death Valley National Monument. Report XVII, 298 pp. Manuscript.

—— 1960. The feral burro in Death Valley. Report XVIII, 54 pp. Manuscript.

WENT, A. V. 1955. Ecology of desert plants. Scientific American (Apr.), vol. 192, pp. 68–75.

WILLIAMS, THOMAS J. 1936–9. Bighorn sheep observations in Death Valley National Monument. 10 pp. Manuscript.

WILBANKS, JOE M. 1959. Patrol and protection problems. Third Desert Bighorn Council Trans., pp. 34–36.

WPA WRITERS' PROJECT. 1939. Death Valley—a guide. Boston, Houghton, Mifflin Co., 75 pp.

WOLF, A. V. 1956. Thirst. Scientific American, vol. 194 (Jan.) pp. 70–76.

——— 1958. Body water. Scientific American, vol. 199 (Nov.) pp. 125–132.

WOOD, JOHN E. 1960. A bibliography of bighorn sheep. Fourth Desert Bighorn Council Trans., pp. 1–11.

The Desert Bighorn Council's Annual Transactions are for sale by the secretary-treasurer of the Desert Bighorn Council at $2 each. Since the office of the secretary-treasurer usually rotates annually from one State or Federal Government land management agency office, or scientific institution, to another, it is suggested that those who desire to secure copies address their inquiries to the National Park Service, Department of the Interior, Washington 25, D.C., or to the Bureau of Sports Fisheries and Wildlife at the same address, to secure the address of the council's current secretary–treasurer.

616472 O—62——15

PHOTOGRAPHS

The following photographs illustrate the methods of research used, the distinguishing characteristics of individual animals, types of habitat, behavior of individuals and groups, types of sign, and the growth and development of bighorn at significant stages.

Figure 1.—This old ewe was the leader of the Badwater band. Her spreading horns, the right horn notched and crimped, and other distinguishing features of her companions, made possible the first uninterrupted month-long series of daily dawn-to-dark observations of a recognizable band of bighorn. This established the subsequent pattern of our research program.

Figure 2.—We also carried on an extensive on-site interpretive program showing the bighorn to as many as 150 carloads of visitors per day during the band's 3-months overall use of the area.

Figure 3.—At the end of each day we left the bighorn bedded down and moved whenever possible to higher elevations to escape the heat. Here, at 5,000 feet in the Cottonwood Mountains, the nights were comfortable for sleeping.

Figure 4.—We returned to the lower elevations during the hot days where the only shade was what we made for ourselves.

Figure 5.—After 4 days, the Badwater band climbed to a gravel- and water-filled basin, or tinaja, where the animals drank. The wide horns of the three adults on the right are a family characteristic. The uniquely down-curved horns of Droopy, the adult to right of center, are unmistakable; the Old Leader is left of center.

Figure 6.—Droopy reappeared 3 years later at Keystone Canyon 5 miles south of Badwater. Her unique set of horns underscores the fact that "hornprints" are as valuable as fingerprints in the identification of individuals. Each year of growth adds a new segment at the base of the horn. Droopy is 8 years old here.

Figure 7.—The membership of bighorn bands does not remain constant, nor are the animals so gregarious that all are unhappy to be alone. For 38 days the Badwater band remained unchanged. But later it diminished from six to four, then one, as various individuals drifted away. The Old Leader seemed as contented alone as when leading the band.

Figure 8.—At Willow Creek, in July 1955, the upper spring in the willows at right had not been used by bighorn for many years. In 1956 they beat trails through these willows and used the water at that place for one summer, but usually they prefer to water at more open spots farther down the canyon.

Figure 9.—Water flows intermittently down Willow Creek for 3 miles. Permanent water situated in rugged escape terrain has made this the home area for one of the region's largest concentrations of bighorn.

Figure 10.—On Paleomesa above Navel Spring, in December 1955, we watched a "band" form, first two, then five, seven, and finally eight. Their leader, Old Mama (foreground), accepted us as a condition of the environment and fed closer as the days passed.

Figure 11.—Within a few days Old Mama led the band down off the mesa into the Big Wash and bedded them on the mesa over a mile from any "cliffy terrain" hitherto supposed necessary to the sense of security of all bighorn at bedding time.

Figure 12.—From Big Wash she led them on down to Deadman's Curve and back up Furnace Creek Wash. *Bebbia juncea* and *Stephanomeria* dominate both these washes, though not the mesa, and began immediately to assume a place of primary importance in the Death Valley bighorn diet.

Figure 13.—By the 5th of January, 1956, Old Mama had not only induced the band to follow her across the highway, but they no longer paid any attention to the cars stopping and people pouring out to photograph them.

Figure 14.—Finally on January 10, following Old Mama's example, the entire band stood stockstill in the middle of the highway, bringing all traffic to a halt. It should be emphasized that such tolerance with respect to humans is most unusual, and it developed in response to a unique leadership.

Figure 15.—At Navel Spring the bighorn demonstrated that while they may not absolutely need water in the winter, they will make an 8-mile trip to get it. In winter they can go at least 3 weeks without water, but in summer they must drink every 3 to 5 days. Navel Spring is one of the key bighorn springs in Death Valley.

Figure 16.—Although these bighorn would feed to within a yard of us in the open wash, at Navel Spring they suddenly found our presence to be an unacceptable condition in that environment. The old hunting blind overlooking Navel Spring probably has contributed to their increased anxiety at the spring.

Figure 17.—At Navel Spring, Old Eighty (note "horn-print" and characteristic carriage of the head and graying muzzle) was photographed at 100 feet with a 500-mm. lens. She reflects the tension of the entire band as she stares suspiciously down at us standing in the shadow of the box canyon below.

Figure 18.—We had to retreat to a point 75 feet from the spring before they would let us observe their watering behavior. With much "spooking," they finally drained all the basins, but this was not enough water to satisfy their needs. Big Sandy paws in the mud and waits for her tracks to fill with water.

Figure 19.—However, not all of the band reacted to the confines of Navel Spring and our presence there in the same way. In open terrain Big Sandy was one of the wariest in the band, but her experience at the waterhole apparently had not included aggressive action from humans, and she was, surprisingly, less wary than even Old Mama.

Figure 20.—The 6-month-old ram lamb played around too long and found nothing but mud when he came to drink at Navel Spring. Here he tries to make up his mind whether to go with the departing band or wait for more water to seep into their hoofprints.

Figure 21.—Rehabilitation of Navel Spring consisted of digging back to the source of each trickle, then channeling it into one or more troughs made from half an oil drum, which we sank flush with the ground. Before the work, the seep shown here produced only 5 gallons per day.

Figure 22.—Lowell Sumner came to our assistance on the water project and by the end of July 1956 we had made about 75 gallons of water available to the bighorn at Navel Spring, shown here, and had brought similar supplies to the surface at Virgin, Scotty's, and Hole-in-the-Rock Springs.

Figure 23.—We began to learn how specific or how transient the bands may be within the herd. During the autumn of 1956, Old Mama's original band was in three small groups. These temporarily joined to become a record band of 18. Shown here are 15 of this group waiting for Old Mama and 2 others (not shown) to join them.

Figure 24.—By the end of summer, 1956, we had established our observation camp at Nevares Springs and had our first glimpse into the preliminary rituals of the rams. However, we saw no actual ram "fights" until the summer of 1957.

Figure 25.—On August 27, 1957, our field identification study began to gain sub-stance when Tight Curl arrived at Nevares Spring. We had known him in Furnace Creek Wash in November 1956 and in upper Echo Canyon in January 1957. His right horn curls much closer than his left, and both are badly marred at the frontal base by heavy fighting.

Figure 26.—Two types of identification. Tight Curl was "positive" because his dis-tinguishing characteristics could scarcely be duplicated by another ram. But Little Whitey is a "relative" type. Her white rump and white face, which is relatively rare, coupled with a peculiar carriage of the head, make her identification "positive" only as long as she remains in the same area.

Figure 27.—Some distinguishing characteristics may be temporary. The lump below the left ear of the Badwater lamb (Mischief), March 1955, was noticeable for 1 day only, then vanished. This is a "relative" type.

Figure 28.—Old Mama, observed at Furnace Creek in 1956 and 1957, had a characteristic figure which could be recognized a mile away with a telescope. Her "horn-prints" were "positive," the right horn plate being chipped out at the base on the inside, which is very rare. Her right horn tip is broomed; her eyes, yellow.

Figure 29.—The accident that gave Scarface her name could hardly be duplicated on another ewe. Once photographed for comparison, her identity could be established anywhere as "positive."

Figure 30.—Rambunctious was present at Furnace Creek Wash in 1955 and 1956 and at Nevares Spring in 1957. The large scar on the right side, high up, of this 2-year-old ram, as shown here, the smaller scar on the shoulder, and the pronounced annular sectioning of the horn-tips made identification fairly "positive."

Figure 31.—Old Eighty has lost her right horntip. The ring near the middle of both horns, over a quarter of an inch deep, was unique. Whether this groove resulted from malnutrition during a bad year or from sickness is unknown.

Figure 32.—Relative horn development is greater in a 6-month-old ram (Bad Boy, foreground) than in a ewe lamb (Little Whitey, left) of the same age.

Figure 33.—Second and third from the left are the same ewe (Little Whitey) and ram (Bad Boy) at 18 months. The trend toward thicker, more outwardly-turned horns continues in the young ram. Animal at far left also is a young ram, the others are ewes.

Figure 34.—When Old Mama returned with her newborn lamb on February 2, 1956, it could scarcely stand, wobbling precariously as it walked, falling down in the brush and rocks. Yet by 4 p.m. it had gained enough strength to climb out of the wash and follow its mother 1½ miles up Pyramid Peak for bedding.

Figure 35.—Within 10 days Old Mama's lamb was beginning to nibble at the same food its mother ate. The sparse and rigid character of the desert bighorn forage shown here is typical.

Figure 36.—Having no other lambs to play with, it played its own games, usually in the semidarkness of early dawn or late evening. It raced along the washes and leaped up cliffs that its mother usually climbed around.

Figure 37.—When Old Mama's lamb was 6 weeks old, New Mama came into the wash with another lamb of the same age.

Figure 38.—Old Mama's lamb went up to meet the new lamb at once, and they became inseparable companions.

Figure 39.—Rough pelage among lambs (this is Old Mama's) is fairly common and is likely to be accompanied by a cough and lethargy. The unknown cause of these symptoms may be a contributing factor to lamb mortality.

Figure 40.—Mesquite is a favorite thrashing post for rams during rut and serves in this respect as an introductory note to sign reading. A dismantled shrub, however, should not always be accepted as the sign of ram activity, because bighorn of all age classes and sexes may attack shrubs, especially during the spring shedding period.

Figure 41.—This typical bighorn bed, 2 to 3 feet long, has been pawed in the loose soil of a rocky slope. This bed, on a slope in rough terrain, accompanied by a large number of pellets, probably is the night bed of an adult. Beds in open washes are likely to be day beds, for we have no record of night bedding there.

Figure 42.—These three sizes of prints do not indicate three animals but probably two: A—four tracks of front feet; B—a hind foot of possibly the same animal; C—a smaller animal, probably a lamb. Since each animal leaves two sizes of prints it would take at least five sizes of prints to indicate three animals.

Figure 43.—A mature ram crushed these cottontop cactuses with the bulge of his horn, then pawed them open with a front foot. But this is our only observation in 8 years of the full use of this cactus by bighorn in Death Valley, indicating that generalizations from such single observations can lead to misconceptions of bighorn life history.

Figure 44.—Small lambs can vanish quickly in the desert. We last saw this lamb (Little Fuzzy) alive on August 23, 1957. After we had searched for 3 days, we were led to its body in this advanced stage of decomposition by circling ravens and buzzards on August 30. Three months later, there were not even any bones left.

Figure 45.—Pack rats often confuse the beginner in sign reading by leaving pellets somewhat similar to lamb pellets and by "browsing" plants both for food and for nest-building. Additional confusion also can be caused by the browsing of chuckwallas.

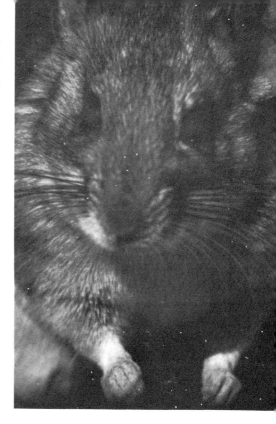

Figure 46.—Game trails are often reported to us as bighorn trails. On such trails the larger tracks usually are made by coyotes, and there is no sign of any of those on the valley floor being used by bighorn. But such tracks still give impetus among the credulous to the legend of the valley crossing by bighorn.

Figure 47.—The rough gauntness of extremely dehydrated adults on their way to water is often mistaken for a generally poor condition. The same animals, fat and sleek from rehydration, can be mistakenly counted the second time as different animals. This astonishing transformation was observed many times.

Figure 48.—A possible cause of mortality is suggested by the propensity of lambs to play on nearly sheer walls, leaping into the air and kicking their heels. This one lived to repeat the same antics the next evening until after dark, but we have found dead ones at the base of cliffs.

Figure 49.—Forgotten Creek was rediscovered during this survey. It flows for nearly a mile down a canyon in the foothills of the Grapevines. We observed no sign of contemporary bighorn use, although old trails converged on the upper springs from the foothills. But sign quickly disappears in similar salty terrain at Nevares Spring as a result of chemical action.

Figure 50.—The ecological undesirability of the feral burro in Death Valley is beyond question, but the actual extent of its threat to the bighorn has not been determined. The condition of Rest Spring shows that burros do not always foul springs. Bighorn will, if other conditions are acceptable, continue to water at springs utilized by burros.

Figure 51.—This and following pictures are the only ones we have seen of desert bighorn on the jousting field. The tournament, which took place in an air temperature of 122° was between Broken Nose and Tabby, both between 10 and 12 years old. Bighorn sometimes mill around for hours "blowing," "growling," and "groaning," in the preliminary phase of the joust shown here.

Figure 52.—The ritual includes an elaborate pretense of disinterest in which one ram turns away and pretends to eat or polish his horns in a nearby shrub. But their eyes are set out so far that they see behind them and know what the other is doing. We have never seen one attempt to "blast" the other during this preliminary maneuver.

Figure 53.—Occasionally they both rear instantaneously from this position and lunge at close range. Usually, however, they turn their backs with every indication of indifference and walk away. But here again each is watching every move of the other, and at varying distances some communication known only to them signals the next move.

Figure 54.—Having walked away a certain number of paces, suddenly they whirl and rise to their hindlegs, then "sighting down their noses" they race toward each other in an upright position, gaining speed and leaning farther forward as they approach.

Figure 55.—When they are about 12 feet apart, with every muscle bulging for a final effort, and with amazing timing and accuracy, they lunge forward like football tacklers.

Figure 56.—Their combined speed at impact has been estimated at 50 to 70 miles per hour and to be the equivalent of a 2,400-pound blow. We counted over 40 such blows between two other rams in one afternoon.

Figure 57.—The remarkable synchronization of movement pictured here is the rule, not the exception. Every effort seems to be made to insure a perfect head-on and balanced contact. Note that both heads are tilted to the same side.

Figure 58.—Sometimes the heads are tilted in opposite directions, resulting in a blow on the forehead itself instead of on the horns, but the encounter is still head-on and in balance.

Figure 59.—Occasionally one slips or miscalculates and a severe neck-twisting or nose-smashing can result. Tabby, the ram on the left, has a scar on the right side. Broken Nose has a dark patch on the left horn. Tabby has not watered for 3 days, and shows the gauntness and rough coat of dehydration.

Figure 60.—This 7-year-old ewe was captured and brought to the Desert Game Range in 1947 when she was a lamb. Her 6-week-old lamb was born in 1954 and registered in the Desert Game Range genealogy as "female No. 7."

Figure 61.—This is "female No. 7," when 6 weeks old in April 1954. At this age, the previously ill-defined rump patch turns white. The horns have not appeared, but the characteristic tufts of hair often are mistaken for beginning horns.

Figure 62.—"Female No. 7," when 7 months old in October 1954.

Figure 63.—"Female No. 7," when 2 years and 7 months old in October 1956, accompanied by her 6½-month-old ewe lamb, which was born on April 4, 1956. These relatively inconspicuous "extra" growth rings appear fairly often in ewes.

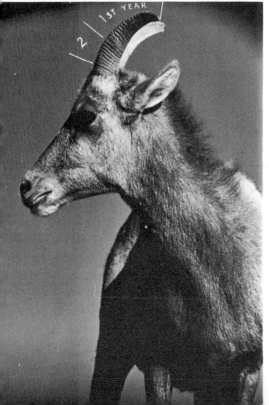

Figure 64.—"Female No. 7," when 2 years and 7 months old in October 1956.

Figure 65.—"Female No. 7's" ewe lamb in September 1957 at the age of 17½ months. She has the relatively slender body, low withers, and high horns of her mother. (See fig. 66.)

Figure 66.—"Female No. 7," at 3 years and 7 months in October 1957. Notch at tip of right horn would be another useful characteristic in field identification. Small dark spot on left horn shows here and also in figures 63 and 67, permitting positive location of horn growth stages.

Figure 67.—"Female No. 7," at 3 years and 7 months (right), her 17½-month-old ewe lamb (left), and her 4-month-old ram lamb (center), showing relative sizes and horn development.

Figure 68.—The following pictures show the growth and development of the Old Man, captured as a lamb in the late summer of 1948 and kept in a large fenced inclosure at the Desert Game Range where he was photographed by us annually from 1953 to the date of this writing. March 1953. Age: 5 years.

Figure 69.—February 1954. Age: 6 years.

Figure 70.—January 1955. Age: 7 years.

Figure 71.—January 1957.   Age: 9 years.

Figure 72.—August 1958.   Age: 10 years.

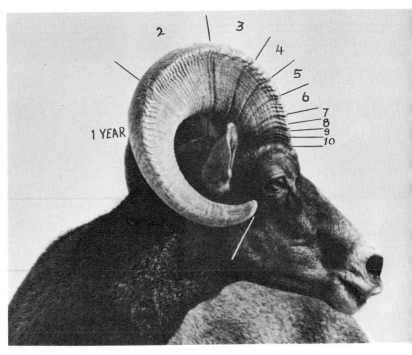

Figure 73.—July 1959.   Age: 11 years.

Figure 74.—April 1960.   Age: 12 years.

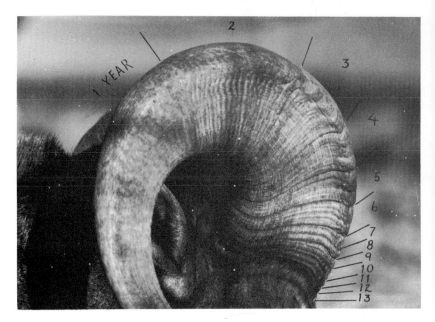

Figure 75.—January 1961. Age 13 years. Note that beginning in 1957 at 9 years, no new light-colored annual ring has matured, so that now in 1961 the dark "ring" at the base of the horn is actually composed of five narrow dark rings, each indicating a year's growth. This is typical of desert bighorn ram horn development.

Figure 76.—As we left in 1961, the Old Man followed along the fence, bleating. We were reminded that he was 13 years old and that his teeth were going now and that when we came another year things might not be the same. For things will not be the same there again—when the Old Man is gone.

Figure 77.—Predictions were made in 1937 that wild burros would drive the bighorn away from Lost Spring. But the 1960 observations of the authors, and this 1961 photograph by Park Naturalist Ro Wauer, indicate that bighorn and burros have shared this water without apparent friction for a quarter of a century.

Index

U.S. GOVERNMENT PRINTING OFFICE: 1962   O—616472